# HANDBOOK OF RECORDING ENGINEERING

## Second Edition

John Eargle

**VNR** VAN NOSTRAND REINHOLD
New York

Library of Congress Catalog Card Number 91–11474
ISBN 0–442–00553–9

Printed in the United States of America.

Van Nostrand Reinhold
115 Fifth Avenue
New York, New York 10003

Chapman and Hall
2–6 Boundary Row
London, SE1 8HN, England

Thomas Nelson Australia
102 Dodds Street
South Melbourne 3205
Victoria, Australia

Nelson Canada
1120 Birchmount Road
Scarborough, Ontario MIK 5G4, Canada

16 15 14 13 12 11 10 9 8 7 6 5 4 3 2

**Library of Congress Cataloging-in-Publication Data**

Eargle, John.
    Handbook of recording engineering/by John M. Eargle—2nd ed.
      p.  cm.
    Includes bibliographical references and index.
    ISBN 0–442–00553–9
    1. Sound—Recording and reproducing. I. Title.
TK7881.4.E16  1991
621.389′3—dc20

           91–11474
           CIP

# PREFACE

The second edition of the *Handbook of Recording Engineering* has been completely rewritten and includes all recent developments in recording technology. In the last five years, the number of degree programs and course offerings in recording arts and sciences has increased significantly. The author has had extensive discussions with teachers in the field, and many of their suggestions have been incorporated in the new edition in order to make it a more effective textbook. There are more (and shorter) chapters grouped under major topic areas. The intent is to provide the student with rapid access to specific topics and enable the instructor to better organize the material for the length of the course. For the professional recording engineer the book retains its organization as a true handbook, offering ready solutions to everyday problems.

The new book is divided into ten major areas.

***Section 1: Acoustical Foundations in Recording.*** The recording engineer must have a thorough understanding of physical and psychological acoustics and how these come together in the recording studio and performance spaces. Added emphasis has been placed on stereo localization phenomena, since this is the means by which the engineer translates acoustical relationships into an acceptable facsimile in the reproducing space.

***Section 2: Microphones.*** Microphone choices, their directional patterns, and placement are the prime ingredients the recording engineer uses in daily practice. This sequence of chapters deals extensively with the electrical and physical aspects of microphones.

***Section 3: Fundamentals of Stereophonic Recording.*** The basic systems of stereo recording are covered here, including coincident, near-coincident, and spaced microphone methods. The discussion emphasizes normal two-channel recording, but multichannel surround-sound techniques are included. Techniques for image broadening and pseudo-stereo processing are presented.

***Section 4: Recording Systems: Architecture, Metering, and Monitoring.*** The modern recording console can be an intimidating affair, and the intent in this sequence of chapters to clarify its evolution in terms of changing musical requirements. While the in-line console dominates multichannel recording, the older split-configuration console is far more prevalent in general use; it is the type on which most young engineers will learn their craft and is accordingly emphasized here.

Metering of signal levels is a subject not often covered in detail. It is the means by which the engineer establishes effective modulation levels with respect to system noise and distortion. Other aspects here have to do with program loudness and interchannel correlation in stereo transmission.

Musical balances are established over monitor loudspeakers, and the large, built-in control room systems are normally supplemented with small loudspeakers, as more music listening is done in the automobile and by means of personal electronics. Control room design considered in terms its acoustical and visual aspects.

***Section 5: Signal Processing.*** This important sequence of chapters deals with the great variety of devices that are used by the engineer to alter and enhance program elements. These can vary from devices that affect the sound of a recording in a profound way, to devices whose role is to shape the program subtly in terms of spectrum and amplitude envelope for better overall transmission. Most of these techniques are covered in chapters devoted to the aspects of frequency domain (equalizers and filters), time domain (reverberation and signal delay), and amplitude domain (compression and noise-gating). A final chapter addresses newer technology that has grown out of advanced digital signal processing.

***Section 6: The Recording Medium.*** Even in this digital age, analog technology dominates in the areas of multitrack recording and general post-production in broadcast and motion picture applications. The coverage of analog tape recording has been appropriately expanded, as has the coverage of code–decode noise-reduction techniques.

Digital recording is given more detailed treatment than in the earlier edition and includes signal processing, data reduction, and interface between various recording systems.

***Section 7: Studio Production Techniques.*** The previous edition presented strong chapters dealing with classical and popular recording and production techniques. These have been updated and supplemented with a useful chapter covering speech recording.

***Section 8: Post-production Techniques.*** Three new chapters cover editing, music assembly, and an overview of sound for film and video. They cover the myriad techniques that are not directly a part of the recording process, but which inevitably follow as the recorded material finds its way into finished form for the consumer.

***Section 9: Consumer Formats for Recorded Sound.*** These chapters cover consumer media both in terms of basic technology and the specific shaping of recorded program to best fit a given medium. Since the compact disc (CD) has virtually replaced the LP record, an argument could have been made for deleting the chapter devoted to disc recording. Nonetheless, the technology of stereo disc cutting is presented in this edition, perhaps for its last time.

The Philips Compact Cassette has long been our most important analog medium for general music and speech program distribution, and of course the CD has emerged during the 1980s as the world's new archival medium. The two digital tape standards, R-DAT and the Philips Digital Compact Cassette (DCC) have not yet reached maturity but are both important in their respective market areas.

*Section 10: Commercial and Operational Aspects of Recording.*   The fundamentals of studio site selection, acoustical design, operating and staffing, and equipment selection are covered in this section.

# CONTENTS

# 1

## PRINCIPLES OF PHYSICAL ACOUSTICS

### 1.1 INTRODUCTION

This chapter will cover the basic elements of sound generation and propagation in both indoor and outdoor environments. Sound fields and directivity of sound sources will be discussed, as will various wavelength-dependent sound transmission phenomena. The concept of the decibel will be introduced.

### 1.2 CONCEPT OF VIBRATION

#### 1.2.1 Periodic Motion

A *sine wave* represents the simplest kind of vibration; it is the natural motion of a weight as it bobs up and down on a spring, or of a pendulum swinging at moderate displacement. Its characteristic motion is shown in Figure 1-1(a) as an undulating movement about a reference line. The motion can also be described as the projection of a point on a circle as that point moves about the circle with uniform angular velocity. One cycle of the wave constitutes rotation through the complete 360 degrees of the circle, and the time required for one cycle of the wave is called its *period* ($T$). A related term is *frequency*, which is the number of periods in a time interval of one second. For example, if a sine wave has a period of one-fourth second ($T = .25$ sec), then its frequency is $1/T$, or 4 cycles per second. The term *hertz* (Hz) is universally used to indicate cycles per second.

> EXAMPLE: Determine the frequency of a sine wave with a period of 1/1000 of a second.

$$\text{Frequency} = 1/T = \frac{1}{.001} = 1000\,\text{Hz} \quad (\text{or 1 kHz}) \tag{1-1}$$

The term kHz, or kilohertz, is equivalent to one thousand hertz.

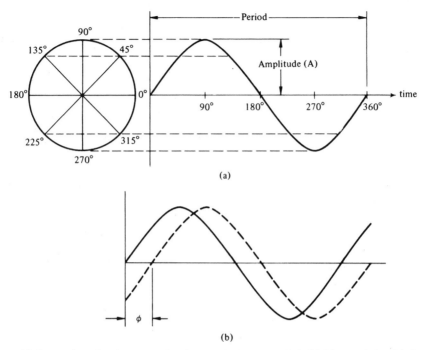

(a)

(b)

**Figure 1-1.** (a) Generation of a sine wave, showing amplitude and period. (b) Phase relationship between two sine waves of the same frequency.

Another characteristic of a sine wave is its *amplitude* $(A)$, which is its maximum displacement from the reference line. Depending on the physical domain we are discussing, this displacement can be in space, as in the case of a pendulum, or in electrical voltage or current, if it is an electrical sine wave. The amplitude of a sound wave is customarily measured in pressure fluctuations above and below normal atmospheric pressure.

The concept of *phase* is important in describing sine waves. It refers to the relative displacement in time between sine waves of the same frequency, and this is shown in Figure 1-1(b). Here, the dashed sine wave is displaced from the solid one by some distance $\phi$, which is usually expressed in degrees, with one period of the wave representing 360 degrees. If two sine waves of the same frequency are displaced in phase by 180°, they are said to be in opposite polarity or, more informally, as being *out of phase*. Obviously, a simple transposition of wiring in a two-conductor signal path can result in this condition.

As common as sine waves are in electrical and mechanical engineering, they are rare in the world of sound, for the reason that nearly all vibrating elements used in the generation of sound have a tendency to execute complex motion. If the motion is a sustained one, as in the case of a bowed string, then the complex waveform can usually be represented as an ensemble of sine waves, beginning with a *fundamental* wave and progressing upward through a set of sine waves whose periods are related as $1, \frac{1}{2}, \frac{1}{3}, \frac{1}{4}, \frac{1}{5}$, and so on. This is shown in Figure 1-2, where four harmonically related waves are

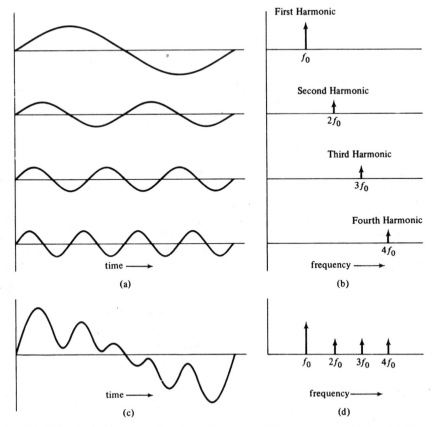

**Figure 1-2.** (a) Illustration of harmonically related sine waves. (b) Frequency spectra for sine waves shown in (a). (c) Generation of a complex wave by adding the sine wave components of (a). (d) Frequency spectrum for the complex wave shown in (c).

added together to produce a complex wave (Figure 1-2c). The components of a complex wave are referred to as *harmonics*. In Figure 1-2(b) and 1-2(d), we have shown the frequency spectrum for each component as well as for the complex wave itself. By specifying the number of harmonics and their relative amplitudes and phase relationships, we can generate any repetitive wave form.

### 1.2.2 Aperiodic Motion: Noise

Although we can describe any unwanted sound as noise, the term is usually reserved for waveforms of the kind shown in Figure 1-3(a). The wave has no discernible period, and is thus called *aperiodic*. Just as a complex repetitive wave form can be shown to consist of harmonically related sine waves, noise can be shown to consist of a *continuous* band of an unbounded number of sine waves. If the array of frequencies present is as shown in Figure 1-3(b), the noise is referred to as *white noise* (similar to the interstation noise

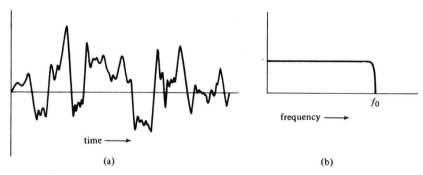

(a)                                    (b)

**Figure 1-3.** Waveform for a typical "white noise" signal (a) and its corresponding frequency spectrum (b).

heard on FM radios). It is normally band-limited, containing frequency components up to some arbitrary cutoff frequency, $f_0$. The term white noise comes from the analogy with white light, which contains all frequencies (visible wavelengths) in equal amount. *Pink noise*, again by analogy with light, has less power at high frequencies; for each doubling of frequency, the power is halved. The waveform shown in Figure 1-4(a) shows noticeably less high-frequency power than the white noise waveform shown in Figure 1-3(a), and the corresponding frequency spectrum in Figure 1-4(b) shows the characteristic roll-off at high frequencies.

White noise contains equal power per cycle, or equal power for each frequency present in the noise signal; pink noise contains equal power per octave (or portion of an octave) and is useful, as we will see in a later chapter, as a test signal for equalizing monitor loudspeakers.

## 1.3 SOUND TRANSMISSION THROUGH AIR

If a vibrating surface is suitably large, then its vibrations will radiate acoustical power to the air around it and sound is thus produced. Generally, we can define sound as cyclic variations above and below normal atmospheric pressure. The frequency range of audible sound is nominally 20 Hz to 20 kHz, and the velocity of sound through air at normal atmospheric pressure is given by the equation:

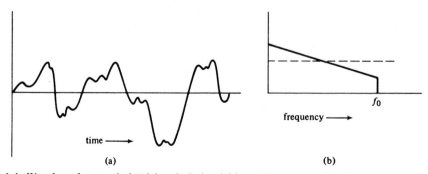

(a)                                    (b)

**Figure 1-4.** Waveform for a typical "pink noise" signal (a) and its corresponding frequency spectrum (b).

$$\text{Velocity} = 331.4 + .607T \text{ meters/sec} \tag{1-2}$$

where $T$ is the temperature in degrees Celsius.

In English units, the equation is:

$$\text{Velocity} = 1052 + 1.106T \text{ feet/sec} \tag{1-3}$$

where $T$ is the temperature in degrees Fahrenheit.

For most applications in recording, we can assume that the velocity of sound is 344 meters/sec. However, wind instruments are quite dependent on ambient temperature in their tuning, and every attempt should be made to keep recording environments at normal and consistent temperatures.

Figure 1-5 shows the range of frequencies that can be produced by various instruments and the human voice.

Let us assume a sound source of a frequency of 344 Hz. At a velocity of 344 meters/sec, the period of the waveform will begin anew each meter, and we can now define wavelength as the distance between the beginnings of those successive periods:

$$\text{Wavelength } (\lambda) = \frac{\text{velocity}}{\text{frequency}} \tag{1-4}$$

The Greek letter lambda ($\lambda$) is universally used to represent wavelength.

EXAMPLES: Determine the wavelength of a 10-kHz signal in air:

$$\lambda = 344/10,000 = .0344 \text{ meter} \quad \text{(or about 1.3 inch)}$$

Determine the wavelength of a 50 Hz signal in air:

$$\lambda = 344/50 = 6.9 \text{ meters}$$

Obviously, given any two the the three quantities, wavelength ($\lambda$), frequency ($f$), and velocity ($v$), we can solve for the third:

$$f = v/\lambda \tag{1-5}$$

$$v = f\lambda \tag{1-6}$$

## 1.4 THE DECIBEL

### 1.4.1 Definition

In both acoustical and electrical measurements, the decibel is a convenient way of expressing ratios of two powers. The *bel* is defined as the logarithm to the base ten of a power ratio:

$$\text{Level} = \log\left(\frac{P_1}{P_0}\right) \text{ bel} \tag{1-7}$$

More conveniently, we use the decibel, which is one-tenth of a bel:

$$\text{Level} = 10 \log\left(\frac{P_1}{P_0}\right) \text{ decibel} \tag{1-8}$$

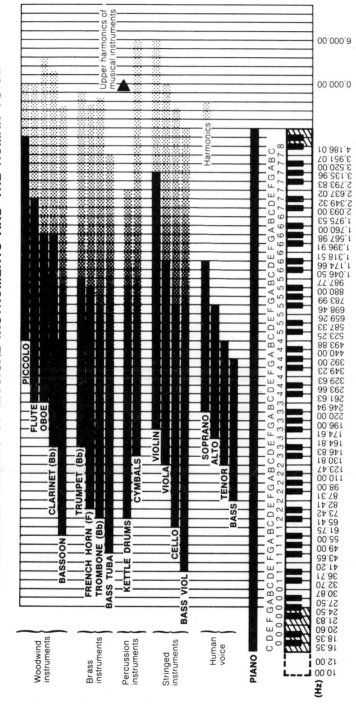

**Figure 1-5.** Range of frequencies for various sources of sound.

Let our reference power, $P_0$, be 1 watt; then 2 watts represents a level of 3 dB:

$$\text{Level} = 10 \log (2/1) = 10(.3) = 3 \text{ dB}$$

Extending the ratio, 4 watts represents a level of 6 dB:

$$\text{Level} = 10 \log (4/1) = 10(.6) = 6 \text{ dB}$$

In a similar manner 10 watts represents a level of 10 dB relative to 1 watt:

$$\text{Level} = 10 \log (10/1) = 10(1) = 10 \text{ dB}$$

Figure 1.6 presents a useful nomograph for determining by inspection the level in dB of power ratios in watts. Simply locate the two power values along the nomograph and read the level difference in dB between them.

> EXAMPLE: Find the level difference in dB between 20 and 500 watts:
>
> Above 20 watts read 13; above 500 watts read 27. Then:
>
> $$\text{Level difference} = 27 - 13 = 14 \text{ dB}$$

The experienced reader will soon note that the relative levels between 100 and 10 watts, 60 and 6 watts, 0.4 and 0.04 watt are all the same: 10 dB. Obviously, the relative level of any 10-to-1 power relationship is 10 dB. Likewise, the relative level of any 2-to-1 power relationship is 3 dB.

## 1.4.2 Electrical Relationships; Ohm's Law

In electrical systems, power is defined as the product of the voltage drop across a load and the current that flows through it:

$$\text{Power } (W) = \text{voltage } (E) \times \text{current } (I) \qquad (1\text{-}9)$$

Equation 1.9 is related to Ohm's law, which is expressed as follows:

$$\text{Current } (I) = \frac{\text{voltage } (E)}{\text{resistance } (R)} \qquad (1\text{-}10)$$

In Figure 1.7(a) shows a 1-volt battery connected in series with a load resistance of 1 ohm. By Ohm's law, 1 volt impressed across a resistance of 1 ohm will produce a current of 1 ampere, and the resulting power will be 1 watt. In Figure 1.7(b), the voltage has

**dB ABOVE AND BELOW A ONE WATT REFERENCE POWER**

POWER IN WATTS

**Figure 1-6.** Nomograph for determining power ratios directly in dB.

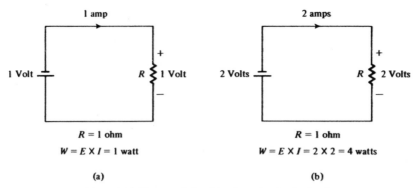

**Figure 1-7.** Power relationships in a simple dc circuit.

been increased to 2 volts, and, again by Ohm's law, the current has increased to 2 amperes:

$$I = E/R = \frac{2 \text{ volts}}{1 \text{ ohm}} = 2 \text{ amperes}$$

Accordingly, the power is:

$$W = E \times I = 2 \times 2 = 4 \text{ watts}$$

Assuming that we are dealing with a fixed load resistance, we can express power levels in dB in terms of voltage or current ratios. Since increasing the voltage across a load by any degree causes the same degree of current increase, we can state that the power dissipated in the load is proportional to the square of voltage or current. Stated another way:

$$W = \frac{E^2}{R} = I^2 R \qquad (1\text{-}11)$$

Thus, by elementary properties of logarithms, power levels in decibels can be expressed as

$$\text{Level} = 10 \log \left(\frac{E_1}{E_0}\right)^2 = 20 \log \left(\frac{E_1}{E_0}\right) \text{ dB} \qquad (1\text{-}12)$$

or:

$$\text{Level} = 10 \log \left(\frac{I_1}{I_0}\right)^2 = 20 \log \left(\frac{I_1}{I_0}\right) \text{ dB} \qquad (1\text{-}13)$$

Thus, a 2-to-1 voltage or current ratio represents the same level relationship, 6 dB, as a 4-to-1 power ratio:

$$\text{Level} = 20 \log (2/1) = 20(.3) = 6 \text{ dB}$$

In a similar manner, a 10-to-1 voltage or current ratio corresponds to a 100-to-1 power ratio:

$$\text{Level} = 20 \ \log \ (10/1) = 20(1) = 20 \ \text{dB}$$

A convenient nomograph that converts voltage or current ratios to levels in dB is given in Figure 1-8. It is used in the same manner as the nomograph shown in Figure 1-6. Only one restriction holds: the two voltage or current readings must be taken with respect to the *same* load resistance value.

EXAMPLE: Find the level difference between 4 volts and 80 volts:

Above 4 volts read 12 dB; above 80 volts read 38 dB.

$$\text{Level difference} = 38 - 12 = 26 \ \text{dB}$$

### 1.4.2.1 Electrical Reference Levels.

In recording engineering there are two common references for voltage calculations in decibels and two common references for power calculations in decibels. These are given in Table 1-1.

Zero dBv is the level of the voltage that will produce a power of 1 milliwatt in a 600-ohm load resistance, while zero dBm is the level corresponding to 1 milliwatt of power. As long as voltage is measured across a 600-ohm load, then levels in dBv and dBm will have the same numerical value. However, a possible point of confusion arises when the reference resistance is something other than 600 ohms. It is possible to express levels in dBm, regardless of the reference resistance, but the dBv and dBm numerical values will be the same only for a reference resistance of 600 ohms.

Today, most console manufacturers indicate voltage levels in dBv in signal flow diagrams, ignoring power levels altogether. When this is done, the effect of load value is likewise ignored.

For higher signal levels, the designations dBW (reference 1 watt) and dBV (reference 1 volt) are often used. Since it is easy to confuse dBv and dBV, many manufacturers prefer the designation dBu instead of dBv; both are in common use.

### 1.4.2.2 Rms and Average Values of Waveforms.

The amplitude of a complex voltage, current, or pressure waveform may be described by its average, rms, or peak values. These concepts are shown in Figures 1-9(a) and (b). The sine wave has a maximum, or

### Table 1-1. Electrical reference levels

| Symbol | Reference for 0 dB |
| --- | --- |
| dBv | 1 volt rms |
| dBv[a] | 0.775 volt rms |
| dBW | 1 watt |
| dBm | 0.001 watt (1 milliwatt) |

[a]dBu is often used as an equivalent to dBv.

**LEVEL IN dB**

**CURRENT OR POTENTIAL RATIOS**

**Figure 1-8.** Nomograph for determining voltage or current ratios directly in dB.

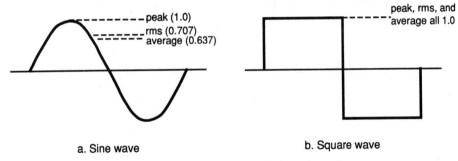

**Figure 1-9.** Rms, average, and peak values of waveforms.

peak, value of 1, and its average value is 0.636. The peak value is obvious, and the average value is simply the arithmetic average of all values over the *half*-cycle of the wave which is shown. Rms is the abbreviation of *root-mean-square*, and it expresses the effective value of the waveform in terms of generating power. (The rms value is arrived at by taking all instantaneous values over the half-cycle, squaring and summing them, and then taking the square root.)

Let us look at an electrical example. If a sine wave voltage of peak value 1 volt is applied across a 1-ohm load, then the power dissipated in that load will be

$$\text{Power} = \frac{E^2}{R} = (.707)^2/1 = 0.5 \text{ watt}$$

In Figure 1-9(b) is shown a square wave. In this case, all three values are 1 volt, and the power dissipated in a 1-ohm resistance produced by an applied square wave of peak amplitude 1 volt will be

$$\text{Power} = 1/1 = 1 \text{ watt}$$

In complex waveforms, the peak value can be many times greater than the rms and average values. We commonly speak of the *crest factor* of a complex waveform as the ratio, often expressed in dB, of the peak-to-rms value. Crest factors of the order of 10 to 15 dB are not uncommon in complex musical signals.

When rms values of voltage and current are multiplied to arrive at a value of power, that value is referred to as average power. The term rms power is a misnomer and should never be used.

## 1.4.3 Sound Pressure Level ($L_P$)

**1.4.3.1 Measurement.** The standard tool for measuring sound pressure level is the sound level meter (SLM), a device that reads directly in $L_P$. A typical sound level meter is shown in Figure 1-10. The model shown has an attached octave band analyzer spanning the range from 31.5 Hz to 20 kHz.

Some of the important characteristics of the meter are its ballistics (dynamic behavior of its meter movement), accuracy of weighting networks, and absolute calibration accuracy.

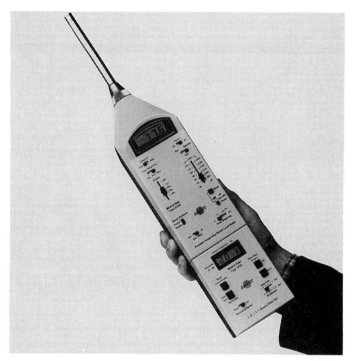

**Figure 1-10.** Illustration of a typical high-quality sound level meter. (*Courtesy B & K Instruments*)

Standard SLMs have both fast and slow meter characteristics; the fast response is more appropriate for impulsive noise readings, while the slow response is more appropriate for determining the levels of more sustained noises or of music.

Standard curves for the three common weighting characteristics are shown in Figure 1-11. The weighting curves are important in determining the annoyance value of noise and they will be discussed later.

**1.4.3.2 Sound Pressure Reference Level.**  Sound pressure is analogous to voltage, and acoustical power is proportional to the square of sound pressure. Thus

$$\text{Sound pressure level} = 20 \log\left(\frac{P_1}{P_0}\right) \text{ dB} \qquad (1\text{-}14)$$

The standard reference, $P_0$, for sound pressure measurements is established as $2 \times 10^{-5}$ pascal (0.0002 dyne/cm$^2$), and sound pressure levels are expressed in dB above or below that value. The reference pressure is quite small, and it is very close to the threshold of audibility in the 1 to 3 kHz range for persons with normal hearing. A value of sound pressure level in dB above the reference level is indicated as $L_P$. Thus. for a pressure of $2 \times 10^{-5}$ pascal, $L_P = 0$ dB; for a pressure of $2 \times 10^{-4}$ pascal, $L_P = 20$ dB, and so forth. Figure 1-12 shows values both in pressure and $L_P$ for a variety of common noise sources.

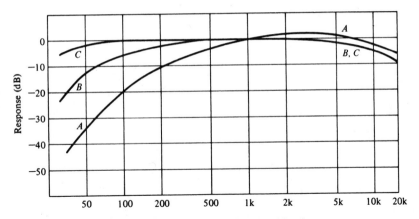

**Figure 1-11.** Weighting curves for sound level meter.

## 1.4.4 Summing levels in dB

If powers of 1 watt and 2 watts are summed, the resulting power will be 3 watts. However, if levels in dB are expressed relative to some reference level, we cannot simply add them together and obtain the resultant level. For example, assume that two sound sources both produce $L_P = 97$ dB. Because they represent identical sound power levels, the summation will be $L_P = 97 + 3 = 100$ dB, not $L_P = 97 + 97 = 194$ dB.

Figure 1-13 illustrates a graphical method for determining the resultant level when two levels in dB are summed.

>   EXAMPLE:  Find the resultant level when two values of $L_P$, 90 and 96 dB, are summed:
>
>   First, determine $D$:
>   D = 96 − 90 = 6. Below 6 read 1.
>   Therefore, $L_P = 96 + 1 = 97$ dB

It is easy to see that if two levels differ by more than about 10 dB, their sum will be insignificant compared to the higher level alone.

## 1.5 ATTENUATION OF SOUND IN FREE SPACE: INVERSE SQUARE LAW

If there are no obstructions near a sound source located outdoors, free space conditions effectively exist. The attenuation of sound we observe as we move away from the source can be described fairly simply. In Figure 1-14 are constructed a number of spheres located at radii of 4, 8, and 16 meters around a sound source. Assume that the source produces a constant power output of 1 acoustical watt. Then, at a distance of 4 meters there will be power of 1 watt passing through a sphere whose area is $4\pi(4)^2$, or 201 square meters. At twice this distance, 8 meters, we will observe the same power of 1 watt passing through an area of $4\pi(8)^2$, or 804 square meters. Since the areas of these two spheres have a ratio of 4-to-1, it follows that the power passing through a given area at a distance of 8 meters will be only *one-fourth* that passing through the same given area at a distance

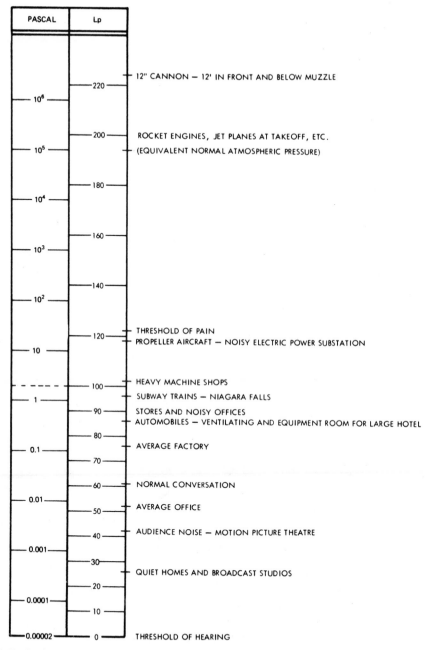

**Figure 1-12.** Sound pressure levels of common sound sources. Persons with normal hearing can detect sound over a range of about 120 dB, a million-to-one power ratio.

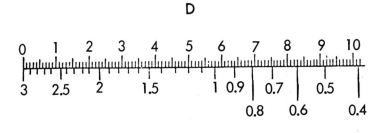

**Figure 1-13.** Nomograph for adding levels in dB. $D$ is the difference between two levels; $N$ is added to the higher of the two levels to derive the summed level.

of 4 meters. Thus, $L_P$ at a distance of 8 meters will be 6 dB lower than at 4 meters. Moving on to a distance of 16 meters, the area is $4\pi(16)^2$, or 3216 square meters, and this is four times the area of the sphere of 8-meter radius. Again, $L_P$ is observed to be 6 dB lower at 16 meters than at 8 meters.

All of this is related to experience; we have all observed that as we walk away from a sound source outdoors the sound level falls off quickly at first, and then more slowly as we get farther away, Each time we double our distance from the source, the level drops about 6 dB. This relationship is known as the *inverse square law,* and its equation is

$$\text{Loss in dB} = 10 \log \left(\frac{r_1}{r_2}\right)^2 = 20 \log \left(\frac{r_1}{r_2}\right) \qquad (1\text{-}15)$$

This equation gives the relative loss in $L_P$ as measured between any two values of $r$.

EXAMPLE: What is the inverse square loss in $L_P$ observed between distances of 10 and 100 meters from a sound source?

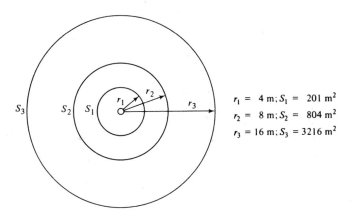

$$r_1 = 4 \text{ m}; S_1 = 201 \text{ m}^2$$
$$r_2 = 8 \text{ m}; S_2 = 804 \text{ m}^2$$
$$r_3 = 16 \text{ m}; S_3 = 3216 \text{ m}^2$$

**Figure 1-14.** Sound behavior in a free field.

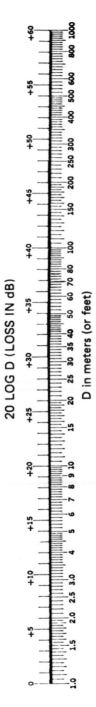

**Figure 1-15.** Nomograph for determining inverse square relationships directly in dB.

Let $r_1$ be 10 meters and $r_2$ be 100 meters; then

$$\text{Loss in } L_P = 20 \log (10/100) = 20 \log (.1) = -20 \text{ dB}$$

As was the case with dB calculations of electrical levels earlier, we can express the equation with a simple nomograph, as shown in Figure 1-15.

EXAMPLE: Using the nomograph of Figure 1-15, find the attenuation of $L_P$ due to inverse square law between distances of 10 meters and 100 meters from a sound source.

Above 10 meters read $-20$ dB; above 100 meters read $-40$ dB;
Then, $+20 - (+40) = -20$ dB.

In an outdoor environment that is free of objects which can obstruct or reflect sound, the inverse square law generally holds. There are two very simple rules to remember for making quick mental calculations When the distance from a sound source in a free field is doubled (or halved), the level decreases (or increases) by 6 dB. When the distance is increased (or decreased) by a factor of 10, the level decreases (or increases) by 20 dB.

As a further observation of the inverse square law, Figure 1-16 shows values of $L_P$ measured at various distances from a talker located on the stage of an open-air theater. Note that the measured levels only approximate inverse square law relationships; in this example, they are within $\pm 2$ dB of the theoretical values because of the many reflecting and absorbing sources.

## 1.6 DIFFRACTION AND REFRACTION OF SOUND

Sound *diffracts*, or bends, around obstacles, and the degree to which this happens depends on the size of the obstacle relative to the wavelength of the sound. Some of the effects are shown in Figure 1-17. If the wavelength is large, as shown in Figure 1-17(a), then the obstacle is virtually "invisible" to the waves, and sound will be propagated as if no obstacle were there at all. At shorter wavelengths, as shown in Figure 1-17(b), there will

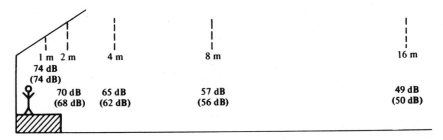

**Figure 1-16.** Departures from inverse square law observed in practice. Measured values of speech peaks are given in $L_P$. Calculated values are indicated in parentheses.

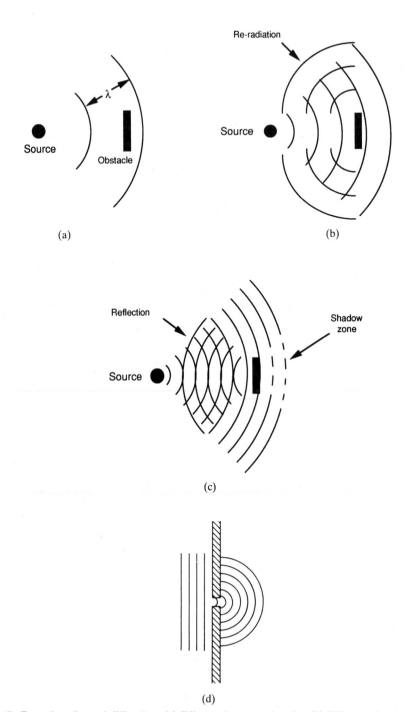

**Figure 1-17.** Examples of sound diffraction. (a) Effect at long wavelengths. (b) Effect at shorter wavelengths. (c) Effect at very short wavelengths. (d) Sound re-radiating spherically as it passes through a small opening in a barrier.

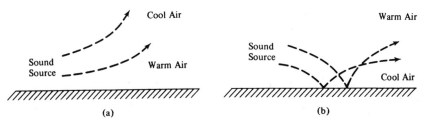

**Figure 1-18.** Illustration of sound refraction due to temperature gradients.

be a degree of shadowing, with some sound reradiating from the obstacle. At very short wavelengths, as shown in Figure 1-17(c), there will be a very clear shadow zone as well as a pronounced reflection of sound from the obstacle. Sound that intercepts a small opening in a barrier is transmitted and radiated as a spherical wavefront, as if from a small source. This is shown in Figure 1-17(d).

Sound *refracts*, or changes its velocity, as it passes between zones of differing temperature. This is usually accompanied by a change in direction of propagation, as shown in Figure 1-18. Wind can have a similar effect. The resulting velocity of sound is the sum its velocity in still air and the velocity of wind in a given direction. Moderate winds will have little effect, but strong winds can, over large distances, affect the distribution of sound, as shown in Figure 1.19.

## 1.7 ATMOSPHERIC LOSSES

Over distance, there is a loss of high frequencies in air, and the effect is greatest when the relative humidity is low. The magnitude of the effect is seen in the data shown in Figure 1-20. In Figure 1-20(a), losses due both to inverse square effects are humidity are shown, while in Figure 1-20(b) losses at several frequencies are shown in terms of relative attenuation over distance and signal transit time through air.

The data presented in Figure 1-20 is useful in determining required high-frequency boosting when sound pickup must take place at large distances, as in recording a pipe organ in a large space.

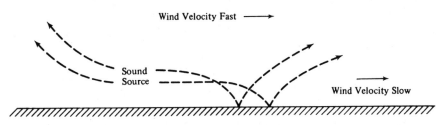

**Figure 1-19.** Effect of wind on sound propagation.

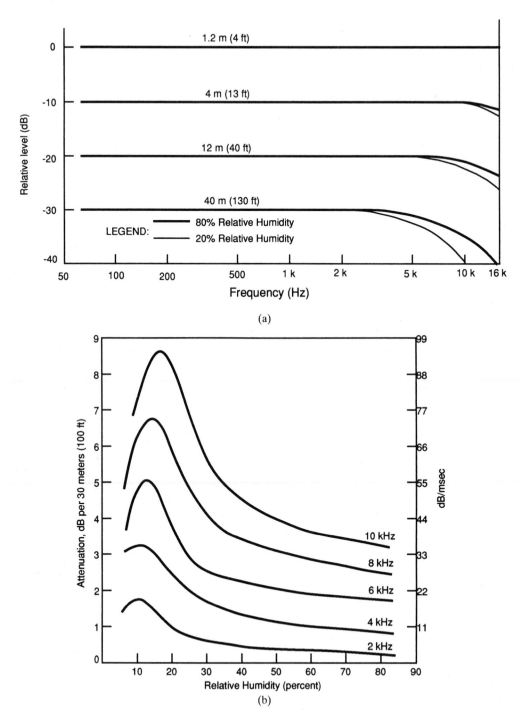

**Figure 1-20.** Atmospheric losses. (a) Losses due to both inverse square and humidity. (b) Relative attenuation versus distance and signal transit time through air.

## 1.8 DIRECTIVITY OF THEORETICAL SOUND SOURCES AND MUSICAL INSTRUMENTS

### 1.8.1 Directivity Index (*DI*) and Directivity Factor (*Q*)

Although we do not normally use the term in relation to musical instruments, *DI* is a useful concept in describing the tendency of most sound-producing devices to radiate preferentially in a given direction. Figure 1-21 illustrates the concept. *Directivity index* and *directivity factor* are related by the following equations:

$$DI = 10 \, log \, Q \tag{1-16}$$

$$Q = (10)^{DI/10} \tag{1-17}$$

Figure 1-22 shows the directivity characteristics of a vibrating piston at the end of a long tube, a condition corresponding roughly to sound radiation from the bell of a brass instrument. Directivity is shown as a function of wavelength, $\lambda$, related to the diameter of the piston. The data shown in Figure 1-23 relates specifically to the directionality of brass instruments, based on the diameter of their bells (2). The highest fundamental frequencies a trumpet can produce are normally in the range of 1 kHz. This corresponds to *2f* in the polar graph, and it can be clearly seen that the instrument is virtually omnidirectional at that frequency. Only the higher harmonics of the instrument exhibit directional response along the axis of the bell.

Figure 1-24 shows the directional characteristics of a vibrating piston mounted in a wall or large baffle, a condition corresponding roughly to the placement of many monitor

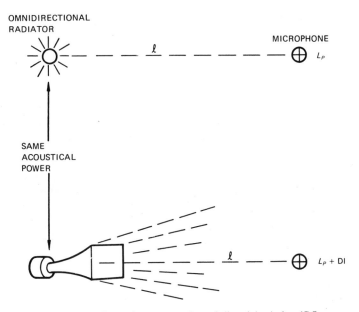

**Figure 1-21.** General representation of directivity index (*DI*).

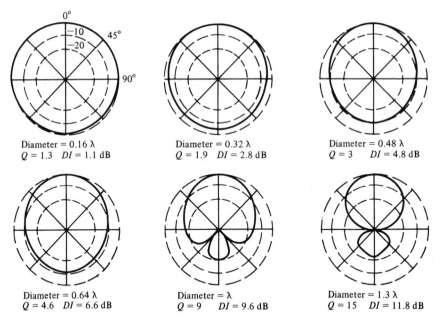

Diameter = 0.16 λ
Q = 1.3  DI = 1.1 dB

Diameter = 0.32 λ
Q = 1.9  DI = 2.8 dB

Diameter = 0.48 λ
Q = 3    DI = 4.8 dB

Diameter = 0.64 λ
Q = 4.6  DI = 6.6 dB

Diameter = λ
Q = 9    DI = 9.6 dB

Diameter = 1.3 λ
Q = 15   DI = 11.8 dB

**Figure 1-22.** Directional characteristics of a piston mounted at the end of a long tube as a function of source diameter and wavelength.

loudspeakers in recording control rooms. Note that when the diameter of the piston is equal to the radiated wavelength, the radiation pattern is fairly directional ($DI = 10$ dB), but without the presence of minor lobes. In practice, it is difficult to operate cone loudspeakers at frequencies corresponding to this wavelength relationship, and at the same time maintain other desirable response characteristics.

The directional characteristics of woodwind instruments are quite complex, inasmuch as they depend on the ever-changing pattern of open key holes. The data presented in Figure 1-25 shows the complex nature of radiation from woodwind instruments along the bell axis (2). Note that response along the axis of the bell is probably the worst, while response in the range of 45 to 60 degrees off-axis is quite smooth. In a later chapter we will discuss microphone placements for accurate close pickup of musical instruments

String instruments are very complex in their radiation characteristics. At their lowest frequencies, radiation is largely by way of cavity resonances in the body of the instrument and is basically omnidirectional. At mid frequencies, radiation is preferential perpendicular to the top plate of the instrument; and at the highest frequencies, radiation is largely from the bridge, which is effectively decoupled from the instrument. The data presented in Figure 1-26(a) shows the directional characteristics of the violin in the vertical plane perpendicular to the strings, while the data shown in Figure 1-26(b) shows the response in the horizontal plane. The recording engineer should note in particular that response along the axis of the top plate is quite directional in the 2 kHz range. Accordingly, experienced recording engineers avoid placing microphones along that axis in order to avoid a strident sound.

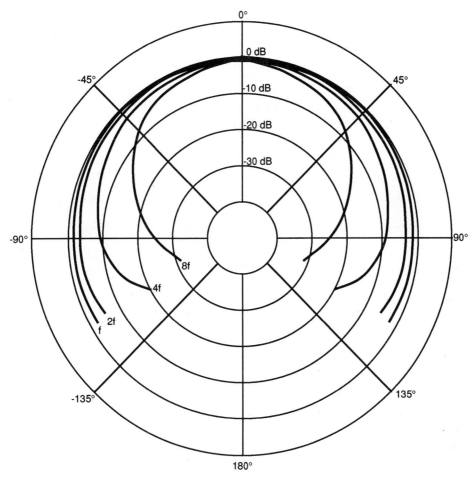

**Figure 1-23.** Directional properties of brass instruments along the axis of the bell. For a trumpet, $f = 500$ Hz; trombone, $f = 250$ Hz; tuba, $f = 167$ Hz. (*Data after Benade (2)*)

Finally, Figure 1-27 the theoretical characteristics of a freely suspended vibrating piston. The principle is that of a *dipole* radiator. The essential characteristics of the dipole are:

a. Response is zero at off-axis angles of ±90 degrees, and
b. The front and back pressure relationships are always in opposite polarity.

Many percussion instruments, such as vibrating plates, the tambourine, and the like, approximate this directional response.

## 1.9 THE NEAR AND FAR SOUND FIELDS

Earlier we discussed inverse square law and stated that each time we halved our distance from a source in a free field, the level increases 6 dB. If we are sufficiently far away

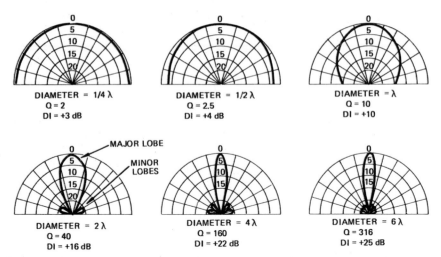

**Figure 1-24.** Directional characteristics of a piston mounted in a large, flat baffle as a function of source diameter and wavelength.

from a source, this is the case; but it is intuitively clear that we cannot continue the process ad infinitum. Actually, as we move within a certain distance from a radiator, significant departures from inverse square law are observed. Figure 1-28 illustrates this for a 0.3-meter diameter loudspeaker. Note that when we move within a distance on the order of the dimensions of the radiator itself, the departure from inverse square law becomes significant. The *near field* is that portion of the free field where inverse square

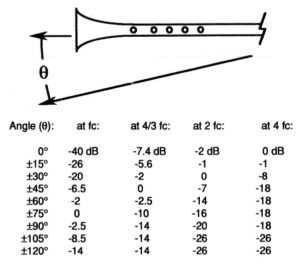

| Angle ($\theta$): | at fc: | at 4/3 fc: | at 2 fc: | at 4 fc: |
|---|---|---|---|---|
| 0° | -40 dB | -7.4 dB | -2 dB | 0 dB |
| ±15° | -26 | -5.6 | -1 | -1 |
| ±30° | -20 | -2 | 0 | -8 |
| ±45° | -6.5 | 0 | -7 | -18 |
| ±60° | -2 | -2.5 | -14 | -18 |
| ±75° | 0 | -10 | -16 | -18 |
| ±90° | -2.5 | -14 | -20 | -18 |
| ±105° | -8.5 | -14 | -26 | -26 |
| ±120° | -14 | -14 | -26 | -26 |

**Figure 1-25.** Directional characteristics of woodwind instruments related to the instrument's cutoff frequency, $f$. For the clarinet and oboe, $f_c = 1500$ Hz; English horn, $f_c = 1$ kHz; bass clarinet, $f_c = 750$ Hz; bassoon, $f_c = 500$ Hz. (*Data after Benade (2)*)

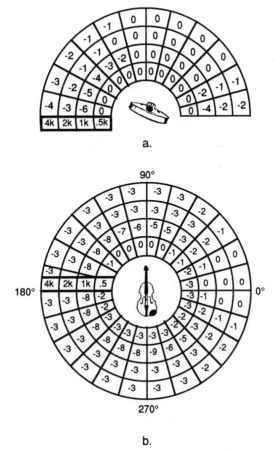

**Figure 1-26.** Directional characteristics of the violin (a) Vertical (b) Horizontal.

relationships do not hold, and the *far field* is that portion beyond it where inverse square relationships do hold. In the far field, the source may be considered to exist at a single point in space.

## 1.10 LINE AND PLANE SOUND SOURCES

Line and plane sound sources represent special cases of the near field and exhibit their own unique properties. For example, the attenuation of sound with distance from a long line array is only 3 dB per doubling of distance. A busy freeway approximates such a sound source, and the noise of a freeway can often be heard at considerable distances, due to the low attenuation rate with respect to distance.

A plane array, which can be approximated at a rock concert by large stacks of loudspeakers, exhibits essentially no attenuation with distance when the observer is fairly close to it. The transition between the three zones of no attenuation, 3 dB with doubling

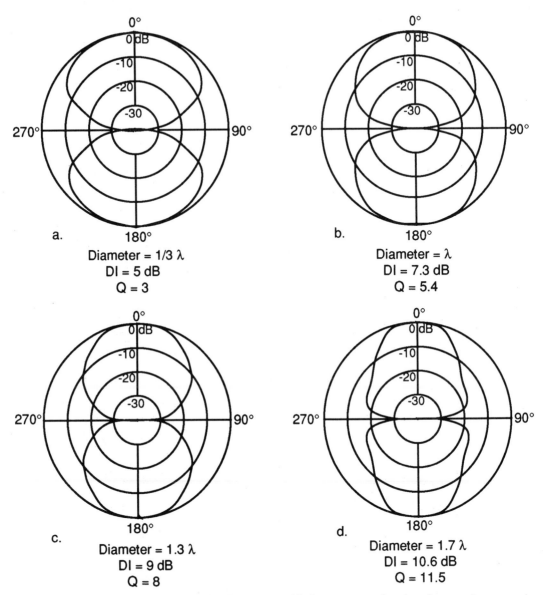

**Figure 1-27.** Directional characteristics of a piston mounted in free space as a function of source diameter and wavelength.

of distance, and 6 dB with doubling of distance, is analyzed in Figure 1-29. Here, we observe attenuation with respect to distance from a large rectangular sound source of dimensions $A$ and $B$, where $A$ is the shorter dimension and $B$ is the longer one. As we moved away from the source, we observe transitions from plane, to line, and finally to point source behavior in terms of attenuation with distance.

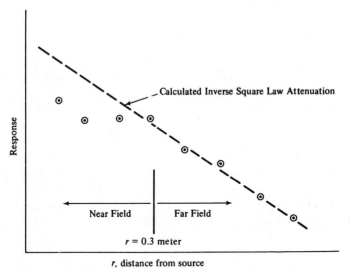

**Figure 1-28.** Illustration of near-field and far-field phenomena.

## 1.11 GROWTH, DECAY, AND ATTENUATION OF SOUND INDOORS

### 1.11.1 The Reverberant Sound Field

The behavior of sound in a large room is very complex, and we need to make a number of simplifying assumptions if we are to acquire an intuitive grasp of it. Let us assume that an impulsive sound is generated on the stage of an auditorium and that we are going

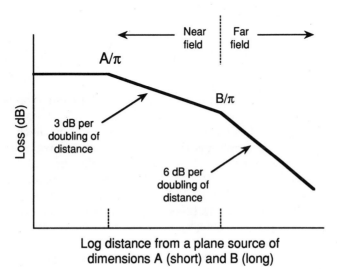

**Figure 1-29.** Attenuation of sound with distance from a rectangular sound source.

to monitor what happens at some location in the audience area. What we would perceive might look something like Figure 1-30(a). The sound is generated at $T = 0$ seconds and is perceived after a short interval as a direct sound. Shortly after, multiple reflections begin to arrive at the monitoring position, few at first, but becoming more dense with time. Figure 1-30(b) presents a spatial representation of these events, showing that direct sound reaches the listener along a single axis, while early reflections come primarily from the front and sides, and the dense reverberant field comes from all directions.

After some time, perhaps a second or so, these many echoes become so dense that they are perceived as a continuous decay of sound called *reverberation*. Reverberation time ($T_{60}$) is arbitrarily defined to be the time it takes for the reverberant field to decay 60 dB after a sound source has been turned off. Subjectively, a room is said to be "live" if its $T_{60}$ is long in relation to its size, or "dead" if it is short in relation to its size. Figure 1-30(c) illustrates the growth of sound, eventually reaching a steady state condition, and finally decaying when the source is turned off. Figure 1-30(d) shows the same growth and decay of sound, but with a logarithmic scale indicating sound pressure levels in decibels. Note that the period of decay appears to be much longer than the period of growth in this representation. This is, in fact, the way we hear reverberation, even though the growth and decay intervals are equal in terms of acoustical power.

Wallace Sabine (13) developed an empirical equation for determining $T_{60}$. If a room is fairly live, then its $T_{60}$ is given accurately by

$$T_{60} = \frac{.16V}{S\bar{\alpha}} \tag{1-18}$$

where

$V$ = volume (m³)
$S$ = surface area (m²)
$\bar{\alpha}$ = average absorption coefficient

In English units:

$$T_{60} = \frac{.05V}{S\alpha}, \quad V \text{ in ft}^3 \text{ and } S \text{ in ft}^2$$

Average absorption coefficient ($\bar{\alpha}$) is a new term; but let us first define what we mean by absorption coefficient.

The *absorption coefficient* ($\alpha$) of a material is a measure of how much sound is absorbed when sound strikes it. If $E$ represents the energy in a sound wave striking a material with an absorption coefficient of $\alpha_1$, then $E\alpha_1$ will be absorbed and $E(1 - \alpha_1)$ will be reflected. This is shown in Figure 1-31.  Perhaps now we can appreciate the complexity and apparent randomness of Figure 1-30(a). Sound strikes surfaces at various distances and values of $\alpha$, and the early reflections clearly show this. Later, only after all the surfaces have been brought into play, does an average value of absorption coefficient become apparent.

The calculation of $\bar{\alpha}$ is a tedious job, but it is a necessary calculation during the design phase of an auditorium. Mathematically it is given by

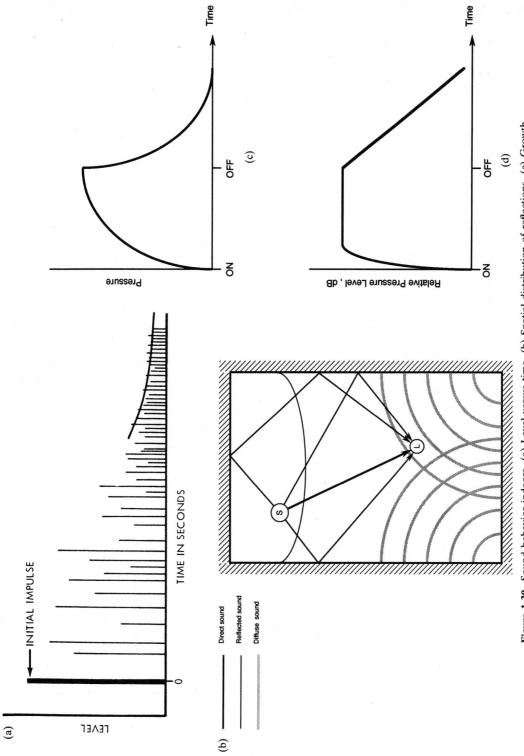

**Figure 1-30.** Sound behavior indoors. (a) Level versus time. (b) Spatial distribution of reflections. (c) Growth and decay of sound. (d) Growth and decay of sound expressed logarithmically.

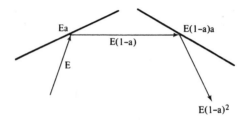

**Figure 1-31.** Illustration of sound loss with subsequent reflections.

$$\bar{\alpha} = \frac{S_1\alpha_1 + S_2\alpha_2 + \cdots + S_n\alpha_n}{S_1 + S_2 + \cdots + S_3} \tag{1-19}$$

Where $S_{(1,\ldots,n)}$ represent the areas of the individual boundary materials, and $\alpha_{(1,\ldots,n)}$ represent, respectively, their absorption coefficients. Typical values of $\alpha$ for some common materials are given in Table 1-2. Note that most materials have a significant variation in absorption coefficient as a function of frequency. Typically, "soft" materials will exhibit lower values of absorption coefficients at low frequencies and higher values at high frequencies.

EXAMPLE: Calculate the reverberation time at 500 Hz for the rectangular room described below.

Room dimensions:
length = 11 m
width = 5 m
height = 3.5 m
volume = 192.5 m³

Details of areas:

| Materials: | $\alpha$ | Dimensions | Area (S) | $S\alpha$ |
|---|---|---|---|---|
| Floor, wood | 0.10 | 11 × 5 | 55 | 5.5 |
| Ceiling, plywood | 0.17 | 11 × 5 | 55 | 9.4 |
| Wall, brick | 0.03 | 5 × 3.5 | 17.5 | 0.5 |
| Wall, brick | 0.03 | 5 × 3.5 | 17.5 | 0.5 |
| Wall, velour | 0.49 | 11 × 3.5 | 38.5 | 18.9 |
| Wall, velour | 0.49 | 11 × 3.5 | 38.5 | 18.9 |
| | | | 222 | |

$$\bar{\alpha} = \frac{\text{Total } S\alpha}{S} = \frac{53.7}{222} = 0.46$$

$$T_{60} = \frac{0.16\,(192.5)}{222\,(0.24)} = 0.58 \text{ sec}$$

## Table 1-2. Absorption coefficients

| Materials | 125 Hz | 250 Hz | 500 Hz | 1 kHz | 2 kHz | 4 kHz |
|---|---|---|---|---|---|---|
| Brick, unglazed | 0.03 | 0.03 | 0.03 | 0.04 | 0.05 | 0.07 |
| Carpet, heavy, on concrete | 0.02 | 0.06 | 0.14 | 0.37 | 0.60 | 0.65 |
| Medium velour (draped to half area) | 0.07 | 0.31 | 0.49 | 0.75 | 0.70 | 0.60 |
| Concrete or terrazzo floor | 0.01 | 0.01 | 0.015 | 0.02 | 0.02 | 0.02 |
| Wood floor | 0.15 | 0.11 | 0.10 | 0.07 | 0.06 | 0.07 |
| Plywood paneling, 9.5 mm thick | 0.28 | 0.22 | 0.17 | 0.09 | 0.10 | 0.11 |

The equation we have used here to determine reverberation time assumes that absorption in the room is fairly evenly distributed, which is not the case in this simple example. The difference between calculated and measured reverberation time is not always reassuring to acoustical consultants, and considerable experience is required to correlate and justify their differences. Acoustical handbooks present absorption coefficients for a wide variety of materials in different mounting configurations, thus enabling the acoustical engineer to make detailed reverberation time calculations. Data is also presented for audience areas, occupied as well as unoccupied. Air absorption is also considered at high frequencies.

### 1.11.2 Norris–Eyring Reverberation Time Equation

Years after Sabine's work, Norris and Eyring (10) developed a reverberation time equation which gives more accurate results in less reverberant rooms. However, the requirements for good diffusion and even distribution of absorption still hold. Their equation is

$$T_{60} = \frac{.16V}{-S \ln (1-\bar{\alpha})} \tag{1-20}$$

In English units the equation is

$$T_{60} = \frac{.05V}{-S \ln (1-\bar{\alpha})} \tag{1-21}$$

EXAMPLE: Solve the previous reverberation time exercise using the Norris–Eyring equation:

$$T_{60} = \frac{(.16)(192.5)}{-(222) \ln (1-.46)} = \frac{30.8}{137} = 0.22 \text{ sec}$$

The value of 0.22 sec given by the Norris–Eyring equation is probably closer to what might actually be measured in the experimental space we have been discussing in this section.

### 1.11.3 Attenuation of Sound with Distance Indoors

As we have shown, the generation of reverberation involves an ensemble of room reflections, and this tends to establish a fairly uniform sound pressure in the room. We have all had the experience of listening to a sound source in a highly reverberant space, perhaps a house of worship or large public building. As we move away from the sound source, the attenuation seems to follow the inverse square law at first, but we soon reach a point beyond which level the remains fairly constant. This is shown in Figure 1-32. Note that at the points where direct and reverberant field are equal (vertical arrows), the resultant sound pressure is 3 dB higher than either field, representing the summation of equal power levels. The distance where the two fields are equal is referred to as the *critical distance*, $D_c$. The equation that describes the indoor attenuation curve is

$$\text{Loss in dB (as a function of } r ) = 10 \log \left[ \frac{Q}{4\pi r^2} + \frac{4}{R} \right] \tag{1-22}$$

The quantity $R$ is known as the *room constant* and is given by

$$R = \frac{S\bar{\alpha}}{(1-\bar{\alpha})} \tag{1-23}$$

where $S$ is the total boundary area in the space and $\bar{\alpha}$ is the average absorption coefficient. The term $Q$ is the directivity factor of the sound source in the direction of observation and $r$ is the distance from the radiator. Equations (1-22) and (1-23) can be solved in any consistent system of units.

The equation (1-22) must be solved for two values of $r$ and gives the difference in $L_P$ between those two distances. The first term in the brackets represents the inverse square law component, while the second term represents the constant reverberant field component.

If we equate the two bracketed terms in the equation, we can solve for $D_c$, the distance at which the two fields are equal:

$$D_c = .14 \sqrt{QR} \tag{1-24}$$

Note from Figure 1-32 that the attenuation of sound beyond $D_c$ is minimal; it can only decrease an additional 3 dB.

The equation for attenuation with distance indoors is rather cumbersome to solve directly, and a number of worked out graphical solutions are shown in Figure 1-33. A $Q$ value of 5, typical for a sound source of moderate directivity has been assumed. A general estimate of the room constant can be determined from the graph of Figure 1-34. Locate the reverberation time along the vertical axis and the room volume along the horizontal axis. They will intersect at or near one of the diagonal lines. Trace the diagonal line to the edge of the graph and read the room constant. The graph is based upon what may be called "normal" rooms, those whose length, width, and height dimensions do not exceed ratios of about 1.6.

EXAMPLE: In an auditorium with a volume of 12,500 m³ and a reverberation time of 2.5 sec, find the sound attenuation in dB between distances of 5 m and 20 m along the major axis of a loudspeaker with a directivity factor of 5.

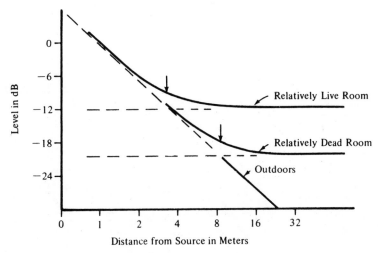

**Figure 1-32.** Sound attenuation with distance indoors. Arrows indicate critical distance. At these points, the level is 3 dB higher than either direct or reverberant field.

*Answer:* Referring to Figure 1-34, locate the volume of 12,500 m³ along the bottom of the graph; then move upward until the horizontal line corresponding to 2.5 sec is intersected. Note that this intersection takes place at the diagonal line representing a room constant of about 800 m². Now, locate the curve in Figure 1-33 representing a room constant of 800 m² and read directly the difference in dB between 5 and 20 m. For 5 m read −2 dB, and for 20 m read −9 dB. Thus, 9 − 2 = 7 dB attenuation from 5 m to 20 m.

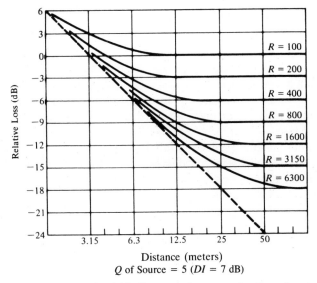

**Figure 1-33.** Sound attenuation with distance indoors as a function of room constant.

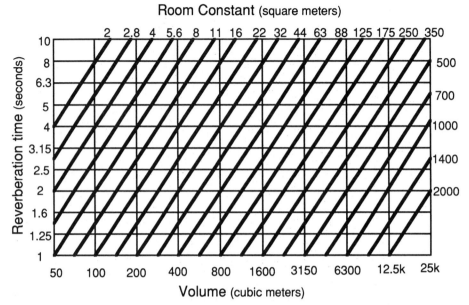

**Figure 1-34.** Estimation of room constant when volume and reverberation time are given.

EXAMPLE: Using the graph of Figure 1-35, determine the value of $D_c$, that distance at which the direct and reverberant sound fields are equal, in the previous example.

*Answer*: 9 meters.

### 1.11.4 Quasi-Steady-State Conditions

The equations presented describing the attenuation of sound indoors are based on theoretical models that assumed a highly diffuse reverberant field. They are fairly accurate in reverberant houses of worship and other spaces, but they tend to give erroneous results when used in small rooms or those rooms with low ceilings in relation to height and width. While the deviations from the theoretical attenuation curve may be only ±2 dB in large reverberant spaces, the errors noted in rooms with low ceilings can be significant, as shown in Figure 1-36.

Peutz (11) presents an empirical equation for determining the approximate slope of level fall-off with respect to distance observed beyond the calculated $D_c$ in large rooms with low reverberation times:

$$\Delta = \frac{0.4\,\sqrt[6]{V}}{T_{60}} \tag{1-25}$$

In this equation, V is the room volume in cubic meters, and $T_{60}$ is the reverberation time. $\Delta$ is the fall-off in dB for each doubling of distance beyond the calculated $D_c$.

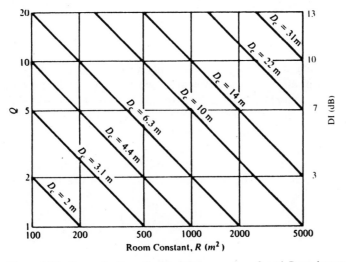

**Figure 1-35.** Determination of critical distance when $Q$ and $R$ are known.

In rooms with low ceilings relative to length and width, the equation is

$$\Delta = \frac{0.4\sqrt{V}}{hT_{60}}$$ (1-26)

In this equation, $h$ is the height of the room in meters.

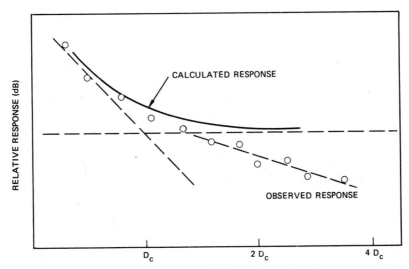

**Figure 1-36.** Departure from calculated attenuation with distance in semireverberant spaces. Rate of attenuation beyond critical distance is given by Equations (1-25) and (1-26).

### 1.11.5 Modification of the Room Constant

Another significant departure from the equations presented earlier is the variation in reverberant field level as a function of absorption coefficient of the first reflecting surface. The equations assume that absorption is evenly distributed and that sound radiation is essentially uniform in all directions. However, we know that when a directional radiator is pointed at a highly absorptive surface, the resulting reverberant field will be considerably less than if that same source of sound were aimed at a highly reflective surface. In sound reinforcement, workers have known for years that aiming directional loudspeakers at the absorptive audience area, which is where the sound is desired, produces a minimum reverberant field. Augspurger (1) has suggested that the equation for room constant be altered to taken into account the absorption coefficient of the first reflective surface:

$$R' = \frac{S\bar{\alpha}}{1 - \alpha_1} \qquad (1\text{-}27)$$

In this equation, $\bar{\alpha}$ is the average absorption coefficient for the space, and $\alpha_1$ is the absorption coefficient of the first reflective surface. Figure 1-37 shows how reverberant levels can be influenced under these conditions.

### 1.11.6 Behavior of Sound in Small Spaces

The equations presented thus far regarding reverberant field behavior are largely statistical, in that they describe the average behavior of many reflections over time. It has been assumed that, because of the great number of these reflections, a generally diffuse condition existed. In small rooms, no such assumptions can be made; the dimensions of the room itself determined its behavior at various frequencies.

All rooms, large or small, have *normal modes*, or *eigentones*, which are the specific frequencies at which the room resonates. For all but the simplest shapes, calculation of normal modes is difficult. For a rectangular space, the equation that determines normal modes is

$$f = \frac{c}{2}\sqrt{\left[\left(\frac{n_l}{l}\right)^2 + \left(\frac{n_w}{w}\right)^2 + \left(\frac{n_h}{h}\right)^2\right]} \qquad (1\text{-}28)$$

where $c$ is the velocity of sound in air; $l$, $w$, and $h$ are the length, width, and height of the room respectively; and $n_l$, $n_w$, and $n_h$ are a set of integers (values 0, 1, 2, 3, . . .) taken in all possible combinations. Figure 1-38 shows the typical pressure level response for a swept source of sound in a rectangular room of dimensions 5.2, 6.4, and 2.7. Note that the room responds primarily to its modal frequencies (indicated here by values of $n_l$, $n_w$, and $n_h$ in parentheses). Note also that the normal modes become more closely spaced with rising frequency.

Smooth reverberant response is a requisite for any space which is to be used for music, and the measure of it depends on both room volume and reverberation time. Schroeder (14) presents an equation which determines the frequency above which room modes overlap smoothly, creating a diffuse field. Often called the *Schroeder frequency*, it is given by

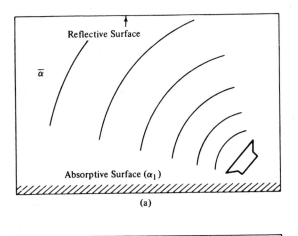

(a)

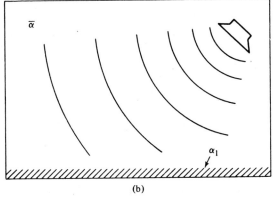

(b)

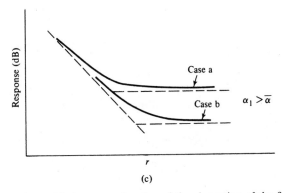

(c)

**Figure 1-37.** Attenuation of sound indoors as a function of the absorption of the first reflecting surface.

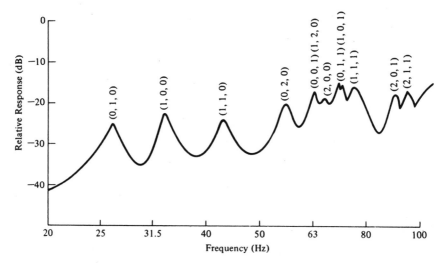

**Figure 1-38.** Illustration of normal modes in the response of a rectangular room 5.2 × 6.4 × 2  meters.

$$f = 2000 \left[ \frac{T_{60}}{V} \right]^{1/2} \tag{1-29}$$

In this equation, $T_{60}$ is the reverberation time and $V$ is the volume in cubic meters. For a typical concert hall of volume 19,000 m³ and a reverberation time of 2.5 sec, the Schroeder frequency is 23 Hz.

Another estimate of the frequency above which diffuse room response exists is simply to multiply the lowest room mode by 10. In the example just cited, the longest room dimension is about 50 m, producing a room mode ($n = 1$) of 3.4 Hz. Multiplying this by 10 gives 34 Hz. Obviously, there is no single frequency above which the room's performance suddenly becomes diffuse, and both answers here may be considered to be broad indicators of the frequency range above which the room's performance has become essentially diffuse.

Most large recording spaces have sufficient modal density; it is the smaller monitoring spaces that are often problematic. Control rooms, which we will study in a later chapter, are physically small and, if undamped, will present problems of insufficient modal density. The only cure is to damp out *all* low-frequency modes, allowing the room to become reflective at mid and higher frequencies where it can be assumed that good diffusion exists.

### 1.11.7 Mean Free Path (MFP)

The concept of MFP grows out of the development of reverberation time equations. It can be shown that, in a wide variety of normal spaces, the average, or mean, free path of sound as it is reflected about a room, is given by

$$\text{MFP} = \frac{4V}{S} \tag{1-30}$$

where $V$ is the volume of the room and $S$ is the area of all exposed surfaces. The equation is consistent in any system of units.

While the concept properly belongs in the study of physical acoustics, it is perhaps more important in shaping certain subjective judgements of sound behavior in performance spaces and in recording studios. MFP translates directly into delay time via the equation:

$$\text{Delay (seconds)} = \frac{\text{MFP}}{c} \tag{1-31}$$

where $c$ is the velocity of sound in the appropriate system of units. Thus, the delay of a first-order wall reflection from a sound source to a listener, relative to the direct sound, may be expressed statistically as two-times MFP less the delay of the direct sound itself. Likewise, the delay of a second-order reflection can be expressed at three-times MFP less the delay of the direct sound, and so forth. This subject will be explored in a later chapter.

## BIBLIOGRAPHY

1. G. Augspurger, "More Accurate Calculation of the Room Constant." *J. Audio Engineering Society*, vol. 23, no. 5 (1975).
2. A. Benade, "From Instrument to Ear in a Room: Direct or Via Recording," *J. Audio Engineering Society*, vol. 33, no. 4 (1985)
3. L. Beranek, *Acoustics*, McGraw-Hill, New York (1954).
4. L. Beranek, *Music, Acoustics and Architecture*, Wiley, New York (1962).
5. L. Cremer and H. Mueller, *Principles and Applications of Room Acoustics* (translated by T. Schultz), Applied Science Publishers, New York (1982).
6. L. Doelle, *Environmental Acoustics*, McGraw-Hill, New York (1972).
7. L. Kinsler et al., *Fundamentals of Acoustics*, Wiley, New York (1982).
8. V. Knudsen and C. Harris, Acoustical Designing in Architecture, Acoustical Society of America, New York (1978).
9. H. Kuttruff, *Room Acoustics*, Applied Science Publishers, London (1979).
10. R. Norris, "A Derivation of the Reverberation Formula," in Appendix II of V. Knudsen, *Architectural Acoustics*, Wiley, New York (1939).
11. V. Peutz, "Quasi-steady-state and Decaying Sound Fields," *Ingenieursblad*, vol. 42, no. 18 (1973) (in Dutch).
12. E. Rathe, "Note on Two Common Problems of Sound Propagation," *J. Sound and Vibration*, vol. 10, pp. 472–479 (1969).
13. W. Sabine, "Collected Papers on Acoustics," Harvard University Press (1927).
14. M. Schroeder, "Progress in Architectural Acoustics and Artificial Reverberation: Concert Hall Acoustics and Number Theory," *J. Audio Engineering Society*, vol. 32, no. 4 (1984).

# 2

## PYSCHOLOGICAL ACOUSTICS

### 2.1 INTRODUCTION

Psychological acoustics, or psychoacoustics, deals with the subjective nature of hearing, and the intention of this chapter is to cover those aspects of the subject that the recording engineer will deal with in his daily work. Such topics as loudness phenomena, sound image localization, pitch perception, masking, and the all-important subject of hearing protection will be discussed.

### 2.2 LOUDNESS PHENOMENA

At the lower limit of audibility, persons with normal hearing can detect air particle velocities of about $2 \times 10^{-6}$ cm/sec. At the upper limit, the threshold of feeling, the ear responds to air particle velocities of about 2 cm/sec. This is a range of some 120 dB. The sensation of *loudness* is a complex function of both level and frequency. Loudness comparisons are complex as well. Over most of our hearing range, we judge a level increase of 10 dB to be "twice as loud," or a decrease of 10 dB to be "half as loud," even though a level difference of 3 dB accounts for twice or half power.

For single tones, the phenomenon can be demonstrated rather simply. Figure 2-1(a) shows the equal loudness curves developed by Robinson and Dadson (8), which represent a refinement of the earlier work of Fletcher and Munson. Loudness level is expressed in *phons*, and individual phon contours represent equal loudness to the ear.

Consider a pure tone of 1 kHz at 100 dB $L_P$. By comparison, a tone of 100 Hz will have to be about 3 dB higher in level to sound as loud. Assume that program spectral judgments have been made at these levels. Now, let us examine the effects that take place 50 dB lower. Again, assuming a reference tone of 1 kHz, note what happens at 100 Hz. We see that the level at that frequency will have to be boosted about 8 dB in order to sound as loud.

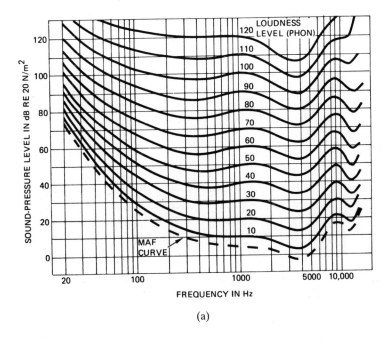

(a)

Level change for "half-loudness" over the
frequency range from 20 to 1000 Hz.

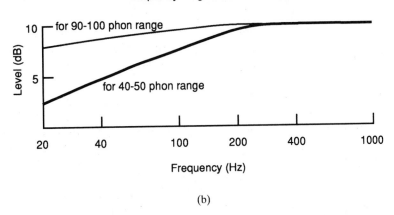

(b)

**Figure 2-1.** Loudness phenomena. (a) Robinson–Dadson equal loudness countours. (b) Plots of narrowing of the 10-dB contours as a function of frequency. (c) Normal level and frequency ranges of speech and music.

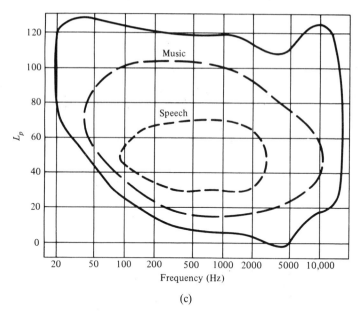

(c)

**Figure 2-1.** Continued.

There is a 5-dB divergence at 100 Hz when we compare the 50-phon and 100-phon curves, and this implies that program balances made in the 100-phon loudness range will sound bass-deficient when they are played back at lower levels.

Many consumer preamplifiers have loudness compensation circuits that boost low frequencies when the playback level is reduced. The aim is to maintain some degree of natural balance at low playback levels.

Sound level meters, which were discussed in Section 1.4.3, include weighting networks that enable the user to adjust the meter readings to that they reflect the relative loudness of noise or program at various levels. The C scale is fairly flat and is it normalized to the curves for 100 phons and higher. The B scale approximates the inverse of the 70-phon curve and should be used for assessing noise levels in that range. The A scale is roughly the inverse of the 40-phon curve and should be used for assessing noise levels in that range and lower.

Another view of subjective loudness is shown in Figure 2-1(b). Here is plotted the narrowing of 10-dB phon contours as a function of frequency. At 1 kHz and above, the 10-dB spacing between phon contours as observed in Figure 2-1(a) is constant. However, at lower frequencies, the contours are closer together. At higher levels (90 to 120 dB) the contours converge moderately as frequency is lowered, while at middle levels (50 to 90 dB) the convergence is more pronounced. At the lowest levels (10 to 50 dB), the convergence is quite pronounced. Remembering that a phon difference of 10 dB at 1 kHz corresponds to judgments of half or twice subjective loudness, it is easy to see how important correct monitoring levels and monitor system bass response are to achieving correct balance of bass information in recording. The implication here is that the recording engineer and producer should monitor their recorded products at levels likely to be encountered in the typical living room.

Figure 2-1(c) shows the level and frequency range of speech and orchestral music superimposed on the envelope of the Robinson-Dadson contours, spanning the range from the minimum audible field (MAF) up to the 120-phon contour. Note that normal speech and music occupy a relatively small range. However, we must consider the limits that are imposed in both dynamic range and bandwidth by typical home playback equipment, as well as the noise floor in most homes.

### 2.2.1 Loudness Dependence on Signal Duration

Figure 2-2 illustrates the dependence of perceived loudness on the duration of a signal. The test signal here is a 1-kHz tone. Observe that a 10-msec burst of tone will be some 10 dB lower in loudness to a listener than a tone with a duration of 400 msec or greater. As will be noted in a later chapter, the ballistic characteristics of some program meters have been designed with these factors in mind. In particular, the persistence of the venerable VU (volume unit) meter over many decades rests, at least in part, on its ability to track the ear in terms of loudness.

## 2.3 LOCALIZATION PHENOMENA

### 2.3.1 Phasor Analysis

With a single ear the listener can determine most attributes of a sound except source direction, or localization. The two ears working together are able to sort out the various cues necessary for binaural hearing, which is analogous to binocular vision. The localization acuity of binaural hearing is in the range of $\pm 2.5°$ in the horizontal plane directly ahead of the listener.

Figure 2-3 presents a simple explanation of localization based on phasor analysis. In the figure, the arrows are known as *phasors*, with length indicating amplitude and angular orientation representing the phase angle lead or lag between them. If a source 1 is located

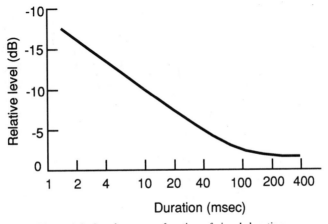

**Figure 2-2.** Loudness as a function of signal duration.

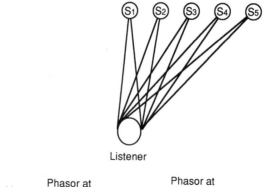

**Figure 2-3.** Phasor analysis of real images. (1) Listener and sound sources. Phasors beginning with center source (2) and progressing to far right source (5).

directly ahead of the listener, then it will produce signal phase relationships at the ears which will be equal due to symmetry (Figure 2-3(2). Source 2, located at the right a small angle away from center, will give rise to a phase difference at the ears due to the slight path length difference at the ears; the phase angle at the right ear will lead that at the left ear (Figure 2-3(3)). In the illustration, the leading phase angle at the right ear is advanced counterclockwise relative to that at the left ear. Phasor relationships for sources at greater angles are shown in Figures 2-3(4) and (5).

Because of diffraction effects around the head, the amplitudes at both ears are very much the same at frequencies up to about 700 Hz, and phase relationships dominate in determining localization. There is a transition region between 700 Hz and about 2 kHz where both amplitude and phase relationships are important, and at frequencies above 2 kHz amplitude cues caused by shadowing around the head are most significant.

Small side-to-side nodding motions of the head may be useful in "zeroing in" on a sound source. The motions are helpful in differentiating between fore and aft sources of sound.

To a remarkable extent a pair of loudspeakers located in front of the listener can simulate sound sources, or phantom images, in the lateral space between the loudspeakers. The basic principle is shown in Figure 2-4(a). This shows the relationships existing at

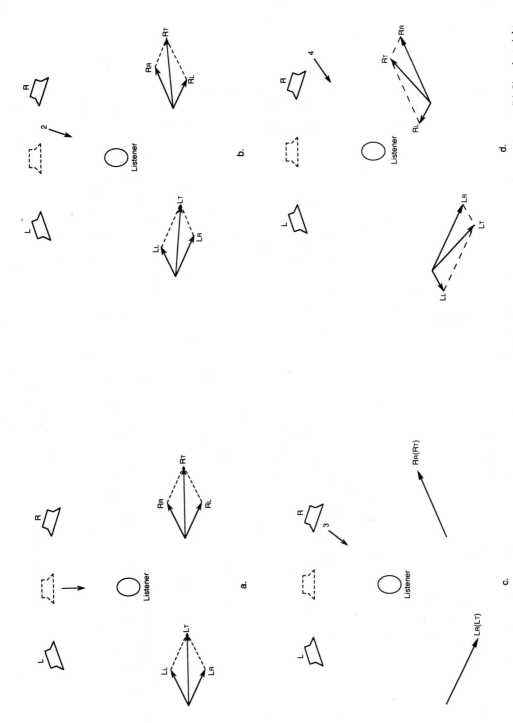

**Figure 2-4.** Phasor analysis of phantom images. (a) Same signal fed to both loudspeakers, producing a center phantom image. (b) Signal at right loudspeaker slightly louder. (c) Signal fed only to right loudspeaker. (d) Left loudspeaker fed signal at 180° polarity.

each ear when identical signals are presented at the loudspeakers. The left ear receives phasors $L_L$ and $L_R$, respectively, from the left and right loudspeakers. In just the same way, the right ear receives phasors $R_L$ and $R_R$. The notation is as follows: $L_L$ is the phasor at the left ear due to the signal from the left loudspeaker, while $L_R$ is the phasor at the left ear due to the signal from the right loudspeaker. A similar situation exists at the right ear with $R_L$ and $R_R$. $L_T$ and $R_T$ represent the total, or summed, phasors at each ear.

When both sets of phasors present the same program material at equal levels at both loudspeakers, we can add the phasors at each ear; these are represented by $L_T$ and $R_T$. Since $L_T$ and $R_T$ have the same magnitude and phase angle, the effect at the ears will be the same as for an actual sound source located directly ahead of the listener.

Now let us observe what happens when the left loudspeaker is powered at a somewhat lower level, as shown in Figure 2-4(b). In this case the net result of adding phasors at the ears produces resultant phasors, $L_T$ and $R_T$, such that $R_T$ leads $L_T$ by some phase angle. The effect at the ears will be the same as for a source located at position 2 between center and the right loudspeaker.

We can extend the examples further with interesting results. Figure 2-4(c) shows what happens when a signal exists only at the right loudspeaker, corresponding to position 3. The only phasors present at the ears are due to the right loudspeaker; thus $L_R = L_T$ and $R_R = R_T$, and localization will clearly be at the right loudspeaker.

If we feed a small amount of signal 180° out of polarity to the left loudspeaker, the phasors will be as shown in Figure 2-4(d). The magnitude of $R_T$ is greater than $L_T$ relative to Figure 2-4(a), and the phase relationship leads by an even greater angle. The effect, which is often subtle, is that of a sound source located *outside* the bounds of the loudspeaker array, roughly at position 4. However, if the level of the out-of-phase signal at the left loudspeaker is increased substantially, then the out-of-bounds localization will give way to confusion for the listener. A practical limit here is that primary out-of-phase signals from the two stereo channels should differ in level by 8 dB or more.

The sound of equal signals presented in the stereo loudspeakers in reversed polarity ("out of phase") is something that all recording engineers should be able to spot almost instantly. It is invariably a sign of mis-wiring in the transmission path.

Phantom images are essential to good stereo, and the analysis we have given here is applicable primarily to listeners located on the plane of symmetry between the loudspeakers. At lower frequencies, the analysis holds for listeners who may be slightly removed from the plane of symmetry. In general, if a listener moves to one side of the plane of symmetry, the effect is that of phantom images tending to "collapse" toward the closer loudspeaker.

Out-of-bounds phantom images are rather unstable, and the effect is usually most convincing when limited to frequencies below about 700 Hz. These images do occur with certain stereo microphone arrays, primarily for ambient information. They will be discussed in a later chapter.

Other aspects of localization have to do with fore–aft and height judgments by the listener. These will be discussed under the subject of binaural sound in a later chapter. The ability to localize in the vertical plane depends on subtle changes in the perceived frequency response of sound sources as they are modified by the convolutions in the external ear. Similar modifications influence our fore–aft localization judgments.

## 2.3.2 Panoramic Potentiometers (Panpots)

The positioning of sound sources by means of the phasor relationships presented in Figure 2-4 can be done through the use of a panpot. Figure 2-5 shows the electrical schematic diagram of a panpot, as well as its relative output positions as a function of rotational settings of the control. When the panpot is in its center position, the resulting equal left and right outputs are both 3 dB down from either full-left or full-right position. As explained in the figure caption, the mathematical relationships in the panpot ensure constant acoustical power output for all panned positions. The panpot operates acoustically on the same phasor analysis as that already discussed.

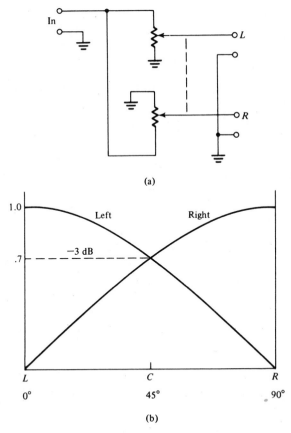

Figure 2-5. Details of a two-channel panpot. (a) Schematic diagram. (b) Response as a function of control position.

### 2.3.3 Analysis of Image Location

During the 1950s, Bauer (2), building on the work of Clark et al. (5), studied stereophonic localization as a function of the effects of relative loudspeaker levels and their included angle subtended with the listener. He referred to this as the stereophonic "law of sines":

$$\frac{\sin \theta_1}{\sin \theta_A} = \frac{S_L - S_R}{S_L + S_R} \tag{2-1}$$

In this equation, $\theta_1$ is the azimuth angle of the phantom image and $\theta_A$ is the azimuth angle of the loudspeakers from the plane of symmetry. $S_L$ and $S_R$ are, respectively, the signal pressures at the listener produced by the left and right loudspeakers. Details are shown in Figure 2-6.

As we have stated, the bulk of our localization of stereophonic phantom images comes from signals below about 700 Hz. Indeed, it can be shown that center images at certain high frequencies actually disappear at the ears and that stereophonic imaging at high frequencies is far from precise. Figure 2-7 shows how the slight displacement of each ear from the plane of symmetry in stereo listening is sufficient to cause pressure cancellations at each ear. Slight changes of head position aggravate this. It is no wonder then that many recording engineers and producers literally agonize over the subjective quality of center panned images, as opposed to those positioned directly at the left or right loudspeakers. In general, the angle subtended by the stereo loudspeakers with the listener ranges from about 45° to no greater than 60°. Larger angles tend to result in less-stable phantom images.

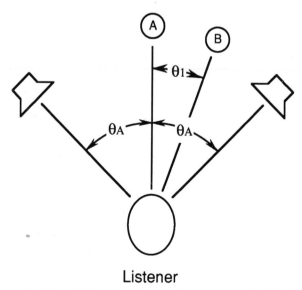

**Figure 2-6.** Bauer's stereophonic law of sines. *A* indicates phantom center signal and *B* indicates position of any arbitrary phantom image.

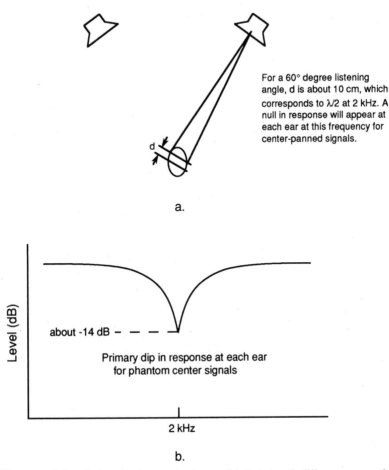

For a 60° degree listening angle, d is about 10 cm, which corresponds to λ/2 at 2 kHz. A null in response will appear at each ear at this frequency for center-panned signals.

a.

b.

**Figure 2-7.** The case of the missing phantom center image. (a) Path length differences around the head. (b) Net frequency response.

### 2.3.4 The Precedence Effect

The precedence effect has been informally described as the "law of the first wavefront." It describes the tendency of the ears to localize in the direction of the first sound arrival, more or less independently of sound levels. Figure 2-8 illustrates the phenomenon. Figure 2-8(a) a stereo loudspeaker pair produces identical levels; however, the right loudspeaker has been delayed by 5 milliseconds. Under this condition, a listener located on the plane of symmetry will localize the sound source at the left loudspeaker.

If the level of the left loudspeaker is reduced approximately 10 dB, the listener will again localize the sound toward the middle, as shown in Figure 2-8(b). However, the center image will not be as precise as in the case of normal center panned images. The trading value of 2 dB per millisecond is fairly linear over this range, as shown in Figure 2-9. Beyond a delay of 5 msec, a constant 10 dB of level imbalance will restore the source

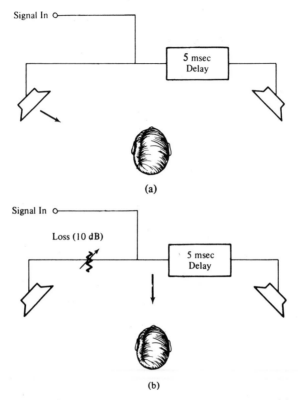

(a)

(b)

**Figure 2-8.** (a) Displacement of apparent sound source using signal delay. (b) Effective cancellation of precedence effect by adjusting levels.

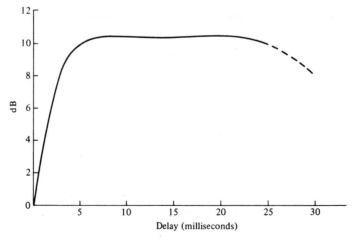

**Figure 2-9.** Approximate delay versus amplitude imbalance relationships for precedence effect.

position to the middle. Above about 25 msec, the listener will hear a distinct echo, and the 10-dB amplitude imbalance will be apparent as such. The data shown in Figure 2-9 is due to Haas (7), and the various phenomena associated with delay are often referred to as the Haas effect. As Haas shows, the data indicates general trends and should be interpreted broadly.

Franssen (4) describes the trade-off between level and time differences in stereo localization for a monophonic signal at both loudspeakers, as shown in Figure 2-10. The delay range covered in the figure is 8 msec, and the horizontal axis indicates the delay (or advance) in the left loudspeaker relative to the right one. For example, if the left loudspeaker leads the right loudspeaker by about 2 msec, the image will be located in the center if the right loudspeaker is about 6 dB louder. If the left loudspeaker leads the right by 4 msec, the image will be located in the center if the right loudspeaker is 8 dB louder. The data thus agrees broadly with that shown in Figure 2-9.

Recording engineers deal with delay effects when multiple stereo microphones are located at different distances from a given sound source. In particular, laterally spaced microphones can give rise to delay cues that may convince the stereo listener that the density of room reflections is greater than it actually is. These effects will be covered in detail in later chapters.

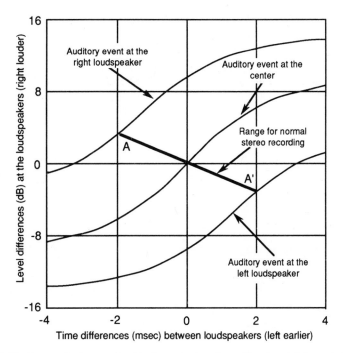

**Figure 2-10.** Franssen's data on localization as a function of level and delay relationships.

### 2.4 PITCH PERCEPTION

Pitch is our subjective judgment of frequency differences. An octave relationship in pitch is generally related to a two-to-one frequency difference, and with complex signals this is the case. With pure tones, the ear discriminates differently. Figure 2-11 illustrates the divergence between two-to-one frequency differences and octave judgments at high frequencies. Pitch perception of frequencies above 3 or 4 kHz is imprecise. Most musical fundamental frequencies occur well below this range, and audio signals above this range consists primarily of harmonics and overtones.

Pitch judgments are dependent on signal level, and the effect is a complex one, as shown in Figure 2-12. Note that higher frequencies generally rise in pitch at higher levels, while lower frequencies tend to sound lower in pitch at higher levels. The term mel is used to indicate subjective frequency relationships.

### 2.4.1 Critical Bandwidth

The ears have great acuity in determining the pitch of complex signals that differ only slightly in frequency. However, with pure tones the precision is much less. In particular, two pure tones that differ only slightly in frequency can be sounded together and fuse into a single pitch with a rising and lowering of amplitude, known as *beating*, that is equal to the difference in frequency between the two pure tones. The frequency range over which the ears will fuse two adjacent pure tones is known as *critical bandwidth*.

Critical bandwidth (9) is shown in Figure 2-13(a), where a fixed tone is combined with an adjustable one. Critical bandwidth is defined as the interval spanning the frequency range over which the listener fuses the two tones. The variation of critical bandwidth over the entire hearing range is shown in Figure 2-13(b). Observe that above 1 kHz the width of critical bands remains a constant percentage about the center frequency of the critical band. For example, a critical band centered at 5 kHz has a bandwidth of about

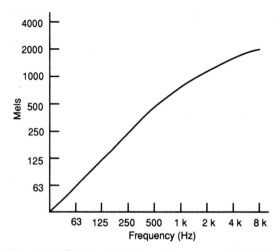

**Figure 2-11.** Relationship between frequency and pitch (mels).

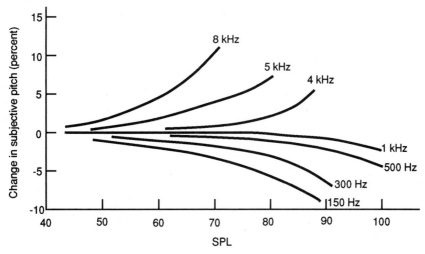

**Figure 2-12.** Subjective pitch versus level.

1 kHz. The dashed line in the figure shows the width of ⅓-octave bands across the frequency range, and it can be seen that critical bands are about ⅓-octave wide.

## 2.5 MASKING PHENOMENA

*Masking* refers to the observation that some sounds mask, or hide, others when they are presented together. In general, loud sounds tend to mask softer ones and lower-pitched sound tend to mask higher-pitched ones. Much of our perception of signal distortion is dependent on the amount of masking that may be taking place in a given program frequency spectrum.

Figure 2-14(a) shows a typical masking contour involving a single masking tone. In this example, a masking tone of 500 Hz is presented at a level of 100 dB. Any other tone below the contour is effectively masked by the 500-Hz tone. Thus, a tone of 2 kHz presented at a level of about 60 dB or lower would be masked by the 500-Hz tone. A 2-kHz tone greater than 60 dB would not be masked. By comparison, a 250-Hz tone presented at any level above about 20 dB would be clearly audible.

Figure 2-14(b) shows a family of masking contours involving the same 500-Hz masking tone, here masking levels of 80, 60, 40, and 40 dB $L_P$. Note that when the level of the masking tone is lowered, the masking contour tends to become narrower and is effectively centered about the masking frequency itself. Note also that at higher masking levels the masking contour extends upward in frequency, but not downward to any significant degree.

In normal recording operations, signal distortion is always present, if only to a slight degree. For wide-band program material, distortion components may be successfully masked by low frequencies present in the program. Consider, however, an unaccompanied women's chorus. In many musical passages in which all the voices lie high in their ranges,

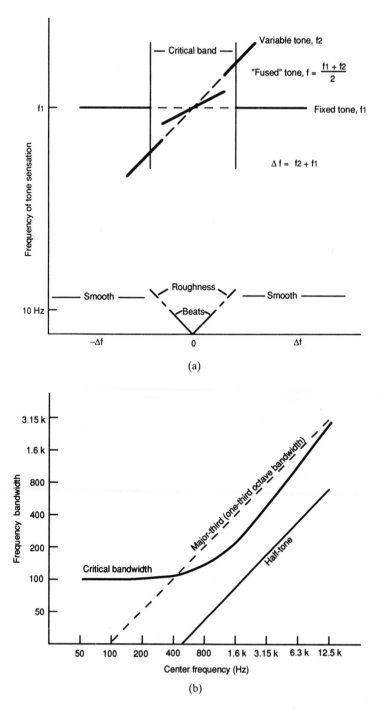

**Figure 2-13.** (a) Definition of critical bandwidth. (*Data after Roederer (a)*) (b) Variation of critical bandwidth over the complete hearing range.

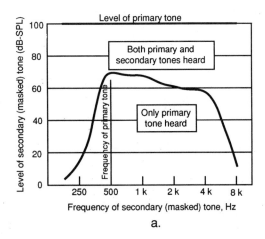

a.

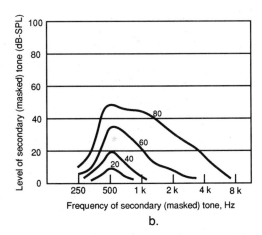

b.

**Figure 2-14.** Masking phenomena. (a) Masking tone at level of 100 dB $L_p$. (b) Masking tone at lower levels.

the masking threshold may resemble that shown in Figure 2-14(a). Since distortion produces difference tones between those frequencies present in the signal, as well as harmonics of the frequencies present, there could easily be distortion components in the frequency region, below 500 Hz. It can be seen that there is little masking in this region and difference tones may be clearly audible.

## 2.6 NORMAL PROGRAM SPECTRA

Figure 2-15 shows some typical recorded program spectra. Note that speech and most classical music diminishes in output significantly above 1000 Hz. This characteristic has fundamentally shaped the pre-emphasis and de-emphasis nature of many analog recording systems, but rock and electronic music has altered the picture.

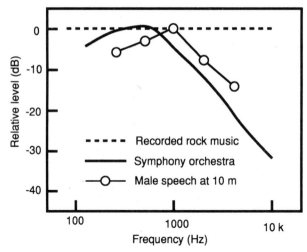

**Figure 2-15.** Typical recorded program spectra.

## 2.7 HEARING PROTECTION

Recording engineers must value their hearing as a precious asset. Even considering the normal effects of aging on hearing acuity, many engineers practice their craft successfully well into their sixties because they have been careful over the years to avoid overexposure to potentially damaging noise levels. The world is ever noisier, and of course music itself is louder than it used to be.

Table 2-1 presents the maximum daily exposure to noise as determined by the Occupational Safety and Health Act (13). The Environmental Protection Agency (EPA) has set even more stringent standards, with 85 dB(A) as a maximum allowable limit for 8 hours and a trading value of 3 dB for each halving of exposure time.

### Table 2-1. Permissible exposure to noise levels under OSHA regulations

| Sound pressure level (dB) (A weighted) | Daily exposure (h) |
|:---:|:---:|
| 90 | 8 |
| 92 | 6 |
| 95 | 4 |
| 97 | 3 |
| 100 | 2 |
| 102 | 1.5 |
| 105 | 1 |
| 110 | 0.5 |
| 115 | 0.25 |

*Source*: Occupational Safety and Health Act, 1970 (13).

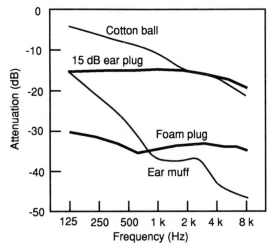

**Figure 2-16.** Attenuation curves for various ear protection devices.

If engineers ever sense a ringing sensation in their ears after a particularly long recording or remixing session, they should take heed. There is a tendency to raise levels as a session proceeds—and there is almost never a tendency to reduce levels once they have been raised! Contemporary musicians generate quite high sound pressure levels, and they want to hear their recordings played back accordingly. Even in the modern symphony orchestra, sound pressure levels can easily reach the range of 100 to 115 dB $L_P$ in the vicinity of certain brass and percussion instruments (12), and a loudly played piccolo can produce levels of 120 dB(A) at the right ear of the player (3).

For those engineers concerned with long-term hearing protection, we strongly recommend the judicious use of ear plugs. The attenuation of traditional materials is shown in Figure 2-16. None of these materials is satisfactory for musical listening and evaluation inasmuch as the spectrum is skewed. In recent years Killion et al. have developed an ear attenuator that is intended for musical use (1). It produces a uniform attenuation of 15 dB over the audible spectrum and is recommended for all applications where judgments of high-level music must be made over extended periods of time. These attenuators are custom-molded for each user.

## BIBLIOGRAPHY

1. M. Altschuler, "Balance Attenuation Ear Protection," *Sound & Communications,* vol. 35, no. 3 (1989)
2. B. Bauer, "Phasor Analysis of Some Stereophonic Phenomena," *J. Acoustical Society of America,* vol. 33, no. 11 (1956).
3. A. Benade, *Fundamentals of Musical Acoustics*, p. 209, Oxford University Press, New York (1976).
4. J. Blauert, *Spatial Hearing*, MIT Press, Cambridge, Mass. (1983).
5. H. A. M. Clark, et al., "The 'Stereosonic' Recording and Reproducing System," *J. Audio Engineering Society,* vol. 6, no. 2 (1958).
6. S. Gelfand, *Hearing, an Introduction for Psychological and Physiological Acoustics,* Marcel Dekker, New York (1981).

7. H. Haas, "The Influence of a Single Echo on the Audibility of Speech," reprinted in *J. Audio Engineering Society,* vol. 20, no.2 (1972).

8. D. Robinson and R. Dadson, *British Journal of Applied Physics*, vol. 7, p. 166 (1956).

9. J. Roederer, *Introduction to the Physics and Psychophysics of Music,* p. 29, Springer-Verlag, New York (1973).

10. E. Schubert (ed.), *Psychological Acoustics,* Dowden, Hutchinson, and Ross, Stroudsburg, Pa. (1979).

11. F. Winckel, *Music, Sound, and Sensation,* Dover Publications, New York (1967).

12. D. Woolford, "Sound Pressure Levels in Symphony Orchestras and Hearing," presented at the 1984 Australian Regional Convention, Audio Engineering Society, Sept. 1984, preprint no. 2104.

13. Occupational Safety and Health Act, 1970, Department of Labor, US Congress, 651 *et seq.*

# 3

# CHARACTERISTICS OF PERFORMANCE SPACES

## 3.1 INTRODUCTION

While popular and rock music is usually recorded (some would say created) in studios, most classical recording takes place in actual performance spaces, be they concert halls, ballrooms, or houses of worship. To the extent that a classical recording attempts to convey a sense of space or ambience appropriate for the music, it will be useful to analyze performance spaces in terms of direct, early, and reverberant fields. The direct field is of course the sound reaching the listener along a straight line from the source on stage. The early field generally describes the ensemble of early reflections from the front and sides of the space to the listener. The time interval usually discussed here is the first 100 msec after the initial onset of sound. The reverberant field has been discussed earlier, and it is the statistical ensemble of many reflections that arrive uniformly at the listener from all directions. The trade-offs inherent in concert hall design will be discussed, as will some numerical methods for rating concert hall performance.

## 3.2 SPACIOUSNESS

Kuttruff (7) relates spaciousness in a listening environment to the presence of reflections that are perceived by the listener after the receipt of direct sound from the stage. Only a few discrete reflections may be required to create the effect of spaciousness if the following conditions can be satisfied:

a. The reflected sounds are mutually incoherent (not arising from symmetrical pairs of side reflections).
b. Their intensities exceed a certain threshold (normally not more than about 20 dB below the direct sound).

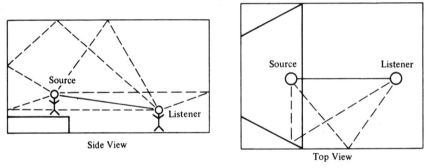

**Figure 3-1.** Direct and early reflected sound paths in an auditorium.

c. Their delay times relative to the direct sound not exceed about 100 msec.

d. They arrive primarily from lateral directions.

Referring to Figure 3-1, note that the pattern of early reflections from the front and sides of an auditorium will satisfy Kuttruff's requirements. Indeed, in concert hall design, it is the scaling of room size, choice of finish materials, and the balance between sound reflection and diffusion from wall surfaces that determine the sense of spaciousness perceived in various parts of the house. The term initial time gap (ITD) is useful in describing the time interval between receipt of the direct sound from the stage and the first reflections.

Barron (2) presents the data shown in Figure 3-2. Here, the subjective impressions for 40° side reflections are given as a function of both level and delay time of the reflections relative to direct sound. Note that the spatial impression is greatest for delays in the range from about 40 msec to 100 msec, with reflected levels spanning a wide range. When delays are large and reflected levels are high, there will be a disturbing effect of distinct echoes. Additionally, when delays are slight and reflected levels are high, there will be a tendency for image shift to take place.

Another factor that enters into the judgment of spaciousness is reverberation time. Figure 3-3 shows recommended values of reverberation time for various musical and speech activities in rooms of different sizes. The desired reverberation time normally increases as volume increases. If any attempt were made to keep reverberation time constant with increasing volume, too much absorption would have to be added to the space, and there would be inadequate program loudness in the space. Alternatively, if a small room is treated so that it has a long reverberation time for its size, the direct-to-reverberant ratio in the space will suffer and both music and speech will sound indistinct and confused.

There is a natural tendency for reverberation time to increase at low frequencies and decrease at high frequencies. Figure 3-4 shows the general trend. The increase in reverberation time at low frequencies comes as a consequence of the fact that most materials exhibit reduced absorption at long wavelengths. The reduction in high-frequency reverberation time is largely a consequence of increased air absorption in the space at frequencies above 2 kHz.

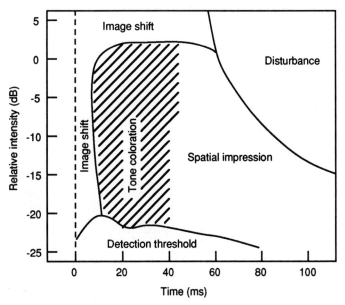

**Figure 3-2.** Barron's data on the effect of lateral reflections as a function of level and delay with respect to the direct signal.

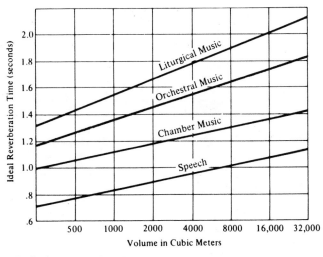

**Figure 3-3.** Optimum reverberation times versus volume for several types of rooms.

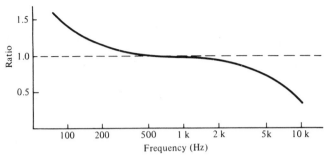

**Figure 3-4.** Variation in reverberation time with frequency in large performance spaces as a ratio of midband reverberation time (500 to 1000 Hz range).

## 3.3 DESCRIPTIONS OF PERFORMANCE SPACES

The subjective vocabulary devoted to architectural acoustics is quite rich, but not at all standardized. Some terms, such as intimacy, liveness, and warmth, have taken on greater meaning through numerical description. Leo Beranek, in his book *Music, Acoustics & Architecture* (3), has provided the basis for the following discussion of these subjective attributes. Where they are applicable, we have indicated those measures the recording engineer may employ in order to simulate these effects with signal processing.

### 3.3.1 Intimacy

Intimacy implies closeness of the listener to a performing group, and it results from an ensemble of early reflections that follow closely on the direct sound by no more than 15 to 20 msec. The degree to which intimacy can be provided at distances up to 20 or 25 meters from the performers through the careful control of reflected sound is often surprising. Figure 3-5 hows the use of overhead reflectors or "clouds" which provide strong early reflections, while allowing egress of low frequencies for extended reverberation time in that frequency range. Articulated arrays of overhead reflectors can adequately provide needed early lateral reflections in halls of large size.

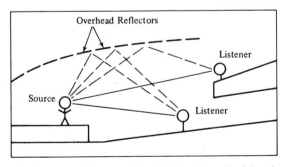

**Figure 3-5.** Use of reflectors to preserve desirable direct-to-early delays in an auditorium.

In recording, the engineer can simulate the effect of multiple reflections through the proper application of time-delay devices, along with the appropriate degree of reverberation. These techniques will be discussed in detail in later chapters.

### 3.3.2 Liveness

Liveness implies a relatively high amount of reverberation in the mid-frequency range (0.5 to 2 kHz) along with initial delay patterns characteristic of moderate sized rooms. The effect is most often observed in old-style ballrooms where there is a good bit of high-frequency reflection because of mirrored surfaces and plaster finishing, along with substantial low-frequency absorption due to plywood and wallboard materials in the construction. Rooms of this sort are often excellent for recording, where the engineer can control the low-frequency content of a recording by electrical means. When such spaces are used as performance venues, there is often a disturbing lack of bass.

Liveness may be added to a recording by applying reverberation in the range of 1.5 to 2.0 seconds equalized to favor the 0.5 to 2 kHz portion of the spectrum. Time delays should be kept on the short side, since liveness is most often an attribute of moderate size spaces.

### 3.3.3 Warmth

Warmth is associated with high reverberation time at low frequencies (125 to 250 Hz) relative to mid frequencies. It is an essential ingredient in any concert hall where music of the romantic period is to be performed. There is no other attribute more difficult to add to a recording by signal processing than this one, due to shortcomings in most reverberation generators. The problem is usually one of insufficient modal density in the reverberant characteristic at low frequencies. Often a moderate increase in low-frequency reverberant response and a slight reduction in high-frequency response may help, but generally a feeling of warmth, if not already present in instrumental timbres or room characteristics, is hard to create later via signal processing.

## 3.4 NUMERICAL RATING OF PERFORMANCE SPACES

While it is relatively easy to assess speech communication in large spaces through articulation tests and through new measurement techniques, it is not so easy to give a numerical rating to a concert hall. Alim (8) suggested the notion of $C_{80}$, or "clarity index," which is a measure of the ratio of acoustical power perceived by the listener from zero to 80 msec to the acoustical power perceived from 80 msec to the end of reverberation:

$$C_{80} = 10 \log \left[ \frac{\int_0^{80} [g(t)]^2 \, dt}{\int_{80}^{\infty} [g(t)]^2 \, dt} \right] \tag{3-1}$$

where $[g(t)]^2$ represents a weighted function of sound pressure.

Schultz (9) proposed the notion of "running reverberance," which he defined as

$$R = 10 \log \left[ \frac{\int_{50}^{400} p^2(t)\, dt}{\int_0^{50} p^2(t)\, dt} \right] \qquad (3\text{-}2)$$

where $p^2(t)$ represents the square of sound pressure.

Values of $C_{80}$ of 0 dB are considered excellent, and this indicates that acoustical power arriving at the listener during the first 80 msec is equal to all acoustical power arriving later. Values in the range of $-3$ dB are tolerable, indicating that the earlier-arriving components are somewhat weaker, with reverberant textures predominating. Values of $R$ in the range of 3 to 8 dB are considered excellent.

$C_{80}$ and $R$ are generally calculated at several frequencies from 200 Hz to 10 kHz. The two rating methods are inversely related, with positive values of $R$ corresponding to negative values of $C_{80}$.

Table 3-1 gives data on several concert halls, as presented by Beranek (3). Note the range of room volumes, seating capacity and ITD. A clear pattern emerges here; rooms that seat many patrons do so at the expense of a too-long ITD. Boston's Symphony Hall, with its relatively narrow "shoe box" design, represents a fine balance between adequate seating capacity, short ITD, and generous reverberation time. In many ways, the long reverberation time of the hall is balanced by the clarity afforded by the short ITD.

### Table 3-1. Acoustical data on major concert halls

| Hall, location | Volume (m³) | Seating | Initial time gap (msec) | Reverberation time (sec) Empty | Reverberation time (sec) Occupied |
|---|---|---|---|---|---|
| Symphony Hall Boston, MA | 18,740 | 2631 | 15 | 2.8 | 1.8 |
| Orchestra Hall Chicago, IL | 15,170 | 2582 | 40 | not available | 1.3 |
| Eastman Theater Rochester, NY | 25,470 | 3347 | 55 | not available | 1.75 |
| Carnegie Hall New York, NY | 24,250 | 2760 | 23 | 2.15 | 1.7 |
| Grosser Musikvereinsaal Vienna, Austria | 15,000 | 1680 | 23 | 3.6 | 1.5 |
| Royal Albert Hall London, England | 86,600 | 6080 | 65 | 3.7 | 2.5 |
| Festival Hall London, England | 22,000 | 3000 | 34 | 1.8 | 1.5 |
| Neues Gewandhaus Leipzig, West Germany | 10,600 | 1560 | 8 | 1.8 | 1.55 |

## 3.5 GENERAL COMMENTS

It is easy to make a good recording in Boston's Symphony Hall, with its near-ideal balance of acoustical attributes. Conversely, it is difficult to make a good symphonic recording in London's Royal Albert Hall, with its excessive reverberation time. To a great degree, recording engineers can ignore many of the problems that patrons experience in concert halls, simply because the microphones can always be placed to good effect. Halls that may not have adequate reverberation time can often be treated by placing large plywood sheets over absorptive surfaces, rendering the space more reverberant. The recording engineer can further place a pair of microphones well in the house to pick up just the desired amount of reverberation. The recording engineer need not worry about ITDs, inasmuch as the microphones tend to swamp them out. Artificial ITDs can be created, both through microphone placement and through signal processing. These topics will be discussed in later chapters.

## BIBLIOGRAPHY

1. Y. Ando, *Concert Hall Acoustics*, Springer-Verlag, New York (1985).
2. M. Barron, "The Subjective Effects of First Reflections in Concert Halls—The Need for Lateral Reflections." *J. Sound and Vibration*, vol. 15, pp. 475–494 (1971).
3. L. Beranek, *Music, Acoustics & Architecture*, Wiley, New York (1962).
4. L. Cremer, *Principles and Applications of Room Acoustics*, Applied Science Publishers, New York (1978).
5. J. Eargle, *Music, Sound, & Technology*, Van Nostrand Reinhold, New York (1990).
6. M. Forsyth, *Buildings for Music*, MIT Press, Cambridge, Mass. (1985).
7. H. Kuttruff, *Room Acoustics*, Applied Science Publishers, London (1979).
8. W. Reichardt, A. Alim and W. Schmidt, *Applied Acoustics*, vol. 7 (1974).
9. T. Schultz, "Acoustics of Concert Halls", *IEEE Spectrum*, vol. 2, no. 6 (1965).

# 4

## BASIC OPERATING PRINCIPLES OF MICROPHONES

### 4.1 INTRODUCTION AND SHORT HISTORY

The use of microphones began with the telephone in the last quarter of the nineteenth century. The requirements were basically those of speech intelligibility, and the carbon microphone, developed early in that art, is still used in telephones today. The carbon microphone works on the loose-contact principle, as first demonstrated by Emile Berliner. Particles of carbon are alternately compressed and relaxed by the diaphragm under the influence of sound pressure, and the resulting alternation of resistance modulates the current proportionally to the change in resistance. Carbon microphones are noisy, have limited dynamic range, and produce high levels of distortion. None of these defects is really serious in its application to telephony, however.

The demands of broadcasting in the early years of this century called for higher-quality performance. Music and speech entertainment demanded more accurate translation of sound pressures into electrical signals, and better microphones were required. The capacitor or "condenser" microphone was developed, and the principle of magnetic induction was applied to moving coil and ribbon devices. Their refinement over the last seventy-five years has formed the basis of present day microphone technology.

It is surprising that the microphone did not become a part of recording technology until about fifty years after its application to telephony. Sound recording remained a purely acousto-mechanical process from the 1870s until the introduction by Western Electric of electrical recording in the mid 1920s. Until this time the performance characteristics of the acoustical medium had been felt to be equal to, or better than, what could be routinely done electrically.

Radio broadcasting developed around the various moving-coil and ribbon devices, and those microphone types were the mainstay of recording in the United States through the mid 1940s. The most significant engineering of microphones during the 1930s was accomplished by RCA and Western Electric, essentially for their broadcast and motion picture interests. Development of capacitors in the United States was more or less restricted to calibration and measurement applications.

Capacitor microphones thrived in Europe during the 1930s, and after World War II they made a significant impact on American recording practice. The introduction of tape recording and the long-playing record in the late 1940s pointed up the frequency response limitations of the dynamic microphones that were in common use; capacitor microphones, with their extended high-frequency response, were quick to fill the need. The 1950s and 1960s saw the introduction of numerous dynamic microphones with excellent performance characteristics, and today's recording studios have both capacitor and dynamic models in abundance. In the last twenty years microphones have become better and cheaper; increased demands for all types has resulted in mass production and the development of better materials.

## 4.2 PRINCIPLES OF TRANSDUCTION

### 4.2.1 Dynamic (Moving-Coil) Microphones

A section view of a dynamic microphone is shown in Figure 4-1. Sound normally impinges on the diaphragm from the left (as shown here), and the diaphragm vibrates accordingly. Attached to the diaphragm is a small coil of wire, which moves to and fro with the diaphragm. The coil is placed in a magnetic field that is largely contained by the magnetic return path and the pole piece. There is a large concentration of magnetic flux in the magnetic gap containing the coil and the voltage generated across the coil is given by

$$E \text{ (voltage)} = Blv \qquad (4\text{-}1)$$

where $E$ is measured in volts, $B$ is the magnetic flux density in teslas, $l$ is the length of the coil in meters, and $v$ is the velocity of the coil across the magnetic field in

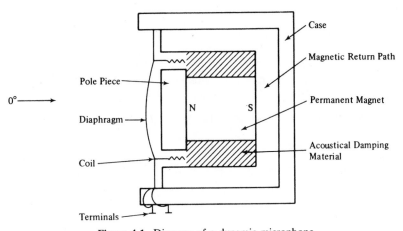

**Figure 4-1.** Diagram of a dynamic microphone.

meters/second. Since the coil velocity is very small, designers use as large a magnet as possible in order to maintain adequate signal output. The coil itself is rarely greater than about 2 cm in diameter; hence, the length of wire in the coil is rather small. As it is, the normal output of a dynamic microphone is in the range of a few millivolts for fairly loud pressure levels.

The frequency response of a dynamic microphone can be maintained fairly flat (smooth) over a wide frequency range through careful attention to resonances and damping.

### 4.2.2 The Ribbon Microphone

The ribbon microphone is electrically related to the dynamic microphone in that the output results from an electrical conductor, the ribbon, moving in a magnetic field. However, in physical appearance and acoustical function it is quite different. Figure 4-2 shows physical details of the ribbon microphone. The ribbon is suspended in a large magnetic gap, as seen in side view. The top view shows the ribbon viewed on end (center of figure). Note that the ribbon is open to the air on two sides, indicated here by 0° and 180°. Sound arriving arriving from those directions will actuate the ribbon. For sound arriving from the directions indicated by the 90° and 270° arrows, there will be no net motion of the ribbon, since sound pressures will be identical on both sides of the ribbon and will cancel. As a consequence, the ribbon microphone exhibits a directional, or polar, pattern, which is shaped like a "figure-8." The figure-8 pattern is also known as a cosine pattern and can be expressed in polar coordinates as $\rho = \cos \theta$. The ribbon microphone is also known as a *pressure gradient* microphone, in that its output voltage depends on the instantaneous pressure gradient, or difference, between the two sides of the ribbon. Another term used is *velocity* microphone, inasmuch as the output voltage depends on the velocity of the air particles in the vicinity of the ribbon.

The forces acting on the ribbon are shown in Figure 4-3. Flat acoustical response can be maintained over the range bounded by $f_0$ and $f_1$ in Figure 4-4. The lower limit is set by the fundamental resonance frequency, while the upper limit is set by the dimensions around the magnetic structure. In most designs, the upper frequency limit is in the range between 15 and 20 kHz.

Another very important characteristic of ribbon microphones is that the voltage output for sounds originating at 180° is of opposite polarity, or "out-of-phase," with sound originating at 0°. As a family, ribbon microphones have rather low output and require careful electrical interfacing. However, for close placement to loud instruments, the low output voltage is not a problem. Earlier models were quite fragile, but newer models are more robust.

### 4.2.3 Capacitor (Condenser) Microphones

Capacitor microphones are mechanically the simplest types used in recording; their only moving part is an extremely light diaphragm which acts as one plate of a capacitor. A capacitor is an electrical component consisting of two plates, separated by a very small distance, capable of storing an electrical charge according to the equation:

$$Q = CE \tag{4-2}$$

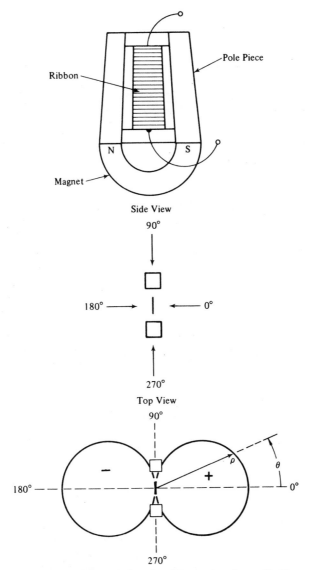

**Figure 4-2.** Diagram and directional characteristics of a ribbon microphone. Positive and negative lobes are indicated.

where $Q$ is the charge in coulombs on the plates of the capacitor, $C$ is the capacitance in farads, and $E$ is the voltage across the plates of the capacitor.

The inverse relationship between charge and voltage is shown in Figure 4-5, where it is shown that, for a fixed charge, a reduction in capacitance caused by separating the plates causes an increase in the voltage across them. This effect is used in the capacitor microphone, as shown in Figure 4-6. Here, the diaphragm moves in and out as a function of sound pressure, and the capacitance is thus varied. The large resistance $R$ in the circuit

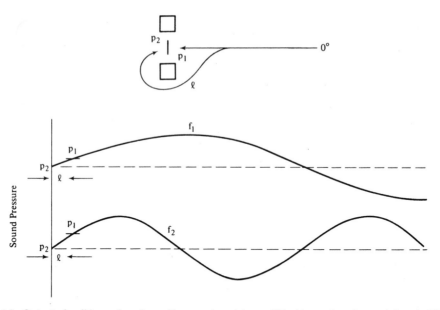

**Figure 4-3.** Output of a ribbon microphone. For sounds arriving at 0° incidence there is a path length difference, $l$, between the two sides of the ribbon. At some frequency, $f_1$, there is a pressure difference, or gradient, equal to $P_1 - P_2$ acting on the ribbon. At $f_2$, which is twice $f_1$, the $p_1 - p_2$ difference is 6 dB greater. The ribbon is *mass-controlled* because of its subsonic resonance, and the net output is a flat (constant) electrical signal with respect to frequency, as shown in Figure 4-4.

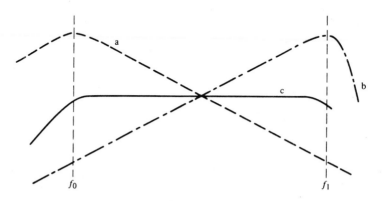

**Figure 4-4.** Forces acting on a ribbon microphone produce flat output with respect to frequency. Curve $a$ is the velocity of the ribbon when exposed to a constant pressure gradient. $f_0$ represents the subsonic resonance frequency of the ribbon and defines the useful lower limit of the device; it diminishes 6 dB/octave with rising frequency. Curve $b$ is the pressure gradient acting on the ribbon; it rises 6 dB/octave, leveling off at $f_1$, and finally reaching a null point where the wavelength for $f_1$ is equal to $l$. The net voltage output of the microphone is shown at curve $c$.

**70**

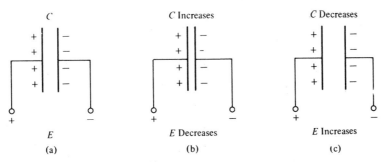

**Figure 4-5.** Relations between voltage and capacitance in a variable capacitor with a fixed charge. The term $Q$ is the charge in coulombs. $C$ is the capacitance farads, and $E$ is the applied voltage (see text). The closer the electrodes are spaced, the higher the capacitance. In (a), the capacitor has been charged by voltage $E$. If the charge remains constant and the electrodes are moved closer together, the voltage between the plates will decrease, as shown in (b). If the electrodes are moved farther apart, as shown at (c), the voltage will increase, as shown in (c).

maintains a constant charge, and the voltage across the plates varies according to the equation

$$\Delta E = \frac{Q}{\Delta C} \tag{4-3}$$

where $\Delta C$ represents the change in capacitance and $\Delta E$ represents the change in voltage across the plates. The signal voltage thus produced is normally amplified by a small amplifier located in the case of the microphone itself.

In construction, the diaphragm is normally made of plastic with a thin metalized layer so that it is both light and conductive. The voltage impressed across the plates of the capacitor is known as the polarizing voltage, and values today are in the range of 45 to 50 volts, depending on the design.

In recent years, the electret principle has been used in the design of some capacitor microphones. An *electret* is a substance which will maintain a permanent electrical charge and accordingly needs no external polarizing voltage source. Details of the design are shown in Figure 4-7. Here, the electret material is placed on the diaphragm; in other

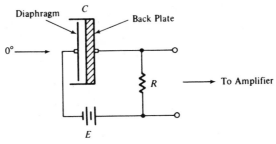

**Figure 4-6.** Basic circuit of the capacitor microphone. The amplifier raises the signal power, reducing the relatively high electrical impedance of the capacitor element to a lower value.

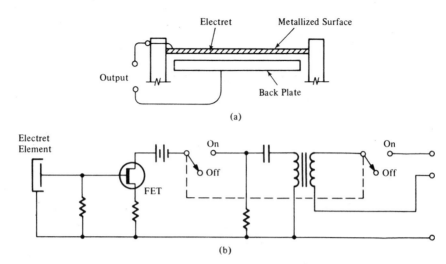

**Figure 4-7.** Structure of the electret microphone (a) and a typical electrical circuit employing a FET transistor, at (b). The electret material is metallized on one side to form an electrode, and the resulting diaphragm and back plate combination behaves like a capacitor in series with a dc voltage source.

designs the material may be located on the back plate. In any event, only a small battery is needed to power the amplifier, and this is usually located in the case of the microphone. While electrets have become more or less standard for applications demanding very small transducing elements, such as miniature microphones or "tietack" types, the principle has been used in certain expensive, high-performance models as well.

### 4.2.4 RF (Radio-Frequency) Microphones

In a few capacitor designs, the change in capacitance is used to alter the tuning of an electrical circuit in much the same manner as a carrier frequency is modulated in FM radio transmission. Early designs were complex and subject to certain operational difficulties. Newer designs have excellent stability and operating characteristics. The better RF microphones are among the quietest available.

## BIBLIOGRAPHY

1. L. Beranek, *Acoustics*, McGraw-Hill, New York (1954).
2. G. Bore, *Microphones*, Georg Neumann GmbH, Berlin (1989).
3. J. Eargle, *The Microphone Handbook*, Elar, Plainview, N.Y. (1982).
4. A. Robertson, *Microphones*, Hayden, New York (1963).
5. G. Sessler and J. West, "Condenser Microphones with Electret Foil," *J. Audio Engineering Society*, vol. 12, no. 2 (1964).
6. *Microphones*, an anthology of articles on microphones from the pages of *J. Audio Engineering Society*, vol. 1 through vol. 27.

# 5

## DERIVATION OF MICROPHONE
## DIRECTIONAL PATTERNS

### 5.1 INTRODUCTION

With the exception of the ribbon microphone with its figure-8 pattern, the basic microphone designs discussed in the previous chapter were all essentially omnidirectional in their pickup pattern. Recording engineers have always desired a variety of pickup patterns in order to solve specific problems in the studio, and the 1930s saw considerable development of directional microphones. The early designs basically made use of dual elements in deriving these patterns. That is, they combined the output of an omnidirectional element and a figure-8, or bidirectional element, to derive a given directional pattern. Such designs as these were often bulky and did not maintain their desired directional patterns at the highest frequencies.

In time, designers found ways of producing directional patterns with single elements, and microphone size could be made quite small. And with the small size came extended high-frequency performance with good pattern control. This chapter will discuss the means that have been used to arrive at the basic patterns, including the various approaches to designing highly directional microphones for special applications.

### 5.2 DIRECTIONAL MICROPHONES

The basic components used to produce directional patterns are the omnidirectional and bidirectional patterns. In polar coordinates, the equation which combines these elements is

$$\rho = A + B \cos \theta \tag{5-1}$$

$A$ is a constant value and represents the output of the omnidirectional element, which is uniform for all directions $\theta$. $B \cos \theta$ represents the output of the bidirectional element, whose directional response over $\theta$ is that of the cosine function. $A$ and $B$ can be varied, and their sum is usually established as unity. The plots in Figure 5-1 show several combinations of the two basic elements. The arrows to the right indicate the principal pickup axes of the resultant patterns.

The family of unidirectional patterns involving components of both omnidirectional and bidirectional elements are known as *cardioids*, because of their generalized heart shape. They are further known as first-order patterns, because they make use of only a single cosine component.

### 5.2.1 Early Directional Designs

Figure 5-2 shows a section view of the Western Electric model 639 microphone from the 1930s. Note that the case contains both ribbon (top) and dynamic (bottom) elements.

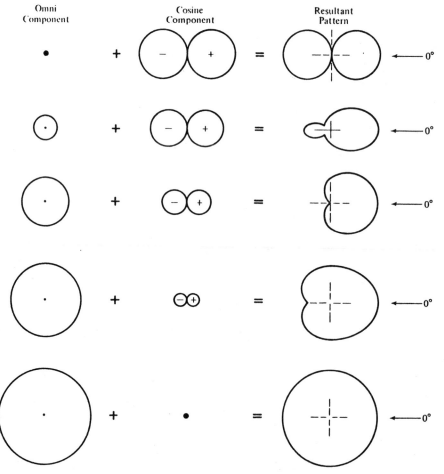

**Figure 5-1.** Various combinations of omnidirectional and figure-8 patterns producing a variety of polar patterns.

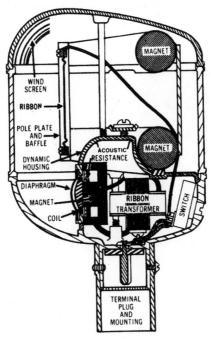

**Figure 5-2.** A cardioid microphone that combines a ribbon element and an omnidirectional pressure element. (*Altec data*).

Their outputs are summed, and cardioid response is produced along the microphone axis to the left.

Figure 5-3 shows a section view of a ribbon element with a shroud on the back side. With the shroud in place, the ribbon is actuated only by the sound pressure on its left side, and the response is essentially omnidirectional (a). When the shroud is opened (b), the ribbon functions as a bidirectional element. When the shroud is at an intermediate setting (c), both bidirectional and omnidirectional components are present and cardioid response is achieved. This principle was used in some of the RCA model 77 designs during the 1930s.

## 5.2.2 Modern Single Element Directional Designs

Today, most directional microphones use a single transducing element that has been optimized for a single pattern. In this way, pattern control can be extended reasonably well into the octave range between 10 and 20 kHz. The design approach used here is as shown schematically in Figure 5-4, which shows what is called a *doublet*, a pair of spaced receivers poled reversely, with a delay placed in one line. In the actual microphone, the doublet results from the single transducing element open to the air on both sides. The delay inserted in one side is made equal to the acoustical delay due to the spacing. For a sound arriving at 0°, there will always be signal output because the negative element

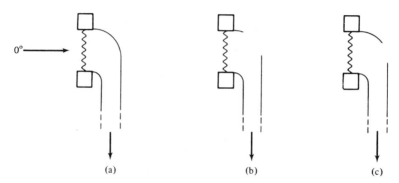

Arrow indicates path to acoustical damping

**Figure 5-3.** Modifications around a single ribbon to produce a cardioid pattern. In (a) the back of the ribbon is sealed with an acoustically inert tube the ribbon thus behaves like a simple dynamic element. In (b) the opening of the tube is large enough that the ribbon behaves as a pressure gradient device with its characteristic figure-8 pattern. With an opening of intermediate size, as shown in (c), both actions are combined, with resulting cardioid response.

of the doublet, through time delay, can never contribute an equal and opposite signal to cause cancellation. For sounds arriving at 180°, the delayed contribution from the negative doublet element will always arrive in step with the positive contribution at the positive doublet element, and cancellation will be total.

Examining Figure 5-5, we can see the doublet path length difference as shown by the two arrows around the dynamic element. The cross-hatched portion in the section view represents the additional delay path which is provided by acoustical damping material. Similarly, Figure 5-6 shows a single-element capacitor design. Here, the back plate is perforated in order to get the required doublet action. Cross-hatching again indicates the additional signal delay. The amount of signal delay introduced into the back path to the transducing element determines the precise cardioid pattern that will be produced by the microphone.

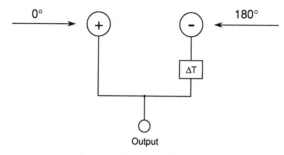

**Figure 5-4.** A doublet with delay in one element. For cardioid response, the delay, $\Delta T$, is set so that it is equal to the acoustical delay path between doublet elements. Thus, sounds arriving from 180° will cancel at the output of the doublet.

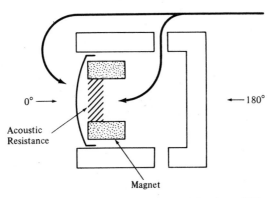

**Figure 5-5.** A single-diaphragm cardioid microphone. Sounds arriving from 180° reach the diaphragm at the same time and thus cancel.

## 5.3 THE CARDIOID FAMILY

There are four specific cardioid patterns discussed widely in the literature. They are known as subcardioid, cardioid, supercardioid, and hypercardioid.

### 5.3.1 The Subcardioid

This pattern is represented by the polar equation:

$$\rho = .7 + .3 \cos \theta \tag{5-2}$$

The pattern is shown in Figure 5-7(a). The directional response is −3 dB at angles of ±90° and −10 dB at 180°. The pattern is of relatively recent development and has found

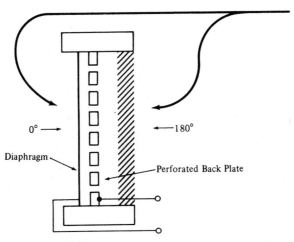

**Figure 5-6.** A single-diaphragm capacitor cardioid microphone. Sounds arriving from 180° reach the diaphragm at the same time and thus cancel.

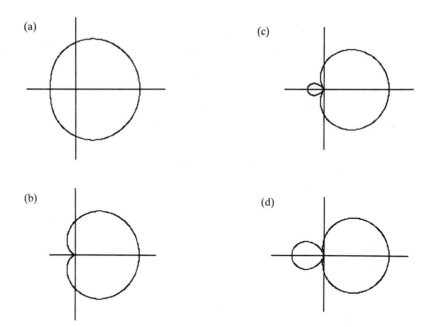

**Figure 5-7.** The family of cardioids. (a) Subcardioid. (b) Cardioid. (c) Supercardioid. (d) Hypercardioid.

great favor with classical recording engineers. It is sometimes referred to as a "forward-oriented omni."

### 5.3.2 The Cardioid

This pattern is represented by the polar equation:

$$\rho = .5 + .5 \cos \theta \tag{5-3}$$

The pattern is shown in Figure 5-7(b). The directional response is −6 dB at angles of ±90° and effectively zero at 180°. The pattern is the original cardioid dating from the 1930s and is commonly found in the recording studio. Its usefulness in the studio arises mainly from its pronounced rejection of direct field sounds arriving at an angle of 180°.

### 5.3.3 The Supercardioid

This pattern is represented by the polar equation:

$$\rho = .37 + .63 \cos \theta \tag{5-4}$$

The pattern is shown in Figure 5-7(c). Directional response is −8.6 dB at ±90° and −11.7 at 180°. (To a close approximation, we can state that the response is −9 dB at ±90° and −12 at 180°.) The pattern exhibits the maximum frontal pickup, relative to total pickup, of the first-order cardioids, and as such can be used for pickup over a wide frontal angle.

### 5.3.4 The Hypercardioid

This pattern is represented by the polar equation:

$$\rho = .25 + .75 \cos \theta \tag{5-5}$$

The pattern is shown in Figure 5-7(d). Directional response is $-12$ dB at $\pm 90°$ and $-6$ dB at $180°$. The pattern exhibits the greatest random energy efficiency, or "reach," in the forward direction of the first-order cardioids. In the reverberant field, the hypercardioid pattern will provide the greatest rejection, relative to on-axis pickup, of randomly arriving reverberant sounds.

### 5.3.5 Summary of the First-Order Cardioids

With the exception of the subcardioid, the essential performance characteristics of the cardioid family are given in Figure 5-8. Most of the terms used in the figure are self-

| CHARACTERISTIC | OMNIDIRECTIONAL | BIDIRECTIONAL | CARDIOID | HYPERCARDIOID | SUPER-CARDIOID |
|---|---|---|---|---|---|
| POLAR RESPONSE PATTERN | 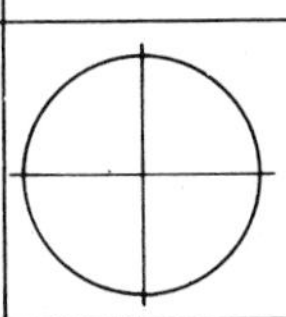 | 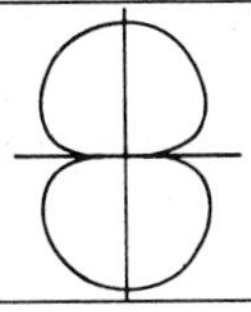 | 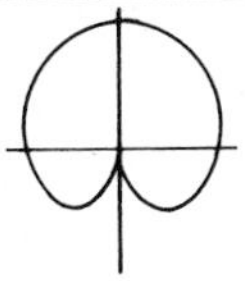 | 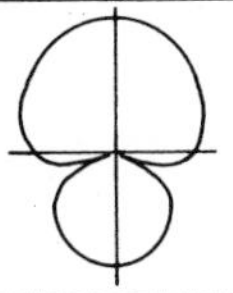 |  |
| POLAR EQUATION F (θ) ∝ | 1 | $\cos \theta$ | $1/2(1+\cos \theta)$ | $1/4(1+3\cos \theta)$ | $.37 + .63 \cos \theta$ |
| PICKUP ARC 3 dB DOWN (θ3) | 360° | 90° | 131° | 105° | 115° |
| PICKUP ARC 6 dB DOWN (θ6) | 360° | 120° | 180° | 141° | 156° |
| RELATIVE OUTPUT AT 90° (dB) | 0 | $-\infty$ | $-6$ | $-12$ | $-8.6$ |
| RELATIVE OUTPUT AT 180° (dB) | 0 | 0 | $-\infty$ | $-6$ | $-11.7$ |
| ANGLE AT WHICH OUTPUT = 0 (θ₀) | — | 90° | 180° | 110° | 126° |
| RANDOM ENERGY EFFICIENCY (RE) | 1 0 dB | .333 −4.8 dB | .333 −4.8 dB | .250 ① −6.0dB | .268 ② −5.7 dB |
| DISTANCE FACTOR (DSF) | 1 | 1.7 | 1.7 | 2 | 1.9 |

① MINIMUM RANDOM ENERGY EFFICIENCY FOR A FIRST ORDER CARDIOID
② MAXIMUM FRONT TO TOTAL RANDOM ENERGY EFFICIENCY FOR A FIRST ORDER CARDIOID

**Figure 5-8.** Data on the family of first-order cardioids. Polar equations are given, along with the pickup angle between the $-3$ dB and $-6$ dB points. Relative outputs at 90° and 180° are given, along with the angle at which the output is zero. (*Courtesy Shure Brothers*)

explanatory; however, random energy efficiency and distance factor may need additional comment. Random energy efficiency (REE) is a measure of the on-axis directivity of the microphone, relative to its response to sounds originating from all directions. REE of $\frac{1}{3}$, for example indicates that the microphone will respond to reverberant acoustical power, which arrives equally from all directions, with $\frac{1}{3}$ the sensitivity of the same acoustical power arriving along the major axis of the microphone. REE is related to the directivity index (*DI*), as discussed in Section 1.8.1, by

$$DI = -10 \log \text{REE} \qquad (5\text{-}6)$$

*Distance factor* (DSF) is a measure of the "reach" of the microphone in a reverberant environment, relative to an omnidirectional. For example, a microphone with a distance factor of 2 can be placed at *twice* the distance from a sound source in a reverberant field, relative to the position of an omnidirectional microphone, and exhibit the same ratio of direct-to-reverberant sound pickup of the omnidirectional microphone. DSF is related to directivity index by

$$DI = 20 \log \text{DSF} \qquad (5\text{-}7)$$

Stated somewhat differently, under reverberant conditions, the recording engineer does not think of directional microphones in terms of their rejection of sounds arriving from some back angle; rather, the microphone is assessed in terms of its ability to reject all reverberant information, relative to the on-axis response.

## 5.4 MODERN VARIABLE-PATTERN MICROPHONES

Today, most variable pattern microphones are of the Braunmühl–Weber design. Details of this design are shown in Figure 5-9. Note that the backplate is in the center, with diaphragms on both sides. The back plate has perforations through it as well as holes which do not go through the plate. The purpose of both sets of holes is to provide the required acoustical stiffness and damping of the diaphragms for the various modes of operation of the microphone.

Figure 5-10 illustrates the operation of the microphone through a set of vector diagrams. Only the left diaphragm has been polarized; the right diaphragm is at zero voltage. First, consider a sound source at a direction 90° relative to the diaphragms. Since both diaphragms are equidistant from the sound source, there will be equal and opposite pressure vectors, as shown in Figure 5-10(b) as $S_1$ and $S_2$. The pressures will push the two diaphragms in and out against the stiffness of the enclosed air. Now, for a source located 0°, as shown at Figure 5-10(a), there will be the same set of vectors plus an *additional* set of vectors caused by the pressure gradient effect at the microphone. These pressures will push the diaphragms and the enclosed air as a unit, because of the interconnection between the two sides of the backplate. These additional vectors are indicated by $s_1$ and $s_2$, and will combine as shown in the figure. Through careful control of damping and stiffness in the diaphragm, the two vectors at the back side (180° relative to the signal direction) can be made to cancel completely, and only the left diaphragm will move, creating an output voltage. For sound arriving at 180°, only the back diaphragm

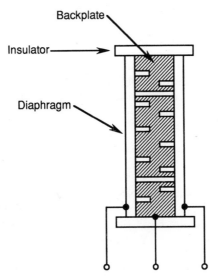

**Figure 5-9.** Diagram of the Braunmühl–Weber dual-diaphragm capacitor microphone.

will move, as shown in Figure 5-10(c), and there will be no electrical output from the microphone, since that diaphragm is not polarized.

This effectively results in a pair of back-to-back cardioid patterns existing in the same structure. If only one diaphragm is polarized, as in our analysis, there will be a cardioid

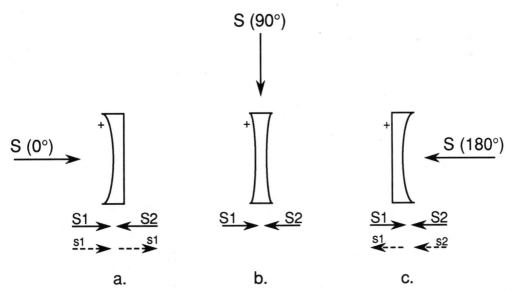

**Figure 5-10.** Operation of the Braunmühl–Weber microphone. (a) Movement of diaphragms for sound incident at 0°. (b) Movement of diaphragms for sound incident at 90°. (c) Movement of diaphragms for sound incident at 180°.

pattern in the direction normal to that diaphragm. If both diaphragms are polarized with the same voltage, the response will be omnidirectional, since the two cardioids will add. If the diaphragms are polarized with equal and opposite voltages, the two cardioids will subtract, and the net response will be bidirectional.

Figure 5-11 shows an electrical configuration that allows the omnidirectional and bidirectional components to be combined for a variety of patterns, through continuously variable voltage changes on one diaphragm.

## 5.5 HIGHER-ORDER AND INTERFERENCE MICROPHONES

For microphones with greater on-axis directivity than that exhibited by the first-order types, the recording engineer has access to certain models that operate on wave cancellation and reinforcement principles. These patterns are not uniform with respect to frequency, as are the first-order types, and most of these microphones are useful only at high frequencies, where the higher-order effects are most pronounced. Figure 5-12 shows two approaches that can be used. The so-called line microphone is shown in Figure 5-12(a). It offers a uniform path for sounds arriving at 0°; however, sounds arriving at off-axis angles will have different path lengths as they travel down the tube toward the diaphragm. Some will cancel, while others may be reinforced. In general, for sounds arriving at large off-axis angles, the cancellations will be predominate. The design's effectiveness is inversely proportional to wavelength, and wavelengths longer than the tube length will show little increase in on-axis sensitivity. Thus, a line microphone that is to be effective at low frequencies will have to be fairly long. In past years, some models have been constructed with a length of about 1.5 meters.

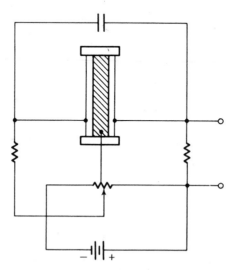

**Figure 5-11.** Connection of Braunmühl–Weber diaphragms for a variety of patterns. By adjusting the wiper on the center-tapped potentiometer, we can vary the response from omnidirectional (wiper at full right position), through cardioid (wiper at center tape), to figure-8 (wiper at full left position).

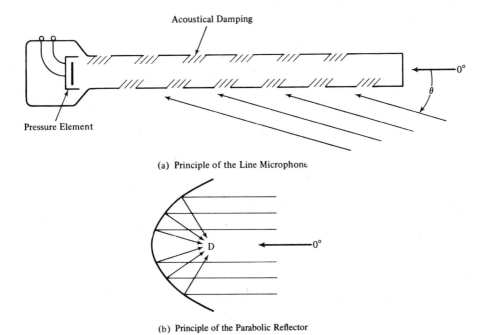

(a) Principle of the Line Microphone

(b) Principle of the Parabolic Reflector

**Figure 5-12.** High-order directional microphones.

The parabolic reflector is shown in Figure 5-12(b). It can be seen that it collects sound waves and concentrates them at a microphone located at the focus of the parabola. As with the line microphone, the design's effectiveness is inversely proportional to wavelength. The design is effective only for those frequencies whose wavelengths are of the dish diameter or shorter.

The recording engineer who has a difficult outdoor recording project may find these devices useful. Certainly, the archivist who records sounds of nature cannot be without them.

Another interference-type microphone is the venerable Neumann M50, a design from the early 1950s that is now in great vogue for studio use. The microphone consists of a pressure diaphragm 12 mm in diameter, which is located on a plastic sphere of 40 mm diameter. At low frequencies, sound diffracts around the sphere and the response is essentially omnidirectional. Above about 2 kHz, the on-axis response rises and the microphone gradually becomes quite directional at the highest frequencies. The intended purpose of the microphone, at the time of its development, was for pickup of classical music in semi-reverberant spaces and at not too-close distances. The increase in forward directivity and increased output at higher frequencies enabled the microphone to maintain signal presence to a higher degree than traditional omnidirectional microphones. At the same time, the M50 does not reduce the reverberant field components below 1 kHz, as would a traditional cardioid microphone.

# BIBLIOGRAPHY

1. B. Bauer, "A Century of Microphones," *Proceedings of the IEEE*, vol. 50, pp. 719–729. [Reprinted in *J. Audio Engineering Society*, vol. 35, no. 4 (1987).]
2. L. Beranek, *Acoustics*, McGraw-Hill, New York (1954).
3. G. Bore, Microphones, Georg Neumann GmbH, Berlin (1989).
4. H.J.Von Braunmühl and W. Weber, "Kapacitive Richtmikrophon," *Hochfrequenztechnik und Elektroakustik*, vol. 46, pp. 187–192 (1935).
5. J. Eargle, *The Microphone Handbook*, Elar, Plainview, N.Y. (1982).
6. H. Olson, "Directional Microphones," *J. Audio Engineering Society*, vol. 15, no. 4 (1967).
7. A. Robertson, *Microphones*, Hayden, New York (1963).
8. J. Sank, "Microphones," *J. Audio Engineering Society*, vol. 33, no. 7/8 (1985).
9. J. Woram, *Sound Recording Handbook*, H. Sams, Indianapolis (1989).
10. *Microphones*, an anthology of articles on microphones from the pages of *J. Audio Engineering Society*, vol. 1 through vol. 27.

# 6

---

# ENVIRONMENTAL EFFECTS AND DEPARTURES FROM IDEAL MICROPHONE PERFORMANCE

---

## 6.1 INTRODUCTION

This chapter will cover the many aspects of microphone performance that depend on the working environment. Such topics as proximity effect, interference effects due to multiple path lengths, and combined microphone outputs will be covered. Departures from ideal performance, including the disparity between random incidence and on-axis response and variations in directional patterns at frequency extremes, will be discussed.

## 6.2 PROXIMITY EFFECT

All directional microphones exhibit some degree of proximity effect, which causes an increase in low-frequency output from the microphone. The effect comes about because, at close working distances, the front and back paths to the diaphragm may differ substantially in their relative distances from the sound source. The pressure gradient component acting on the diaphragm diminishes at lower frequencies, while the inverse-square component remains constant for a given working distance. When this distance is small, as shown in Figure 6-1, it dominates at low frequencies and causes the output to rise.

Since the bidirectional pattern consists solely of gradient response, its proximity effect is quite significant, and typical response at various working distances is shown in Figure 6-2(a). Figure 6-2(b) shows the proximity effect for a cardioid microphone at various working distances. For cardioid microphones, the proximity effect will vary with the pickup angle, as shown in Figure 6-2(c).

Proximity effect can be used to advantage, and many a vocalist has taken advantage of the increased "richness and warmth" that the bass boost provides. But too much can

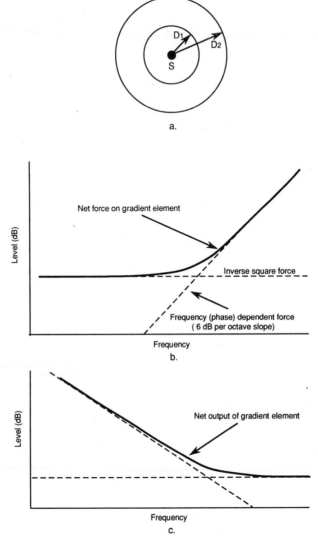

**Figure 6-1.** Proximity effect in pressure-gradient microphones. (a) Sound pressure levels are proportional to the square of the distance from the source. (b) The combination of inverse square and frequency dependent forces on the ribbon. (c) Electrical output of a ribbon microphone, due to the forces shown in (b).

be a problem, and manufacturers of microphones have in many cases reduced the low-frequency sensitivity of their vocal microphones so that close response is only partially boosted. The response of such a microphone is shown in Figure 6-2(b), where the low-frequency output at a distance of 30 cm and greater is considerably rolled off.

Most directional capacitor microphones are provided with switchable low-frequency attenuation for close use, and the typical effect of the rolloff is as shown in Figure 6-3.

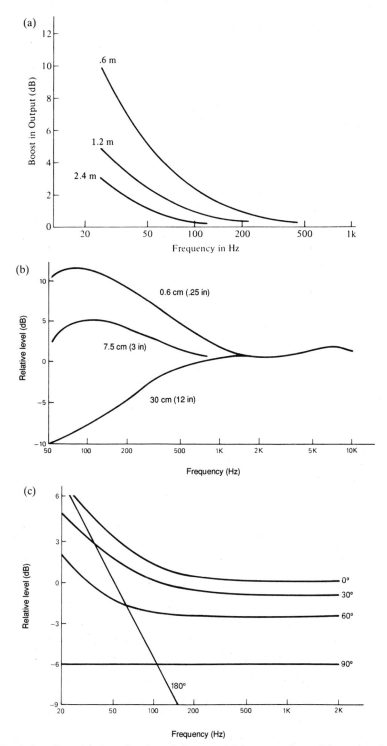

**Figure 6-2.** Proximity effect. (a) As a function of distance and frequency for a ribbon microphone. (b) As a function of distance and frequency for a capacitor cardioid microphone. (c) Calculated for a cardioid microphone as a function of angle (fixed distance).

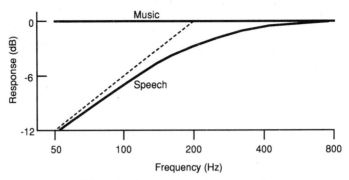

**Figure 6-3.** Effect of voice–music switch on microphone response.

Older dynamic and ribbon microphones often had a switch labeled "music" and "speech." The music position was flat, while the speech position, intended for close use, was rolled off.

## 6.3 HIGH-FREQUENCY AXIAL RESPONSE VERSUS RANDOM INCIDENCE RESPONSE

Depending on diaphragm size, all microphones will exhibit a sharpening of polar response along their primary axis. The response of a typical omnidirectional microphone is shown in Figure 6-4. In (a), the on-axis high-frequency response has been maintained flat, while the response of the microphone at off-axis angles has been allowed to roll off. The larger the diaphragm, the lower the frequency at which the rolloff becomes significant. The manufacturer can equalize the microphone acoustically so that the off-axis, or random, response is maintained flat, as shown in (b). In this case, the on-axis response will rise at high frequencies.

A few high-quality omnidirectional microphones are equipped with a switch that will convert the microphone from flat on-axis response to flat random incidence response. The flat random incidence response would be indicated when the microphone cannot be

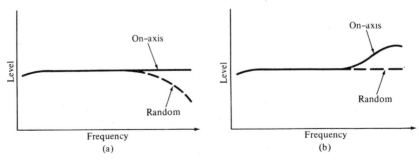

**Figure 6-4.** On-axis and random incidence response of microphones. The microphone in (a) has flat on-axis response, and the microphone in (b) has flat random-incidence response.

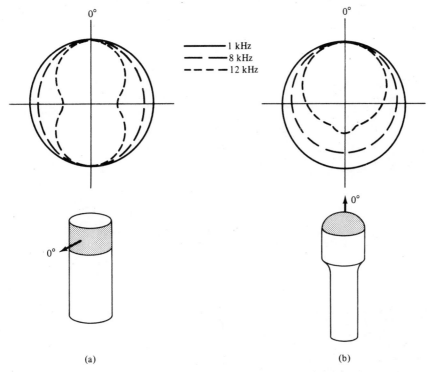

**Figure 6-5.** High-frequency pattern narrowing for a radially sensitive microphone (a) and an axially sensitive microphone (b).

pointed directly at its target. An example here would be a recording in which a single microphone was oriented vertically in order to pick up evenly sounds that were arriving from a number of lateral directions.

The nature of microphone high-frequency polar response depends on the axis of maximum sensitivity. Figure 6-5 shows typical high-frequency pattern sharpening for omnidirectional microphones that are radially and axially sensitive. Directional microphones are prone to these problems as well, and engineers should familiarize themselves with manufacturers' literature and specification sheets.

## 6.4 POLAR RESPONSE ABERRATIONS AT FREQUENCY EXTREMES

While high-frequency polar response aberrations in microphones are wave-length dependent, aberrations at low frequencies are a consequence of design trade-offs. Figure 6-6 shows two views of the polar response of the same cardioid microphone. The response shown in (*a*) is in the normal polar form, while the response shown in (*b*) is presented as a family of off-axis frequency response curves. Both methods of presenting directional data are useful to the recording engineer.

What we note so clearly here is that the microphone's nominal pattern is only approximate and that the response from certain off-axis directions can be fairly uneven with respect to frequency. The example shown here is typical of a high-quality model; lesser designs may have greater anomalies in directional response. The fundamental lesson here is that microphones, regardless of their nominal pickup pattern, should be carefully oriented with respect to the sound sources at hand.

In general, large diaphragm microphones will have greater high-frequency pattern aberrations than smaller diaphragm microphones. However, this should be no deterrent to the use of the large diaphragm models for all kinds of close on-axis placement in the studio, where these aberrations are of no consequence.

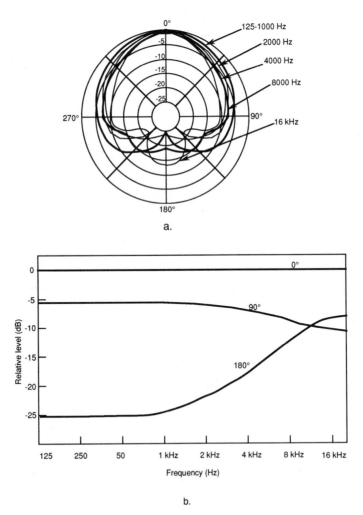

**Figure 6-6.** Polar aberrations at high frequencies. (a) Polar response. (b) Off-axis frequency response.

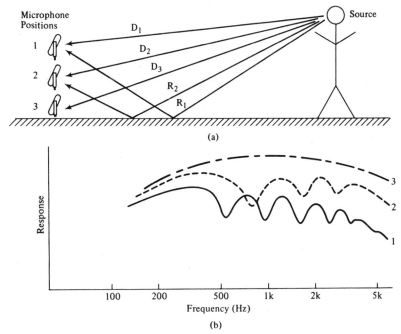

**Figure 6-7.** Illustration of the effect of microphone height above a floor on the pattern of reinforcements and cancellations in response.

## 6.5 EFFECTS OF SIGNAL INTERFERENCE

### 6.5.1 Reflections from Nearby Surfaces

Figure 6-7 shows what happens when sound reaches a microphone by way of two paths. Interference effects give rise to a series of peaks and dips in response. When the path length difference is minimized, as at position 3, the microphone's output is maximized and the response is smoothest.

Short working distances minimize the reflection problem, but in many environments, close boundary reflections are significant. In many cases it is desirable to place a microphone directly on a boundary, and for this purpose a so-called boundary layer microphone will be useful.

### 6.5.2 Boundary Layer Microphones

A boundary layer microphone is a small omnidirectional element placed at a wall or floor surface. The Crown PZM (Pressure Zone Microphone) models are perhaps the best known. They are designed around very small electret elements and, for the most part, have uniform random incidence response.

Since these microphones operate in proximity to a reflective surface, there is an effective acoustical image which doubles the pressure at the microphone's diaphragm, increasing

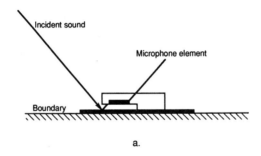

a.

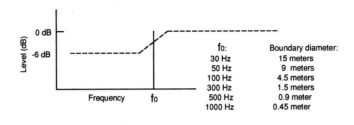

b.

**Figure 6-8.** Boundary layer microphones. (a) Section view. (b) Response as a function of boundary size.

its output by 6 dB. The size of the boundary is important in ensuring extended low-frequency response. In some applications, boundary layer microphones are placed on Plexiglas sheets, and the size of the sheet will determine the range above which the pressure doubling is significant. Details are shown in Figure 6-8.

### 6.5.3 Combined Microphone Outputs

In many cases, microphones may overlap substantially in their coverage of the same sound source. If the microphones are at different distances from the sound source, and if their outputs are combined, then the familiar pattern of peaks and dips will occur. A typical example of this is shown in Figure 6-9. Here, a stereo recording of a piano is made with rather widely spaced microphones. While the recording may be workable in stereo, a monophonic summation of the two channels will result in signal cancellation at frequencies that are integral multiples of

$$f = \frac{0.5c}{D_1 - D_2} \tag{6-1}$$

Here, $D_2$ is the longer distance and $c$ is the velocity of sound. At frequency multiples of $\frac{3}{2}f$, $\frac{5}{2}f$, $\frac{7}{2}f$, and so forth, there will be signal reinforcements in the combined output of the microphones.

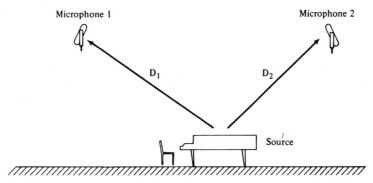

**Figure 6-9.** Illustration of different path lengths between a sound source and a pair of microphones. When the microphones are combined for mono reproduction, reinforcement take place at a frequency (and its integral multiples) whose wavelength is equal to $D_1 - D_2$. Partial cancellation will take place at points between these frequencies.

## BIBLIOGRAPHY

1. L. Beranek, *Acoustics*, McGraw-Hill, New York (1954).
2. G. Bore, *Microphones*, Georg Neumann GmbH, Berlin (1989).
3. J. Eargle, *The Microphone Handbook*, Elar, Plainview, N.Y. (1982).
4. A. Robertson, *Microphones*, Hayden, New York (1951).

# 7

## STEREO AND SOUNDFIELD MICROPHONES

### 7.1 INTRODUCTION

For many applications in stereo recording, it is convenient to use single microphone housings in which two transducers have been positioned for stereo pickup. In recent years, the Soundfield microphone has been developed as an extension of the traditional stereo microphone, and it allows the sound field at a given position in space to be sampled in terms of sound pressure and the three velocity components existing at that position.

This chapter, will describe the construction of these models in detail, reserving for a later chapter specific discussion of how to use them in actual stereo recording.

### 7.2 STEREO MICROPHONES

A typical stereo microphone is shown in Figure 7-1 with grilles partially removed. Upper and lower capacitor elements are visible, and they are both of Braunmühl–Weber design. The lower element is fixed, while the upper one can be rotated over a range of 270°. Both upper and lower elements can be altered in pickup pattern remotely at a control unit. Thus, it is possible to combine a variety of polar patterns at any given splay angle between them.

The general microphone type described here is quite expensive, and only a handful of designs are available. The engineer may encounter a somewhat simplified design in which only a pair of fixed cardioid elements are mounted together. While this design is much less flexible, it has considerable use as an accent microphone in orchestral recording, where the engineer may desire a degree of stereo spread that does not cover the full included angle of the loudspeaker array. These designs are much less expensive than those using the Braunmühl–Weber approach shown in the photograph.

**Figure 7-1.** Details of the Neumann SM-69 stereo microphone. Both elements have remotely variable patterns; the bottom element is fixed, while the upper element can be rotated over at least a 270° range. (*Courtesy G. Neumann GMBH and Gotham Audio Corporation*)

Stereo microphones are commonly used in broadcasting and are often more or less permanently mounted in auditoriums where a variety of musical activities are carried out. Under these conditions, their advantages are:

a. Simple, out of the way, mounting. A single cable and two guy wires can position the microphone, and a third guy wire can be used to tilt the microphone as desired.
b. Remote pattern control allows easy "fine tuning" of the array for a particular type of musical event.
c. The "coincident" stereo pickup is inherently mono compatible.

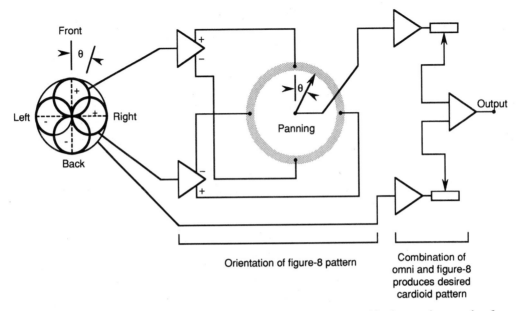

Orientation of figure-8 pattern

Combination of
omni and figure-8
produces desired
cardioid pattern

**Figure 7-2.** A steerable microphone array. The two figure-8 elements are combined to produce another figure-8 oriented in any direction in the horizontal plane. The resulting pattern is then combined with the omnidirectional element to produce the desired cardioid pattern.

 d. The array can easily be supplemented with additional accent microphones for pickup of soloists.

The only drawback to the array is that the splay angle can only be changed directly at the microphone, often requiring a tall ladder.

## 7.3 STEERABLE MICROPHONE ARRAYS

Figure 7-2 shows details of a microphone consisting of one omnidirectional and two bidirectional elements. The three outputs can be combined to provide any first-order cardioid pattern oriented at any angle in one plane. Such a microphone array as this can easily be assembled from commercially available microphones; however, the necessary control circuitry must be custom-designed for the job at hand.

In this design, the outputs of the two bidirectional elements are combined to create a new bidirectional pattern oriented at any desired angle in the plane. Then, its output is combined with that of the omnidirectional element to create a first-order cardioid oriented at any desired angle. Multiple outputs may be used simultaneously.

Although this approach has not been used at the basis of any commercial stereo microphone, it has the advantages that greater "coincidence" can be attained over the dual Braunmühl–Weber elements, and that no physical splaying of the elements is necessary. All orientations are achieved solely through electrical addition of signals.

## 7.4 THE SOUNDFIELD MICROPHONE

The extension of the approach shown in Figure 7-2 to provide three-dimensional control is possible in theory, but very difficult to accomplish. The Soundfield microphone, developed by Gerzon (2), represents a more elegant solution to the problem. In this design, four subcardioid elements are positioned as shown in the left portion of Figure 7-3. In this view, the array of elements is seen from behind, and the four outputs can be combined to produce the three required bidirectional patterns (left-right, up-down, and fore-aft) as well as the omnidirectional pattern.

Figure 7-4 shows a photograph of the microphone element array and a diagram of the control unit. In use, the Soundfield microphone can function as a very flexible stereo microphone, or it can be used to encode positional information in a recording for playback over a variety of loudspeaker arrangements that convey height information in addition to lateral spatial information. In this application, the name *periphonic* is used describe the technology.

When used as a stereo microphone, the Soundfield microphone has the advantage of being electrically (and remotely) adjustable in terms of patterns, effective tilt angle, and pattern splay angle. A version of the Soundfield transducer array is available in a format optimized for stereo (two-channel) use in which patterns and splay angles can be remotely selected.

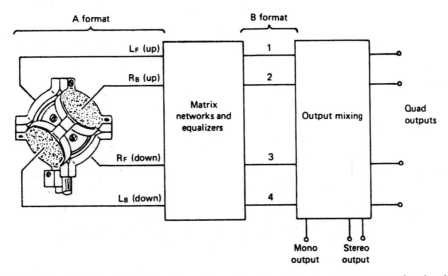

**Figure 7-3.** Details of the Soundfield microphone. The various directional components are produced as follows:

$$1 = \text{Omnidirectional component} = L_F + R_B + R_F + L_B$$
$$2 = \text{Bidirectional (up–down)} = L_F + R_B - (R_F + L_B)$$
$$3 = \text{Bidirectional (left–right)} = L_F + L_B - (R_F + R_B)$$
$$4 = \text{Bidirectional (fore–aft)} = L_F + R_F - (L_B + R_B)$$

(a)

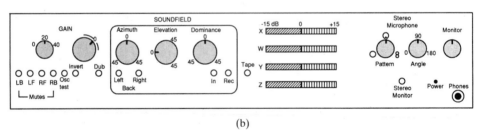

(b)

**Figure 7-4.** Soundfield microphone and associated control unit. (*Courtesy AMS Industries*)

## 7.5 OTHER MULTICHANNEL MICROPHONES

While not gaining the success of the Soundfield microphone, several models of four-channel microphones have been designed and produced on a limited basis. Most of these consist of four cardioid elements arranged in a single plane at angles of 90°. As such, they provide excellent localization for playback in the lateral plane. The recording engineer will rarely encounter such designs.

### BIBLIOGRAPHY

1. J. Eargle, *The Microphone Handbook*, Elar, Plainview, N.Y. (1982).
2. M. Gerzon, "Periphony: With-Height Sound Reproduction," *J. Audio Engineering Society*, vol. 21, no. 1 (1973).

3. C. Huston, "A Quadraphonic Microphone Development," *Recording Engineer/Producer*, vol. 1, no. 3 (1970).

4. T. Lubin, "The Calrec Soundfield Microphone," *Recording Engineer/Producer*, vol. 10, no. 6 (1979).

5. J. Mosely, "Eliminating the Stereo Seat," *J. Audio Engineering Society*, vol. 8, no. 1 pp. 46–53 (1960).

6. J. Smith, "The Soundfield Microphone," *db Magazine,* vol. 12, no. 7 (1978).

7. T. Yamamoto, "Quadraphonic One Point Pickup Microphone," *J. Audio Engineering Society*, vol. 21, no. 4 (1973).

# 8

## MICROPHONE ELECTRICAL
## SPECIFICATIONS AND ACCESSORIES

### 8.1 INTRODUCTION

In addition to the acoustical properties of microphones there are many electrical aspects which the recording engineer must be aware of. Chief among these are microphone sensitivity, impedance, self-noise level, and distortion at high operating levels. These will be discussed along with aspects of remote powering of capacitor microphones. Microphone accessories will be covered as well.

### 8.2 MICROPHONE SENSITIVITY AND IMPEDANCE RATINGS

Microphone sensitivity ratings state either the microphone's output power into a specified load, or the open-circuit voltage developed, when the microphone is placed in a known sound pressure field. A sound pressure of 1 pascal (10 dyne/cm$^2$) is standard for most measurements today and is equivalent to 94 dB $L_P$. The output voltage may be stated either in terms of actual value or in dB relative to some reference voltage. The term dBV is often used to express levels relative to 1 volt: level in dBV = 20 log $V_0$. Figure 8-1 shows the open-circuit measurement method schematically.

When output power is used for expressing microphone sensitivity, it is usually stated in dBm, and is expressed as: level in dBm = 10 log (power in watts/0.001 watt). Such ratings are still common for many types of dynamic microphones. For example, assume that a given model is rated as follows:

| | |
|---|---|
| Impedance: | 50 ohms |
| Sensitivity: | −53 dBm *re* 10 dynes/cm$^2$ (1 pascal) |

This implies that the microphone can deliver a power level into a load of 50 ohms of −53 dBm, and this is shown schematically in Figure 8-2.

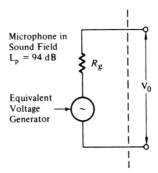

**Figure 8-1.** Equivalent circuit for a microphone in a sound field looking into an open circuit. Because there is no current flow, there is no voltage drop across the generator impedance $R_g$.

In the early days of recording and broadcasting, it was customary to operate microphones into matching loads to get maximum power transfer from the microphone and maintain proper signal-to-noise ratios. In most applications today, microphones are operated essentially into an open circuit. A microphone rated at, say, 50 to 200 ohms will operate into an input impedance of perhaps 3000 or 4000 ohms, and this will not load down the microphone to any appreciable extent. Under these conditions, there is very little power transfer from the microphone to the load.

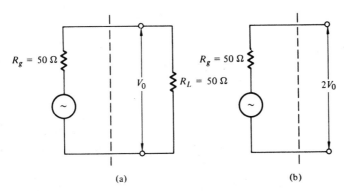

(a)    (b)

**Figure 8-2.** Illustration of the doubling of output voltage between a loaded microphone (a) and an unloaded microphone (b). In (a), the microphone is viewed as a single voltage generator in series with a source resistance of 50 ohms and loaded externally with another 50-ohm resistance. Computing the voltage across the load:

Calculate power from power level of $-53$ dBm:

$$\text{Power } (P) = .001 \text{ antilog } 10 \, (-53/10) \text{ watt}$$
$$= 5 \times 10^{-9} \text{ watt}$$
$$\text{Voltage } (V_0) = \sqrt{PR_L} = 5 \times 10^{-4} \text{ volt}$$

Operating this microphone into an open circuit rather than into a matching impedance, the voltage would double. When $R_L = R_g$, the voltage drop across $R_L$ is the same as across $R_g$, and the sum of the two voltages (in series) is equal to the generator voltage. In (b), $R_L$ has been removed, and there is no current flow or power transfer; in this case the full generator voltage appears unattenuated at the output terminals.

While various dynamic microphones are often rated in terms of power output, virtually all capacitor microphones are rated in terms of the open circuit output voltage that the microphone produces when it is placed in a sound field of 1 pascal. Typical ratings for capacitor microphones are generally from about 5 millivolts to about 20 millivolts *re* 1 pascal.

Some manufacturers of dynamic microphones specify open circuit voltage when the microphone is placed in a stated sound field. Generally, their output voltages are in the range of one-tenth that of a typical capacitor microphone, which corresponds to an output level difference of −20 dB.

## 8.3 MICROPHONE NOISE RATINGS

Today, the output voltage of most capacitor microphones is high enough that the dominant electrical noise floor in an input channel is not likely to be that of the input preamplifier, but rather that of the microphone's electronic circuitry. The fundamental limiting factor in noise is the acoustical resistance present in the microphone's transducing element.

The preferred method of rating the noise of a capacitor microphone is to state its self-noise in terms of its dB(A) weighted noise floor (see Section 2.2). For example, if a given capacitor microphone has a rated self-noise level of 15 dB(A), that microphone will produce an output noise level equivalent to that of a perfect (noiseless) microphone located in a room with a noise level measuring 15 dB on the A scale of a sound level meter.

The best studio capacitor microphones today have noise floors in the range of 10 dB(A). Many good models run as high as 17 dB(A), and levels of 25 dB(A) may be encountered in some small electret models. While such a rating may seem too high, we should remember that many microphones are placed very close to their target instruments in the recording studio, which means that the sound output from the instrument will almost always swamp out the microphone's own noise floor. It is only in classical recording, where the microphones may be placed at some distance from the instruments, that noise generally becomes a matter of concern.

Dynamic microphones do not generally carry a noise rating. Since their output is fairly low, most of the noise encountered in their use is due to the input noise floor of the first stage of amplification in the recording console. Calculations of noise must then be made based on the equivalent input noise of the first stage of amplification in the console.

On some occasions, the engineer will come across a noise rating that indicates the microphone's susceptibility to generating hum in its output due to external alternating magnetic fields. There are several standards here, and comparison of manufacturer's data must be done carefully. Usually, the microphone is placed in a reference hum field of $10^{-4}$ tesla (1 millioersted). Typical hum ratings for both dynamic and capacitor microphones are in the range of 14 to about 24 dB, equivalent SPL.

## 8.4 MICROPHONE DISTORTION RATINGS

The distortion produced by a microphone at high sound pressure levels represents a limit to its usefulness in high-level recording applications. The standard today is to specify the maximum sound pressure level at which the microphone will generate no more than 0.5% total harmonic distortion (THD). Most capacitor microphones in use today carry ratings ranging from about 120 to 140 dB $L_P$ for the maximum upper limit.

The onset of distortion in a capacitor microphone can be quite abrupt, since it may be a function of internal electrical overload. With many dynamic microphones, the onset of distortion at high levels may be more gradual.

## 8.5 MICROPHONE PADS

In many applications, the distortion encountered with microphones may not be due to the microphone itself, but rather to overload of the input circuitry following it. In such cases, some kind of signal attenuation, or padding, will be necessary. Many capacitor microphones have built-in, switchable 10- or 12-dB pads that will reduce their output accordingly. All modern recording consoles have variable input padding so that the signal level from the microphone can further be properly set for the level and gain requirements at hand.

## 8.6 SIGNAL-TO-NOISE RATIO AND DYNAMIC RANGE

The overall operating range between system noise floor and onset of distortion of a recording system can never be better than that which is established at the microphones. The maximum signal-to-noise ratio of a system is the range in level between a defined noise floor and a defined distortion limit. Figure 8-3 shows the maximum signal-to-noise ratio for a typical studio-quality capacitor microphone, with and without the switchable 10-dB pad. Note that when the pad is engaged, the entire operating range of the microphone is shifted upward by 10 dB. Note in particular that the noise floor of the microphone has deteriorated by 10 dB when the pad is engaged. It is clear that the maximum signal-to-noise capability of the microphone shown in Figure 8-3 is some 126 dB, better by far than any commercial recording system.

The dynamic range of a recording system is a measure of the range in levels which the system can handle, taking into account certain properties of hearing. For example, a recording system with a maximum signal-to-noise ratio of 96 dB can exhibit a dynamic range of the order of 110 dB, inasmuch as we can clearly hear a sinewave in the 3 kHz range some 12 to 15 dB below the wideband noise floor of the system. Likewise, an analog tape recording system operating with noise reduction can exhibit a dynamic range which is some 20 dB greater than the maximum signal-to-noise ratio the system can handle, depending on the amount of noise reduction employed.

## 8.7 REMOTE POWERING OF CAPACITOR MICROPHONES

Most capacitor microphones today are powered by a 48-volt phantom powering system. Details of this are shown in Figure 8-4. Note that positive voltage is applied to pins 2 and 3 through carefully balanced resistors, with the return path through pin 1. In this way, the microphone signal can be transmitted between pins 2 and 3, with no interaction

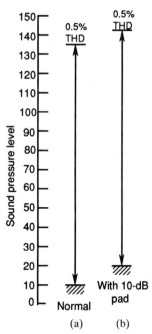

**Figure 8-3.** Illustration of noise floor and maximum output of a studio-quality microphone. (a) Without internal pad. (b) With internal 10-dB pad.

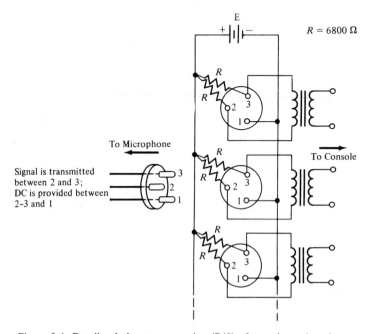

**Figure 8-4.** Details of phantom powering (P48) of capacitor microphones

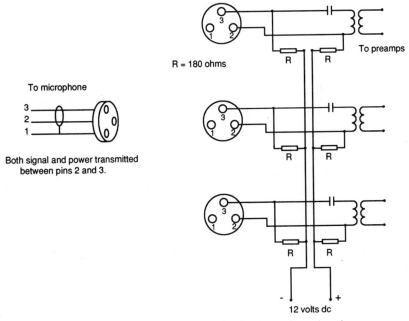

**Figure 8-5.** Details of T-powering (T12) of capacitor microphones.

with the power source. The designation P48 is used to indicate this method of microphone powering.

On rare occasions, T-powering will be encountered. Details of this are shown in Figure 8-5. T-powering is normally at 12 volts, and the standard designation is T12.

Older tube-type capacitor microphones are normally powered individually with a power supply.

## 8.8 MICROPHONE LINE LOSSES

In normal recording activities, remote-powered capacitor microphones may be located as far as 75 meters (250 ft) from the console input. If low-impedance microphones are used, and this is normal, then there will be negligible high-frequency losses if microphones with output impedances in the 150-ohm range or less are used. Figure 8-6 presents typical cable losses as a function of length and source impedance. Longer runs should be avoided. If they are absolutely essential, then it would be wise to incorporate microphone preamplifiers ahead of the long cable runs, then feed the signal into the console at line level.

In many urban locations, long cable runs can be responsible for a variety of RF (radio frequency) interferences. The recording engineer should take note of where local television antennas are located, and be aware of the problem before it occurs. There are no easy cures for RF interferences. Sometimes, a slight repositioning of excess microphone cable will take care of the problem. Some microphones models and some console input stages are more susceptible to the problem than others.

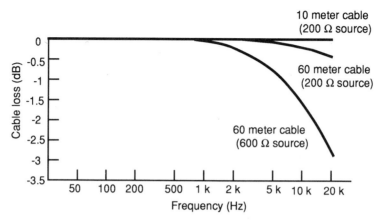

**Figure 8-6.** Microphone line losses as a function of cable length and microphone source impedance.

## 8.9 MICROPHONE ACCESSORIES

### 8.9.1 Mechanical

The following brief descriptions of mechanical accessories are given:

a. *Booms and stands*: To permit placing the microphone exactly where desired.
b. *Shock mounts*: To isolate the microphone from external mechanical vibrations.
c. *Stereo mounts*: To facilitate mounting two microphones on a single stand for stereo pickup.
d. *Wind screens*: To reducing "popping" of plosive sounds, such as can be produced by close-in vocalists. In outdoor applications, wind screens can reduce the low-frequency random noises generated by gentle breezes. Strong winds are a difficult problem.

### 8.9.2 Electrical

The following brief descriptions of electrical accessories are given:

a. *In-line loss pads*: To reduce the signal level from a microphone so that it can better match a given input.
b. *In-line transformers*: To provide impedance matching for better electrical interface with input circuits.
c. *In-line filters*: To reduce rumble or proximity effect.
d. *Male-to-male or female-to female adaptors*: To facilitate setups where there are not enough of the right cables.

## BIBLIOGRAPHY

1. G. Bore, *Microphones*, Georg Neumann GmbH, Berlin (1989).
2. J. Eargle, *The Microphone Handbook*, Elar, Plainview, N.Y. (1982).
3. *Microphones*, an anthology of articles on microphones from the pages of *J. Audio Engineering Society*, vol.1 through vol. 27.

# 9

---

# TWO-CHANNEL STEREO

---

## 9.1 INTRODUCTION AND SHORT HISTORY

Stereophonic sound, or *stereo* as it is usually called, refers to any system of recording or sound transmission using multiple microphones and loudspeakers. Signals picked up by the microphones are routed to loudspeakers that are placed in a geometrical array corresponding to the microphone array. In this manner, many of the spatial aspects of the recording environment are preserved, and the listener can perceive, more or less accurately, the spatial perspective of the original performance in its acoustical surroundings.

Stereo need not be limited to two channels. Motion picture systems have included upwards of six channels. For home use, however, stereo is presently limited to two transmission channels.

A distinction is made between stereo and *binaural sound* transmission. Binaural transmission uses two microphones located at ear position in an artificial head. The outputs are fed to a listener via headphones, with each ear hearing only the signal originating at the corresponding microphone, as shown in Figure 9-1.

Stereo was first demonstrated at the Paris Opera in 1881, making use of primitive carbon microphones and armature earphones. Serious studies of stereo were not undertaken until the early 1930s. The pioneering work of Alan Blumlein in England and workers at Bell Laboratories in the United States is significant here. Stereo did not become commonplace until the advent of multichannel motion picture recording in the 1950s. About that same time, two-track stereo tapes became available, and in 1957 the stereo LP was introduced.

## 9.2 COINCIDENT MICROPHONE ARRAYS FOR STEREO

We begin our study of stereo with a discussion of coincident microphone techniques. These are arrays in which the microphones are placed as closely together as possible, thus minimizing timing differences between the microphones. Coincident microphone

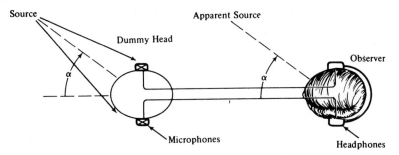

**Figure 9-1.** Principle of binaural sound transmission. Microphones located at ear positions on an artificial head are fed to headphones worn by the listener. Lateral localization cues, such as time and amplitude differences, are preserved.

arrays may be referred to as "panning" microphones arrays, since they can produce amplitude balances between loudspeakers that result in precise phantom image localization in the same way that a panpot does (see Section 2.3.2). Blumlein (2) first described the technique in his 1931 patent. The crossed figure-8 pair shown in Figure 9-2 is commonly known as the Blumlein configuration, although it was not the first stereo array he experimented with.

## 9.2.1 The Blumlein Configuration

This array will be analyzed for three source positions. The positive lobes of the crossed microphones are set at 90° to each other, and the space between the positive lobes is

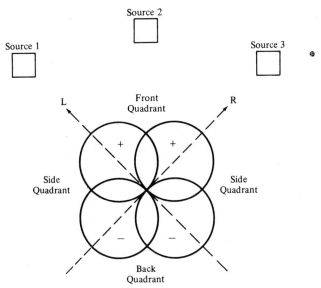

**Figure 9-2.** The earliest coincident microphone array. Blumlein placed a pair of bidirectional microphone one atop the other in close proximity.

aimed toward the performing group. It is clear that for positions 1 and 3 localization will be, respectively, at the left and right loudspeakers only. This is simply because the source, which is precisely on the major axis of one microphone, lies in the null plane of the other microphone. On the other hand, a source positioned at 2 will be picked up equally by both microphones. Furthermore, the amplitude of the sound picked up by each microphone will be 0.7 (−3 dB) relative to on-axis, and this corresponds exactly to the output produced by a panpot set for center localization.

Making use of the sine and cosine nature of the bidirectional pickup pattern, we are able to simulate exactly the operation of the panpot itself, and all images located between the left and right axes of the microphone array will appear in the stereo playback array as precisely as through they had been panned there.

In addition to its precise panning function in the front quadrant, the Blumlein configuration has the following characteristics:

1. *Opposite polarity side quadrant pickup.* Since both side quadrants are picked up by both positive and negative lobes of the bidirectional microphones, any sources of sound located there will appear ambiguously in the playback array and should be avoided.
2. *Reverberation pickup.* Since reverberation may enter the microphone array more or less equally through the back and the two side quadrants, it will benefit from both the out-of-phase pickup and the in-phase pickup in the back quadrant. The result is quite natural reverberant pickup with just a hint of localization coming outside the bounds of the loudspeaker array.

In actual practice, the Blumlein array requires careful judgment in positioning. It must be far enough from the ensemble to fill the front quadrant properly, and it must not be so far from the ensemble that direct-to-reverberant relationships suffer.

## 9.2.2 Other Coincident Arrays

Crossed cardioids are often used in a manner similar to the Blumlein array. It is customary to spread the angle between the major axes out to perhaps 120° in order to avoid too much pickup along the central axis of the array, which would give the sound a strong center, or monophonic, dominance. Supercardioid and hypercardioid microphones are often used in a similar manner, and these would be the natural choice in spaces that were too live for the Blumlein array. That is to say, the front dominance of the various crossed cardioid arrays will allow the recording engineer to move away from the ensemble, while still controlling down the amount of reverberation being picked up. Examples are shown in Figure 9-3.

When cardioid, supercardioid, and hypercardioid microphones are used in a coincident array, it is common to splay them at the angles at which their overlap is −3 dB, relative to on-axis. Table 9-1 gives this information.

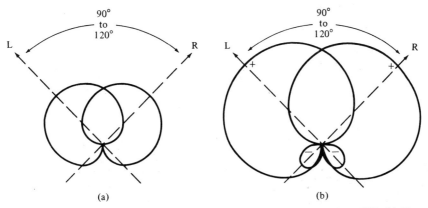

**Figure 9-3.** Other coincident arrays. (a) Axes of crossed cardioids oriented 90° to 120°. (b) Hypercardioids treated similarly.

### 9.2.3 Middle-Side (MS) Pickup

Coincident microphones are very often manipulated by way of the MS technique, which, in its normal application, employs a directional microphone aimed straight ahead, emphasizing the *middle* of the performing group. A second microphone, always bidirectional, is oriented at 90° so that its two lobes emphasize *side* pickup.

The output of the MS pair is not listened to directly, but rather is processed through sum and difference circuits that yield left and right (sometimes referred to as *XY* output) signals suitable for normal stereo listening. The process is shown in Figure 9-4.

When used in MS form, coincident microphones benefit from a good bit of flexibility. By varying the amount of the S component, the apparent width of the array can be altered electrically. A position control allows shifting of the array left or right, as desired. Details of these controls are shown in Figure 9-5 with application shown in Figure 9-6.

When the MS stereo signals are summed for monophonic presentation, the S signal drops out completely, leaving only the M signal, as shown in Figure 9-7. Thus, mono compatibility is generally excellent.

Regardless of the pickup method, some recording engineers prefer to take their stereo channels, convert them to MS, and them convert them back again to stereo. While in

### Table 9-1. Recommended splay angles for coincident cardioid microphones

| Pattern | Total angle between microphones for −3 dB overlap |
| --- | --- |
| Bidirectional | 90° |
| Cardioid | 131° |
| Supercardioid | 115° |
| Hypercardioid | 105° |

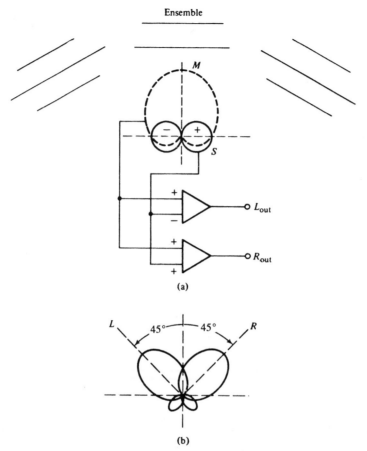

**Figure 9-4.** Principle of MS (middle–side) microphone technique. (a) Cardioid and figure-8 microphones are located in front of a performing ensemble and connected electrically as shown. The respective outputs are:

$$L = 1 + \sin\theta + \cos\theta = 1 + \sqrt{2}\cos(\theta + 45°)$$
$$R = 1 + \sin\theta - \cos\theta = 1 + \sqrt{2}\cos(\theta + 135°)$$

(b) The left and right outputs are directional patterns aimed, respectively, at left and right. Maximum response is at angles of ±45°.

the MS domain, the M and S components can be manipulated so that the eventual stereo sound stage can be widened or narrowed, as desired. The technique, which is shown in Figure 9-8, may be useful for widening any stereo recording that, for whatever reason, may have been recorded with too much front dominance.

Figure 9-9(a) shows the relationship between various MS arrays and their equivalent XY (stereo) forms. Figures 9-9(b) and (c) present a method for determining the specific M and S patterns that will correspond to a given XY microphone array. For example, assume that we are working with an XY array consisting of a pair of supercardioids at

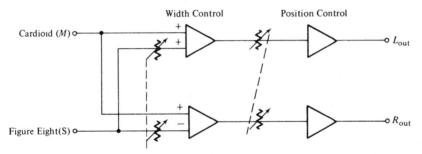

**Figure 9-5.** Width and position control of MS microphones. The width control alters the amount of figure-8 or S component relative to the fixed cardioid or M component. The position control consists of a pair of attenuators connected differentially to act as a balance control.

an angle of 120°. First examining Figure 9-9(b), locate the supercardioid pattern along the bottom and move upward to intersect the 60° curve. From that point move to the right edge of the graph and note that the normal cardioid pattern is indicated for the M pattern. We know that the S pattern is always a figure-8, and we now need to determine its correct operating level, relative to the M pattern. Moving on to Figure 9-9(c), locate the supercardioid pattern at the bottom and move up to the 60° curve. Then, move to the right edge and note that a level of about −1.5 dB is indicated. Thus, an MS pair consisting of a normal cardioid for M operated at −1.5 dB relative to S can be sum-and-difference matrixed to yield an *XY* equivalent of a pair of supercardioids splayed at a total angle of 120°.

Implementation of MS normally requires a special sum-and-difference arrangement of transformers or amplifiers. When such a unit is not available, a method using three input

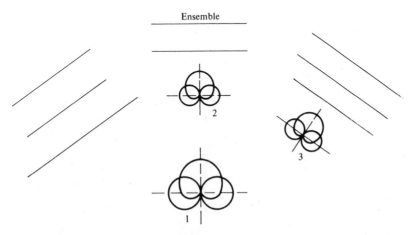

**Figure 9-6.** Use of width and position controls in MS recording. The MS pair 1 is for overall pickup; it should be adjusted for desired width and centered in the stereo loudspeaker array. Pairs 2 and 3 are for highlighting soloists and would be adjusted for narrower presentation. Pair 2 would be centered in the array, and pair 3 would be positioned to the right.

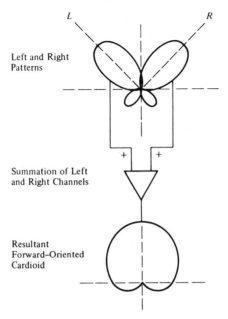

**Figure 9-7.** Monophonic compatibility of the MS technique. The MS pair yields left and right pickup patterns as shown in Figure 9-4. When these expressions are combined $(L + R)$, the cosine terms cancel, leaving only the forward-oriented cardioid pattern:

$$L + R = 2(1 + \sin \theta)$$

positions on a recording console can be used to derive the MS output. This is shown in Figure 9-10.

All coincident techniques discussed in this section, *XY* and *MS*, are most easily implemented with the Braunmühl–Weber type stereo microphones discussed in Chapter 7. The Soundfield microphone also provides the same flexibility with perhaps a bit better overall coincidence, due to the relatively small volume occupied by the four-transducer array.

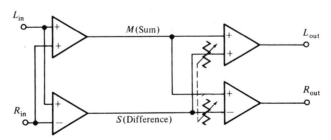

**Figure 9-8.** Sum and difference processing for left–right (*XY*) microphone pairs or stereo channels.

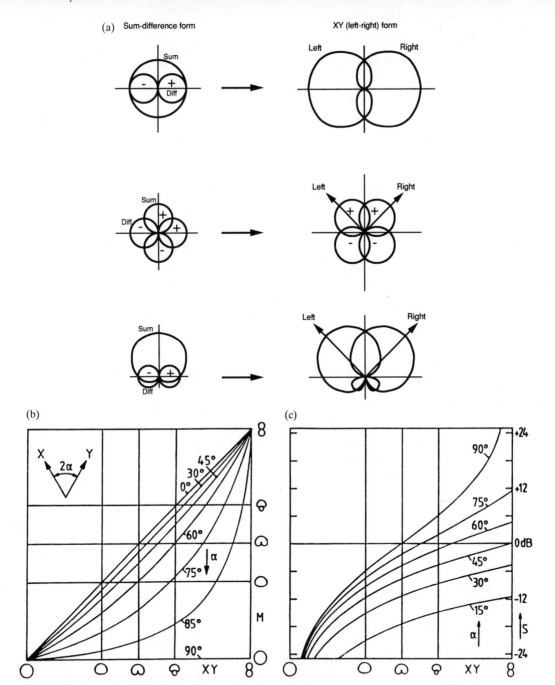

**Figure 9-9.** Various MS arrays and their equivalent *XY* forms. (b and c) Graphical determination of equivalent MS parameters for any given XY form. The M directivity pattern can be obtained from graph (b), while the required S level can be determined from graph (c).

For example, let the *XY* pair consist of a pair of supercardioids at an angle (2α) of 120°. From the upper graph (b), locate the supercardioid symbol on the right axis and move to the left until the 60° curve is intersected. Then read downward to the horizontal axis and note that the required M directivity pattern will be almost halfway between supercardioid and figure-8. Then, going to the same position on the horizontal axis of (c), move upward until the 60° curve is intersected. Move to the right axis and note that the S level will have to be raised about 2 dB relative to the M level. (*Parts (b) and (c) courtesy of Sennheiser; see reference 11*)

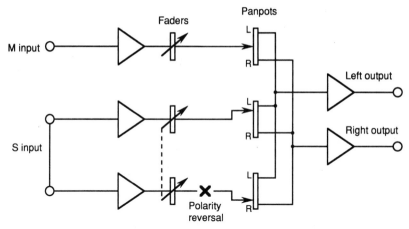

**Figure 9-10.** Implementation of MS recording using three input faders on a recording console when no MS matrix is available.

## 9.3 SPACED MICROPHONE ARRAYS FOR STEREO PICKUP

### 9.3.1 The Multichannel Approach

While Blumlein was developing the coincident approach to stereo in England, engineers at Bell Telephone Laboratories were laying the groundwork for a different kind of stereo recording. They reasoned, as shown in Figure 9-11 that a large number of microphone-loudspeaker channels placed horizontally would reproduce lateral space perspectives quite

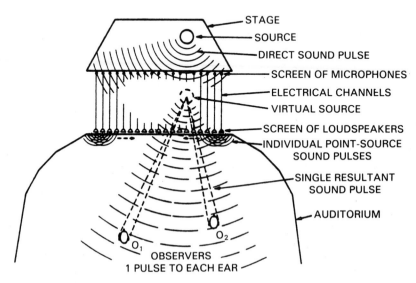

**Figure 9-11.** Multichannel stereo recording with wavefront reconstruction. (*W. Snow, "Basic Principles of Stereophonic Sound," Journal of the Society of Motion Picture and Television Engineers, vol.61 (Nov. 1953)*)

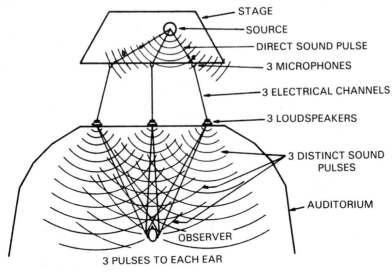

**Figure 9-12.** Three-channel wavefront reconstruction. (*Data after Snow, Journal of the Society of Motion Picture and Television Engineers, vol.61 (Nov. 1953)*)

accurately. Furthermore, the listener would not be limited to a preferred listening location. Their approach was motivated by the demands of large-scale multichannel presentation, such as we now enjoy in the motion picture theater. Their practical embodiment had only three channels, as shown in Figure 9-12 and it is surprising how well three channels can convey accurate localization for listeners seated over a broad area.

### 9.3.2 Panned Arrays

The spaced microphone approach for stereo pickup has its strong adherents, and the technique is often integrated with coincident pickup. The spaced approach has basically evolved into the form shown in Figure 9-13 where a center microphone is panned into the stereo array and produces a phantom center image. The total distance spanned by the left–center–right microphone array will vary according to the size of the performing ensemble, but it will rarely exceed 3 to 4 meters (10 to 13 feet). The level of the center microphone is critical, and it is usually mixed into the stereo channels at a level 4 to 6 dB lower than the left and right microphones.

Many recording engineers prefer the spaced approach for its "warmer" sound, as opposed to the coincident approach. In addition to the early side reflections present in the recording venue, the spaced microphones generate, through the time delays between them, additional delayed signals that have the effect of of early reflections. Through microphone placement, these delays are in the hands of the engineer, who can accordingly use them to advantage. While the various coincident techniques produce superb recordings in the correct acoustical setting, the spaced approach seems to offer the engineer greater flexibility in coping with less than ideal acoustical circumstances. In general, a coincident recording will convey ensemble spatial details to a remarkable degree, while the spaced

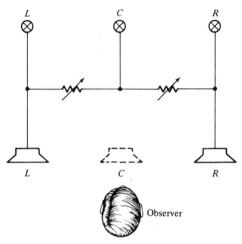

**Figure 9-13.** Center placed microphone. The signal contributed by the center microphone creates a center phantom image in the stereo array.

technique will often convey a heightened sense of the acoustical characteristics of the recording environment itself. Both are valid concerns of the recording engineer.

It is certainly worth stating that many of the famous and highly esteemed American stereo recordings dating from 1953 to about 1970 were made with three spaced microphones. The present CD catalogs of RCA Victor, CBS, and Mercury Records attest to this.

## 9.4 NEAR-COINCIDENT STEREO MICROPHONE ARRAYS

Near-coincident arrays make use of a pair of directional microphones laterally spaced no more than about 30 cm. The intent with these arrays is to combine some of the excellent imaging of coincident arrays with the added sense of space or ambience that even small displacements between microphones can convey. Blumlein's first experiments in stereo were done with a near-coincident array which he referred to as a "binaural pair." Since the seventies, a number of specific techniques have been described in detail.

### 9.4.1 The ORTF Technique

Developed by the French Radio Organization, the ORTF technique employs a pair of cardioid microphones spaced 17 cm apart and angled at 110°. In detailed listening tests (4) the system has rivaled the Blumlein array localization acuity, while at the same time offering immunity to excessive reverberation. The array is shown in Figure 9-14(a).

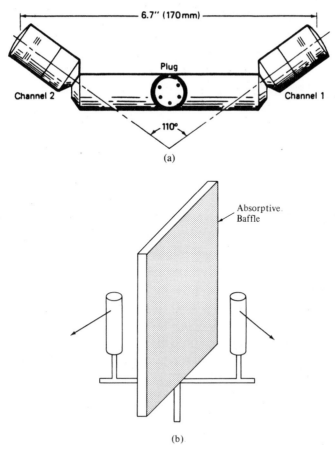

**Figure 9-14.** Near coincident pickup techniques. (a) ORTF. (*data courtesy of Schoeps*) (b) Two spaced microphones separated by a baffle.

### 9.4.2 The NOS Technique

This approach was developed by the Dutch Broadcasting Organization and employs a pair of cardioid microphones spaced 30 cm apart at an angle of 90°. It has many of the advantages of the ORTF array.

### 9.4.3 The Stereo-180 Array

Olson (14) describes an array of two hypercardioid microphones spaced 46 mm apart at an angle of 135°. The array picks up sound over a very wide frontal angle with accuracy.

### 9.4.4 Microphones with a Baffle

Figure 9-14(b) shows a typical arrangement. A baffle is used to ensure greater left–right separation at high frequencies (above about 1 kHz), while the basic microphone pattern itself will provide separation at lower frequencies. There are many variations as regards baffle size, microphone spacing, and pickup pattern. In most applications, the microphone spacing is normally no more than 10 to 20 cm.

## 9.5 ACCENT MICROPHONES

### 9.5.1 Purpose of Accent Microphones

Sometimes called "spot" microphones, accent microphones are often used in orchestral recording in conjunction with the main stereo pickup array to accent, or limn out, certain parts of the ensemble. As a rule, accent microphones (or pairs of accent microphones) are mixed with the main stereo array at levels ranging from about $-6$ dB to about $-12$ dB. If mixed at higher levels than about $-6$ dB, they really qualify as "solo" enhancement; if mixed at lower level than $-12$ dB, they are not likely to be effective at all. Their basic functions are:

a. To correct for fore–aft balances in the ensemble. Because the main stereo microphones are closer to the front of the ensemble, those instruments toward the front tend to be emphasized in the main pickup array. Accent microphones can correct this problem.
b. To correct balances for weak instruments. Some instruments, such as the harp and celesta, often require accent microphones so that the players do not have to force their sound output, or try to play more loudly than is comfortable.
c. To correct for spectral imbalances. In many ensembles, the bass line may seem deficient, due to there being too few players or to absence of reflective boundaries near the basses. Accent microphones can correct the problem.
d. To add "presence." In large ensembles, and in reverberant recording venues, certain instruments toward the rear of the ensemble may lack presence due to a low direct-to-reverberant ratio. Accent microphones can correct this. Some examples include xylophone, timpani, and other percussion instruments, which, because they are often played loudly, tend to stir up a good bit of reverberation.

### 9.5.2 Implementation of Accent Microphones

Accent microphones are never intended to be heard as such; the aim is to correct a given problem without creating another, and they are best used only to the degree that they accomplish an intended purpose. The following guidelines are recommended.

*Microphone position.* Accent microphones should not be placed too close to the instrument or instruments they are covering. Good working distances are in the range of 1 to 1.5 meters for single instruments and 2 to 3 meters for groups of instruments (e.g., the woodwind section).

*Proper panning.* Accent microphones should be panned into the main stereo array at positions which exactly match the position of the instruments as they appear in the main stereo array. Placing them otherwise may create conflicting localization cues.

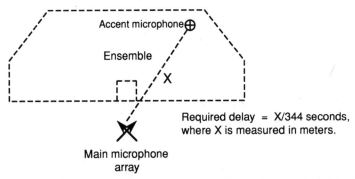

Required delay = X/344 seconds, where X is measured in meters.

**Figure 9-15.** Determining correct signal delay for accent microphones. The required delay is equal to $X/344$ seconds, where $X$ is the distance (meters) from the accent microphone to the main stereo pair.

*Use of signal delay.* It is always correct to delay accent microphones so that their signals can be timed to correspond with the acoustical delay existing at the main microphones. However, such delay may not be necessary, depending on certain time and amplitude thresholds. Figure 9-15 shows how the requisite delay values are calculated, and Figure 9-16 presents empirical guidelines for delay implementation. For relatively short distances between the accent microphones and the main microphones, delay is indicated when the accent-to-main level ratio is fairly high, in order to minimize comb filtering effects. At the other extreme, delay is indicated at large distances, even when the accent-to-main level ratio is fairly low, in order to minimize any possibility of hearing discrete echoes.

*Use of equalization.* Where the purpose of accent microphones is to add presence, careful use of equalization is recommended. Since the accent microphones may be fairly close to the instruments they are covering, it would be advantageous to attenuate low frequencies and raise high frequencies slightly in order that the overall level of the accent microphone can be kept at a minimum.

*Two-channel implementation of accent microphones.* Figure 9-17 shows a method of using only two delay units to provide required delay for an ensemble of accent microphones. The rationale here is that both delay values should be identical and should be set for the most distant accent microphone that requires delay. (The excess delay on accent microphones near the main microphones will rarely be apparent as such.)

*Level changes of accent microphones.* With care, and with musical justification, accent microphones can be altered in level during recording or remix activities. As a rule, gain shifts should not exceed about 3 or 4 dB.

*Careful comparisons, with and without accent microphones.* During the process of setting levels of the accent microphones, the recording engineer should carefully compare, or "A-B," the stereo sound stage with and without each accent microphone. If this is not rigorously done, the engineer may find to his regret later that he has used too much of them and created a subjectively "flat, two-dimensional" sound stage. Remember that an accent microphone should be used only to the extent that it accomplishes its intended purpose—and no more.

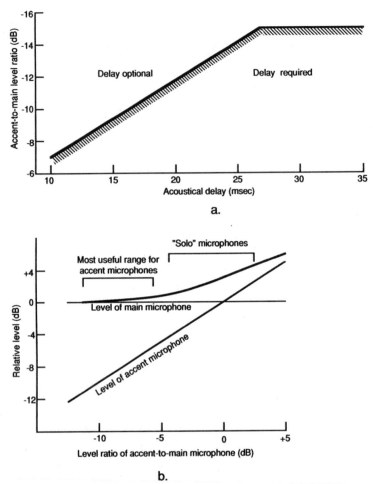

**Figure 9-16.** (a) Threshold determination for signal delay as a function of operating level and acoustical time anticipation of accent microphones. (b) Power summation of main and accent microphones as a function of relative levels.

## 9.6 HEAD-RELATED STEREO PICKUP

While artificial-head recordings are normally intended for binaural playback, the signal can be processed for presentation over loudspeakers, as shown in Figure 9-18. The critical elements in this scheme are the delay and filter characteristics that are used for crosstalk cancellation, and the intent is to produce at each ear only that signal originally picked up by the corresponding "ear" of the artificial head. Obviously, the crosstalk cancellation in space will exist only along the plane of symmetry of the loudspeakers, and any movement of the listener's head away from the plane will nullify to some extent the intended effect. Actually, the method provides only a first-order cancellation of crosstalk, but this is sufficient in most cases to create an illusion of sounds originating over a wide frontal angle far exceeding the loudspeaker placement.

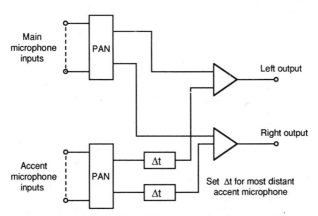

**Figure 9-17.** Two-channel implementation of signal delay for the entire ensemble of accent microphones. Choose the accent microphone farthest from the main stereo pair and calculate the required delay; set both delay units to this value.

## 9.7 TWO-CHANNEL TECHNIQUES FOR IMAGE BROADENING

The recording engineer often has to process monophonic sound sources to produce some degree of spread across the stereo stage. Signals so processed often take on a degree of naturalness that leads even experienced listeners to think that they were recorded in stereo. Many a pop mixdown session has benefited from such treatment. Some of these techniques will be described.

### 9.7.1 Image Broadening Due to Phase Shift

A degree of image broadening can result from phase shifting of one loudspeaker signal relative to the other. The networks that are used for this effect produce constant phase differences with flat amplitude response over a large part of the audible spectrum. The basic technique is shown in Figure 9-19. The network in the left transmission channel produces a certain phase shift, $\phi$, with respect to frequency; the network in the right transmission channel produces the same phase shift plus an additional phase lag, $\theta$, which is adjustable. When $\theta = 0°$, both loudspeakers receive the same signal, and there will be a phantom center signal for listeners on the plane of symmetry. As $\theta$ is varied from zero up to about 135°, the image broadens; it is no longer perceived as a point source in the middle, but appears to come from a large area in front of the listener. As $\theta$ is shifted beyond 135°, the image begins to split apart; finally, at 180°, the familiar out-of-phase condition exists and localization is ambiguous.

As with the effects of time delay and amplitude differences between loudspeakers, the role of phase shifts depends largly upon listener orientation. If the listener is substantially off the plane of symmetry, then the effects as described here are less distinct.

### 9.7.2 Image Broadening Due to Frequency Distribution

If a monophonic source is fed to a stereo pair of channels with their frequency responses shaped as shown in Figure 9-20 the listener will hear a spread of sound between the

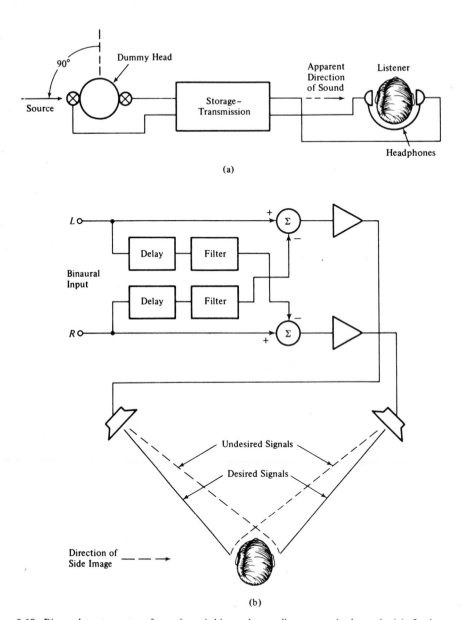

**Figure 9-18.** Binaural-to-stereo transformation. A binaural recording system is shown in (a). It gives accurate localization of sounds in the azimuthal plane. In (b) the binaural signals are processed by providing delay and equalization simulating the acoustic path around the listener's head. These signals are then added in opposite polarity to that the desired cancellation of crosstalk will take place at each ear.

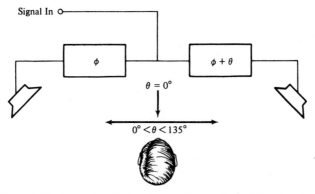

**Figure 9-19.** Image broadening due to all-pass phase shift networks.

loudspeakers. Actually, this technique is equivalent to panning each portion of the frequency spectrum individually from left to right. For maximum effect, the frequency at which both signals are equal should be about 500 Hz.

### 9.7.3 Image Broadening Due to Signal Incoherence

If two microphones are placed some distance apart in a reverberation chamber, their respective outputs will be largely incoherent; amplitude and phase relationships between the two outputs will be randomly related, on a frequency-by-frequency basis, but the overall spectral distribution between them will be largely the same. The result when these two signals are reproduced over stereo loudspeakers will be a spread of sound between the loudspeakers, as shown in Figure 9-21.

### 9.7.4 Image Broadening Due to Time Delay

A related technique is shown in Figure 9-22. Here, the reverberation chamber has only one output. If this out were fed to both loudspeakers, there would be a single phantom center image of the reverberated signal with no impression of spread between the loudspeakers. If a suitable time delay is placed in one of the signal paths, the listener

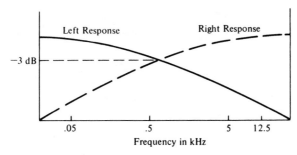

**Figure 9-20.** Image broadening by frequency distribution.

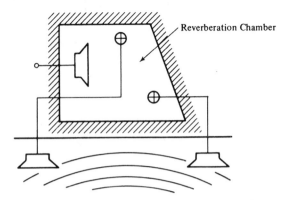

**Figure 9-21.** Incoherent signals from a single reverberation chamber using spaced microphones.

will sense the incoherence between the loudspeakers and the sound will be spread between them. Suitable delays for this effect are in the range of 40 to 60 msec.

In the earlier discussion of the effect of time delays on localization, it was stated that localization tended toward the earlier of the two signals. When the signal consists primarily of reverberation, this is not necessarily the case. Reverberation is largely devoid of significant transient, or impulsive, sounds because of the relatively slow attack and decay times of typical reverberation devices. Thus, a delay of 60 msec (even greater when the reverberation time is longer) will not be noticed as such.

## 9.8 PSEUDOSTEREO PROCESSING

While the techniques presented in Section 9.7 produce a degree of image broadening, they tend to be rather subtle in their effect of creating the natural spread of a stereo array. Pseudostereo refers to specific methods that can be used to convey to the listener a strong sense of lateral spread, which is often suggestive of true stereo itself. Such

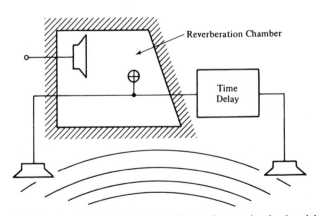

**Figure 9-22.** Incoherent signals from a single reverberant signal using delay.

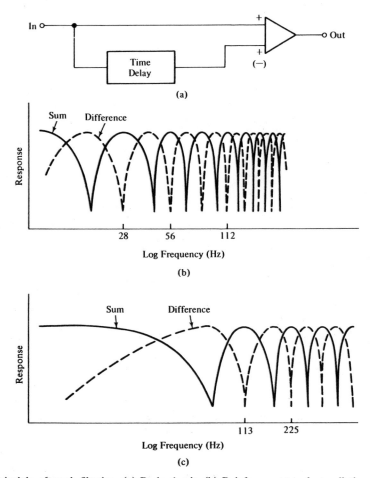

**Figure 9-23.** Principle of comb filtering. (a) Basic circuit. (b) Reinforcement and cancellation patterns shown on a log frequency axis for a delay of 40 msec (reinforcements and cancellations at multiples of 28 Hz). (c) Reinforcement and cancellation patterns for a signal delay of 10 msec (reinforcements and cancellations at multiples of 113 Hz). Characteristic cancellation and reinforcement frequences are given by $f_n = n/T$, where $T$ is the delay time and $n = 1,2,3,4, ....$

techniques have been used over the years, with greater or lesser success, in the transfer of older archival recordings for modern playback.

### 9.8.1 Lauridsen's Method

Lauridsen introduced the notion of complementary comb filters to create an artificial stereo effect. The principle of the comb filter is shown in Figure 9-23. If a delayed signal is recombined with the original signal, there will be a series of peaks and dips in the frequency response. The delayed signal can be either added or subtracted, producing two

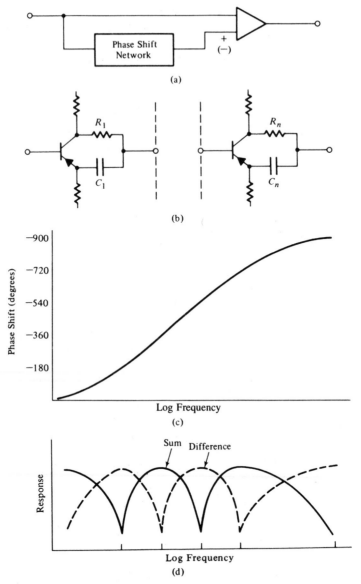

**Figure 9-24.** Phase shift techniques for pseudostereo. (a) The circuit arrangement resembles the comb filter except that an all-pass phase shift network is used instead of signal delay. (b) One section of an all-pass phase shift network. Usually, a number of these sections are connected in series, providing a broad phase shift with respect to frequency, on the order of 1000°, as shown in (c). (d) Combining the phase shifted signals with the non-phase-shifted, which results in cancellations at $(180° + n360°)$ and reinforcements at $(360° + n360°)$, where $n = 1,2,3,4, \ldots.$

complementary comb filter responses, as shown in the figure. The time delay should not exceed 30 to 40 msec for best effect.

### 9.8.2 Pseudostereo Using Phase Shifts

The method shown in Figure 9-24 is a variant of Lauridsen's method. Here, time delay has been replaced with all-pass phase shift networks. Adding and subtracting the phase-shifted signal from the main signal produces a familiar set of alternating peaks and dips in frequency response. The density of the peaks and dips is a function of the total range of phase shift employed. Devices which produce this effect are commonly available under the general description of stereo synthesizers.

## BIBLIOGRAPHY

1. J. Blauert, *Spatial Hearing*, MIT Press, Cambridge, Mass. (1983).
2. A. Blumlein, "British Patent Specification 394,325 (Directional Effect in Sound Systems)," *J. Audio Engineering Society*, vol. 6, pp. 91–98 (reprinted 1958).
3. G. Boré and S. Temmer, "MS Stereophony and Compatibility," *Audio Magazine* (April 1958).
4. C. Ceoen, "Comparative Stereophonic Listening Tests," *J. Audio Engineering Society*, vol. 20, pp. 19–27 (1972).
5. H. Clark et al., "The 'Stereosonic' Recording and Reproducing System," *J. Audio Engineering Society*, vol. 6, pp. 102–133 (1958).
6. M. Dickreiter, *Tonmeister Technology*, Temmer Enterprises, New York (1989)
7. W. Dooley and R. Streicher, "MS Stereo: a Powerful Technique for Working in Stereo," *J. Audio Engineering Society*, vol. 30, pp. 707–717 (1982).
8. J. Eargle, "Stereo/Mono Disc Compatibility," *J. Audio Engineering Society*, vol. 19, pp. 552–559 (1969).
9. J. Eargle, *The Microphone Handbook*, Elar, Plainview, N.Y. (1982).
10. M. Gardner, "Some Single- and Multiple-Source Localization Effects," *J. Audio Engineering Society*, vol. 21, pp. 430–437 (1973).
11. M. Hibbing, "XY and MS Microphone Techniques in Comparison," *Sennheiser News*, June 1989 (Sennheiser Electric Corporation).
12. F. Harvey and M. Schroeder, "Subjective Evaluation of Factors Affecting Two-Channel Stereophony," *J. Audio Engineering Society*, vol. 9 pp. 19–28 (1961).
13. J. Mosely, "Eliminating the Stereo Seat," *J. Audio Engineering Society*, vol. 8, no 1 pp. 46–53 (1960).
14. L. Olson, "The Stereo-180 Microphone System," *J. Audio Engineering Society*, vol. 27, pp. 158–163 (1979).
15. M. Schroeder, "An Artificial Stereo Effect Obtained from a Single Channel," *J. Audio Engineering Society*, vol. 6, pp. 74–79 (1958).
16. W. Snow, "Basic Principles of Stereophonic Sound," *J. Society of Motion Picture and Television Engineers*, vol. 61 (November 1953).
17. *Stereophonic Techniques*, an anthology prepared by the *J. Audio Engineering Society*, 1986.

# 10

---

# MULTICHANNEL STEREO

---

## 10.1 INTRODUCTION

*From Tinfoil to Stereo* by Read and Welch (13) describes a Columbia phonograph model (ca. 1899) that could record and play back through three large horns simultaneously. While it was not exploited as multichannel stereo, it is clear that it was the first machine capable of recording in three channels. Nearly forty years later, Disney introduced Fantasound in the motion picture *Fantasia*. Three optical sound tracks were presented in a left–center–right format behind the screen (9). In the early 1950s, a surround track was added to the three behind the screen, and some semblance of "surround sound" could be created in the theater. Subsequent years saw the introduction of 70-mm film releases and the audio capability of six magnetic tracks. The original implementation called for five loudspeakers behind the screen, along with a single surround channel distributed over multiple loudspeakers. Later, the surround loudspeakers could be split into two channels for special effects. During the early 1950s, Cinerama provided six channels to accompany its wide screen presentation (14).

In the home, multichannel stereo has not fared so well. The early 1970s saw several quadraphonic (four-channel) formats introduced into the home market via the LP record. By 1978, they were all gone. What had killed the effort was lack of industry standardization, infighting among manufacturers, and a lack of clear musical direction in generating the recorded product itself.

By comparison, the motion picture art always knew what it wanted its multichannel systems to accomplish, and it is little surprise that today the biggest force for multichannel sound in the home comes by way of directional matrix encoded stereo sound tracks on today's videocassettes and laserdiscs.

This chapter deals with the fundamentals of surround sound localization as it applies both to sound with picture and sound without picture. In the former, we are concerned with enhancement of the more dominant visual aspects; with the latter, we are concerned with the creation of credible sound fields which can, under proper conditions, transport the listener into another venue.

## 10.2 LOCALIZATION IN THE LATERAL (AZIMUTHAL) PLANE

### 10.2.1 The Four-Loudspeaker Problem

As we saw in the previous chapter, the localization of phantom images between a stereo pair of loudspeakers depends critically on the listener's position. Early motion picture stereo presentation always included a center channel, which was used to "anchor" dialogue firmly at center screen. Thus, a listener seated far to one side could appreciate the full stereo sound stage with little collapsing of it into the nearest loudspeaker. Figure 10-1(a) and (b) shows details of a three-channel panpot used in the motion picture industry to steer a given sound across the screen channels to create either fixed or moving phantom images. With only three channels used in this manner, it is possible for a listener to perceive unambiguous localization over a frontal horizontal angle of about 120 to 140°. Figure 10-1 (c) and (d) shows details of a four-channel panpot as used by the record industry during the 1970s to assign the location of individual tracks in quadraphonic mixdown.

There are problems when one tries to use too few channels to create a continuous 360° wrap-around effect. It can obviously be done if enough channels are used, but setting a practical limit of four physical channels is problematic. In the conventional implementation of four channels, there are two in front and two in the rear, all spaced 90° apart as shown in Figure 10-2. Phantom images do not appear clearly between the side loudspeakers—unless the listener turns to face the direction he expects the sound to originate from. Overall, in such an array as this, side and back localization is best when there are "leakage" signals from all loudspeakers. For instance, a sound intended to originate from far left would normally be panned evenly between the left-front and left-back loudspeakers, with no contribution from the two loudspeakers on the right. A signal so panned would be perceived as coming more from the left-front than from far left, due primarily to the presence of greater high-frequency output reaching the ears from the left-front loudspeaker as opposed to the left-back loudspeaker. Certain crosstalk signals in the opposite loudspeakers can actually improve the stability of the phantom image at the left (3).

Stated differently, the designer of a four-channel recording system must make an important decision regarding the attitude of the listener's head. If the listener is to be forward-oriented at all times, then one set of panning parameters will be used. If the listener has the freedom to look in various directions, then another set will be required. These questions have not generally been answered, although some workers, notably Cooper and Shiga (3) have addressed the problem.

In general, we can give the following summary about localization in the horizontal plane:

1. Image stability improves with more channels. If a stable image is desired at a given position, there should be a loudspeaker placed at that position. This is especially true if the listening area is fairly large.
2. Phantom images are best kept within the forward portion of the stereo stage between loudspeakers that are not separated in angle, as perceived by the listeners, by more than about 60°.

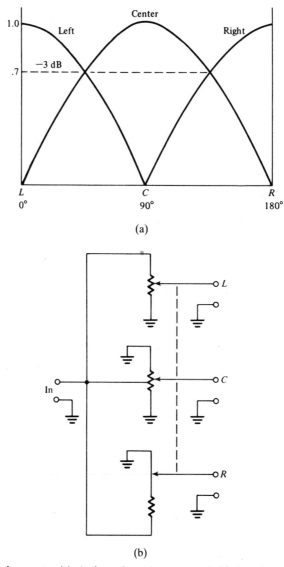

**Figure 10.1.** Multichannel panpots. (a) A three-channel panpot and (b) its schematic. (c) A four-channel (quadraphonic) "joy-stick" panpot and (d) its schematic. (*Photograph courtesy of Automated Processes*)

3. The illusion of panned images in motion can be very good with limited channels. The key here is to keep the images in motion so that the ear does not have time to "analyze" what may wrong with them!
4. The rear loudspeakers fare very well when they carry ambient information. In many cases, it is difficult for the listeners to identify the source of the loudspeaker carrying such program material.

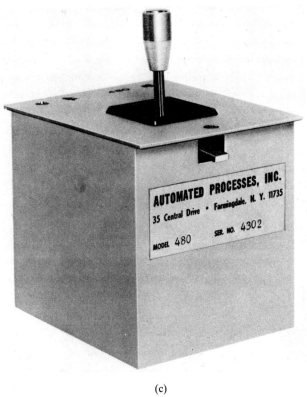

(c)

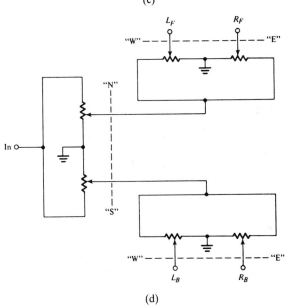

(d)

**Figure 10-1.** Continued.

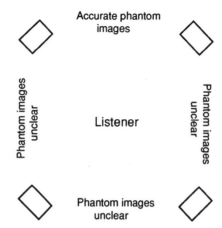

**Figure 10-2.** Conventional quadraphonic loudspeaker arrangement.

### 10.2.2 Motion Picture Formats

It is significant that the first four-channel technique used in motion pictures used three channels behind the screen and a multi-loudspeaker presentation of the fourth channel to the sides and back of the spectators, as shown in Figure 10-3(a). This arrangement allowed spectators to appreciate the intended sound balances and localization effects over a wide area. The surround channel was generally relegated to special effects.

The introduction of the 70-mm six-track format extended the screen complement of channels from three to five, while maintaining a single surround channel, as shown in Figure 10-3(b). In time, film sound mixers returned to only three channels behind the screen, relegating the added channels to such things as low-frequency (subwoofer) enhancement and split surround use.

Cinema Digital Sound, as jointly developed by Eastman Kodak and Optical Radiation Corporation, uses the format shown in Figure 10-3(c). Five wideband channels provide three behind the screen and split surrounds. A band-limited low-frequency channel is intended for subwoofer special effect enhancement, a development of the decade of the 1980s. A similar system has been introduced by Dolby Laboratories under the name SR·D.

### 10.3 MULTICHANNEL MATRIX FORMATS

Matrix systems encode directional information into two stereo channels and decode those channels for playback over three or more loudspeakers. There is loss in separation when this is done, and many schemes of separation enhancement have been devised to assist these systems. Matrix formats came to the fore during the 1970s when many attempts were made to use existing two-channel media, such as stereo tape and the stereo LP, for multi-loudspeaker presentation in the home.

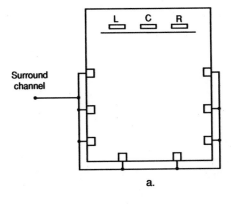

a.

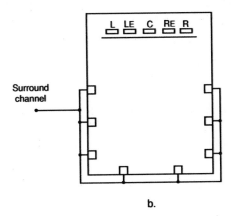

b.

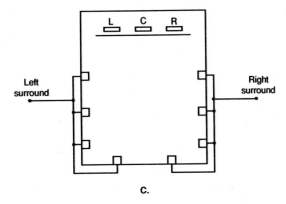

c.

**Figure 10-3.** Motion picture formats. (a) Three screen channels and a single surround channel with multiple loudspeakers. (b) Five screen channels and a single surrounded channel. (c) Three screen channels with subwoofer and split surround channels.

### 10.3.1 A Three-Channel Matrix system

The simplest three-channel matrix system is one that can be implemented to add more focus to the familiar center-panned image in an ordinary stereo recording. The following equations apply:

$$\text{Left channel } (L_T) = L + .7C$$

$$\text{Right channel } (R_T) = R + .7C \tag{10-1}$$

$$\text{Derived center channel} = .7(L_T + R_T) = C + .7(L + R)$$

The left and right transmission channels ($L_T$ and $R_T$) are the two normal stereo channels, and the derived center channel is simply their sum reduced in level by 3 dB. There is a loss in separation, which is evident from the crosstalk terms that appear in the equations.

While most listeners are content with the phantom center as it normally appears in stereo, the three-channel matrix shown here can be modified to reproduce reverberant information in a convincing manner. Details are shown in Figure 10-4 Here, $L$ and $R$ represent the left and right stereo pickup of the ensemble, and $B$ represents the signal from a microphone placed back in the hall to pick up reverberation. These three quantities are encoded as follows:

$$L_T = .965\,L + .258\,R + .7\,B$$

$$R_T = .258\,L + .965\,R - .7\,B \tag{10-2}$$

The decoding equations are

$$L' = .965\,L_T + .258\,R_T = L + .5\,R + .5\,B$$

$$R' = .258\,L_T + .965\,R_T = R + .5\,L - .5\,B \tag{10-3}$$

$$B' = .7\,L_T + .7\,R_T = B + .5\,L - .5\,R$$

Each signal is recovered with the other two appearing as crosstalk terms at half amplitude ($-6$ dB). The inverted polarity of several of the crosstalk terms is a problem that has been dealt with through the use of all-pass phase shift networks, as will be discussed shortly.

### 10.3.2 Four-Channel Matrix Systems

It is standard nomenclature to speak of the preceding matrices as 3–2–3. What this means is that three input channels have been encoded into two transmission channels (indicated by the subscript $T$), and recovered over the three reconstructed, or derived, channels (indicated by the primes).

A 4–2–4 matrix is just a step away from the 3–2–3 approach. Peter Scheiber (15) is generally credited with introducing the first of these in 1969. The encoding equations are

$$L_T = .924\,L_F + .924\,L_B + .383\,R_F - .383\,R_B$$

$$R_T = .924\,R_F + .924\,R_B + .383\,L_F - .383\,L_B \tag{10-4}$$

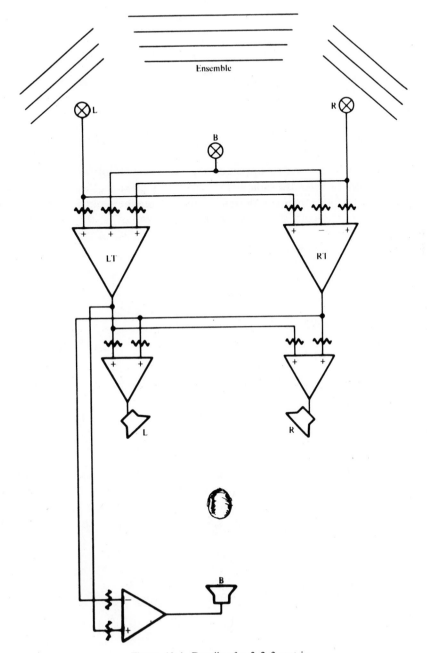

**Figure 10-4.** Details of a 3–2–3 matrix.

The corresponding decoding equations are

$$L_F' = .924\,L_T + .383\,R_T = L_F + .707\,L_B + .707\,R_F$$

$$R_F' = .383\,L_T + .949\,R_T = R_F + .707\,L_F + .707\,R_B$$

$$L_B' = .924\,L_T - .383\,R_T = L_B + .707\,L_F - .707\,R_B$$

$$R_B' = -.383\,L_T + .924\,R_T = R_B + .707\,R_F - .707\,L_B \tag{10-5}$$

Note that the four signals are recovered along with the adjacent signal pair at .707 amplitude (−3 dB).

Shortly after the Scheiber matrix appeared, Sansui of Japan introduced their QS matrix. It has the same numerical coefficients as the Scheiber matrix, but avoids the out-of-phase crosstalk terms in the rear recovered signals of the Scheiber matrix through the use of all-pass phase shift networks. The use of these networks is shown in the following equations by the symbol "$j$," indicating a relative phase shift of 90°.

The encoding equations of the Sansui matrix are

$$L_T = .924\,L_F + .383\,R_F + j\,.924\,L_B + j\,.383\,R_B$$

$$R_T = .924\,R_F + .383\,L_F - j\,.924\,R_B - j.383\,L_B \tag{10-6}$$

The corresponding decoding equations are

$$L_F' = .924\,L_T + .383\,R_T = L_F + .707\,R_F + .707\,L_B$$

$$R_F' = .383\,L_T + .924\,R_T = R_F + .707\,L_F + .707\,R_B$$

$$L_B' = -j\,(.924\,L_T - .383\,R_T) = L_B + .707\,R_B - j\,.707\,L_F$$

$$R_B' = j\,(.383\,L_T - .924\,R_T) = R_B + .707\,L_B - j\,.707\,R_F \tag{10-7}$$

The CBS SQ matrix is significantly different from the two previously discussed in that its basic crosstalk characteristics are not to the adjacent channels. Rather, left and right separation is maintained in both front and back pairs, while the crosstalk from either front channel is into both back channels, and from either back channel into both front channels.

The encoding equations for the SQ matrix are

$$L_T = L_F + .707\,R_B - j\,.707\,L_B$$

$$R_T = R_F + j\,.707\,R_B - j\,.707\,L_B \tag{10-8}$$

The corresponding decoding equations are

$$L_F' = L_T = L_F + .707\,R_B - j\,.707\,L_B$$

$$R_F' = R_T = R_F + j\,.707\,R_B - .707\,L_B$$

$$L'_B = j\,.707\,L_T - .707\,R_T = L_B + j\,.707\,L_F - .707\,R_F$$

$$R'_B = .707\,L_T - j\,.707\,R_T = R_B + .707\,L_F - j\,.707\,R_F \qquad (10\text{-}9)$$

Both the QS and SQ matrix systems were commercialized during the 1970s with a variety of separation-enhancing techniques. The earliest methods involved determining the dominant signal, on an instantaneous basis, and turning down the adjacent channels so that crosstalk would be minimized. This method of separation enhancement was not successful, inasmuch as listeners often complained of a "pumping" sound. Later methods of separation enhancement made use of coefficient manipulation and went by such names as "Variomatrix" and "Paramatrix."

Basically, these schemes did the following. If a signal was determined to be dominant (on the basis of relative level in some part of the frequency band), then that signal was added out of phase to the two adjacent channels to partially cancel the dominant crosstalk term. This was a continuous action, controlled by carefully chosen attack and release time constants. In the better systems, the coefficient manipulation action is rarely apparent to the ear, and the effect can be remarkable. Notable today is the Dolby Pro-logic matrix used in many motion picture theaters and in virtually all home theater installations based on videotape and laserdisc. Its characteristics will be discussed in a later chapter.

While not gaining the popularity of either QS or SQ, the Cooper–Nippon Columbia BMX matrix was unique in that it defined an encoding locus, rather than a set of four points around the listener. Our presentation of the BMX matrix here is in complex notation, which will be unfamiliar to many recording engineers. Basically, this is a shorthand notation for indicating both amplitude and phase relationships between the two transmission channels, and it is used here inasmuch as the BMX matrix does not rely only on four specified inputs, as do the other 4–2–4 matrices. Signal inputs can be made at any angular position $\theta$:

$$L_T = \frac{1 + e^{j\theta}}{2}$$

$$R_T = \frac{1 - e^{j\theta}}{2} \qquad (10\text{-}10)$$

Outputs can be chosen at any angle $\theta'$ for any number points. For standard quadraphonic arrays, both inputs and outputs would be chosen at values of $\theta$ equal to 45°, 135°, 225°, and 315°, according to the equation:

$$\theta' = \frac{L_T + R_T}{2} + \frac{(L_T - R_T)\,e^{-j\theta}}{2} \qquad (10\text{-}11)$$

With four equally spaced decoding points, the BMX matrix exhibits the same crosstalk properties as the QS matrix.

Generally speaking, the various 4–2–4 matrices are compatible with normal stereo requirements; that is, the two transmission channels $L_T$ and $R_T$, are usable as stereo signals. While differing from each other in some degree, they can all be said to provide adequate stereo presentation. Mono performance is another matter. The original Scheiber

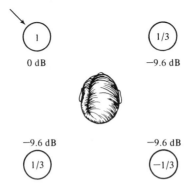

**Figure 10-5.** Characteristics of a 4–3–4 matrix. If a signal is intended for one loudspeaker, then crosstalk terms will exist at the other three loudspeakers down 9.6 dB. The minus sign at the *opposite* loudspeaker indicates a polarity reversal in the crosstalk term.

and QS matrices both exhibit front–back imbalances of 7.6 dB in the mono playback mode, while the SQ matrix exhibits equal output of all signals in mono.

## 10.4 HIGHER-ORDER MATRIX SYSTEMS

We have examined in detail the characteristics of 4–2–4 matrix systems and seen that a degree of crosstalk is inherent in all of them. What about a 4–3–4 matrix? Four signals can be encoded into three channels and recovered with far better separation than is characteristic of 4–2–4 systems. In the following sets of equations, $A$, $B$, $C$, and $D$ represent the four signal inputs to the encoding matrix. $X$, $Y$, and $Z$ represent the three transmission channels. Encoding:

$$X = \tfrac{2}{3}(A + B)$$
$$Y = \tfrac{2}{3}(C + D)$$
$$Z = \tfrac{1}{3}(A - B + C - D) \tag{10-12}$$

Decoding, we recover $A$, $B$, $C$, and $D$ as prime signals along with whatever crosstalk terms there are. These combined recovered signals are indicated by $A'$, $B'$, $C'$, and $D'$:

$$A' = X + Z = A + \tfrac{1}{3}(B + C - D)$$
$$B' = X - Z = B + \tfrac{1}{3}(A - C + D)$$
$$C' = Y + Z = C + \tfrac{1}{3}(D + A - B)$$
$$D' = Y - Z = D + \tfrac{1}{3}(C - A + B) \tag{10.13}$$

The recovered signals in this 4–3–4 array exist along with the remaining terms as crosstalk at one-third the amplitude (down 9.6 dB), as shown in Figure 10-5.

Cooper and Shiga have generalized the theory of matrix systems as regards azimuthal (horizontal plane) presentation. It is based on the theory of *azimuthal harmonics*. The more harmonics (or channels) there are present, the more accurately directional information can be presented. The Cooper–Shiga theory takes into account any number of inputs, transmission channels, and outputs, and makes use of amplitude as well as phase angle relationships between the transmission channels.

As an example of their approach, Figure 10-6 shows typical signal resolution in a 6–4–6 array (six signals encoded into four channels and then resolved back into six loudspeaker inputs).

Under the term *periphony*, Gerzon (10) discusses multichannel systems that convey height as well as azimuthal information surrounding the listener. As an example of how this can be applied to a four-channel transmission system with six loudspeakers, consider the following 6–4–6 matrix. Four loudspeakers would be located in the horizontal plane of the listener; an additional loudspeaker would be located above him, and a sixth loudspeaker would be located below him (imagine if you will a listener suspended in space). The input signals are $A$, $B$, $C$, $D$, $E$, and $F$, and the transmission channels are $W$, $X$, $Y$, and $Z$. The encoding equations are

$$W = \tfrac{2}{3}(A - B)$$

$$X = \tfrac{2}{3}(C - D)$$

$$Y = \tfrac{2}{3}(E - F)$$

$$Z = \tfrac{1}{3}(A + B + C + D + E + F) \tag{10-14}$$

The recovered signals are then given by

$$A' = Z + W = A + \tfrac{1}{3}(C + D + E + F - B)$$

$$B' = Z - W = B + \tfrac{1}{3}(C + D + E + F - A)$$

$$C' = Z + X = C + \tfrac{1}{3}(A + B + E + F - D)$$

$$D' = Z - X = D + \tfrac{1}{3}(A + B + E + F - C)$$

$$E' = Z + Y = E + \tfrac{1}{3}(A + B + C + D - F)$$

$$F' = Z - Y = F + \tfrac{1}{3}(A + B + C + D - E) \tag{10-15}$$

All outputs are recovered at full level, and in each output the remaining signals also appear at one-third amplitude (9.6 dB down). The matrix presented here is typical of what can easily be accomplished with the Soundfield microphone discussed in Chapter 7.

In general, 4–3–4 and 6–4–6 matrices, whatever their derivation, have no need for separation enhancement and can be used directly as presented here.

## 10.5 SIGNAL PROCESSING IN MULTICHANNEL PRESENTATION

### 10.5.1 Chowning's Method of Simulating Moving Sound Sources

Chowning (2) has described a method of processing monophonic sources for presentation over a four-loudspeaker array so that the illusion of motion is realistically produced. The following parameters determine the illusion:

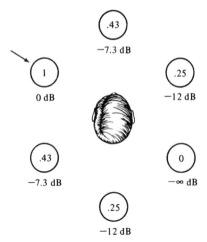

**Figure 10-6.** Crosstalk characteristics of a Cooper–Shiga 6–4–6 matrix. There are two crosstalk terms down 7.3 dB and two terms down 12 dB. There is no crosstalk into the opposite loudspeaker.

1. Amplitude relationships between the four synthesized channels, as manipulated by a panpot of the sort described in Figure 10-1(c).
2. Simulation of Doppler frequency shift proportional to the velocity of the simulated source away from or toward the listener.
3. Reverberant level in both global and local contexts. Global reverberation reaches the listener from all four loudspeakers equally when the simulated sound source is fairly close. Global reverberation is proportional to $(1/r)(1/\sqrt{r})$, where $r$ is the simulated distance. When the source moves away from the listener, local reverberation signals follow it and are simulated to come from the same direction. Local reverberation is proportional to $(1 - 1/r)(1/\sqrt{r})$ and provides cues for directionality, even when the simulated source is at considerable distances from the listener. Distance cues are the result of the direct-to-total reverberation ratios established.

## 10.5.2 Processing of Recordings to Enhance Ambience:

A number of methods have been devised for adding ambience to normal stereo recordings. Most of these use two additional channels so that the ambience information can be presented at the sides or at the back of the listening area. The stereo channels can be delayed and treated with reverberation so that they effectively simulate what might have been picked up in the actual recording venue with an extra pair of microphones placed in the reverberant field (7). Details of this technique will be shown in a later chapter dealing with signal processing in the time domain.

Another method, shown in Figure 10-7 simply delays the stereo channels and reproduces them from the sides (12). By the precedence effect, direct sound will be primarily located at the front loudspeakers, while ambience information will be perceived from all the loudspeakers. Damaske (5) observed that listeners were far more sensitive to interfering

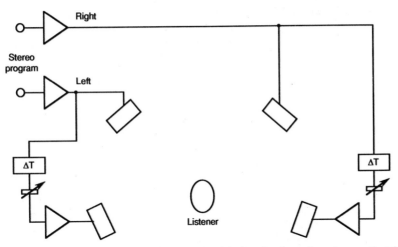

**Figure 10-7.** Madsen's method for "enhancing" stereo by delaying the channels and presenting them from the sides.

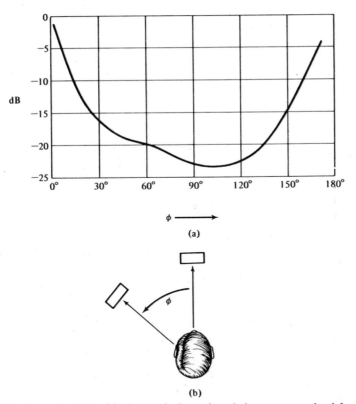

(a)

(b)

**Figure 10-8.** The Damaske effect. (a) The graph shows the relative annoyance level for an interfering sound source located at some angle Ø away from a signal source located to the front of the listener in (b). For example, an annoyance source located at an angle between 90° and 120° from the front of the observer will be about 20 to 25 dB more annoying than it would be if it were located to the front of the listener behind the main source.

noises at levels below a frontal source when those noises were incident from the sides rather than from the front, as shown in Figure 10-8 The implication here is that only the ambient information present in the stereo program will be perceived as coming from the sides, inasmuch as the precedence effect will steer the direct sound to the front.

# BIBLIOGRAPHY

1. B. Bauer, D. Gravereaux, and A. Gust, "A Compatible Stereo-Quadraphonic (SQ) Record System," *J. Audio Engineering Society*, vol. 19, pp. 638–641 (1971).

2. J. Chowning, "The Simulation of Moving Sound Sources." *J. Audio Engineering Society*, vol. 19, pp. 19–27 (1971).

3. D. Cooper and T. Shiga, "Discrete-Matrix Multichannel Stereo," *J. Audio Engineering Society*, vol. 20, pp. 346–360 (1972).

4. J. Cunningham, "Tetraphonic Sound." *db Magazine*, pp. 21–23 (December 1969).

5. P. Damaske, "Subjective Investigation of Sound Fields," *Acustica*, vol. 22, no. 4 (1967–68).

6. P. Damaske and V. Mellert, "A Method for True Reproduction of All Directional Information by Two-Channel Stereophony," *Acustica*, vol. 22, no. 3 (1969–70).

7. J. Eargle, "On the Processing of Two- and Three-Channel Program Material for Four-Channel Playback, *J. Audio Engineering Society*, vol. 30, pp. 707–717 (1971).

8. J. Eargle, "Multichannel Stereo Matrix Systems: An Overview," *J. Audio Engineering Society*, vol. 19, pp. 552–559 (1971).

9. J. Frayne and H. Wolfe, *Elements of Sound Recording*, Wiley, New York (1949).

10. M. Gerzon, "Periphony: With-Height Sound Reproduction," *J. Audio Engineering Society*, vol. 21, pp. 2–10 (1973).

11. R. Itoh and S. Takahashi, "The Sansui QS Four-Channel system," presented at the Audio Engineering Society Convention, Los Angeles, May 1972.

12. E. Madsen, "Extraction of Ambience Information from Ordinary Recordings." *J. Audio Engineering Society*, vol. 18, pp. 490–496 (1970).

13. O. Reed and W. Welch, *From Tinfoil to Stereo*, 2nd edn., H. Sams, Indianapolis (1976).

14. H. Reeves, "The Development of Stereo Magnetic Recording for Film," *J. Society of Motion Picture and Television Engineers*, vol. 91, nos. 10 and 11 (1982).

15. P. Scheiber, "Analyzing Phase-Amplitude Matrices." *J. Audio Engineering Society*, vol. 19, pp. 835–839 (1971).

16. *Quadraphony*, an anthology of papers taken from *J. Audio Engineering Society*, 1969–1975.

# 11

## RECORDING CONSOLES

### 11.1 INTRODUCTION

Audio transmission systems are the means by which audio signals are mixed, processed, and assigned to the desired output and monitoring channels. Today the term *console* generally refers to the familiar desk-like arrangement of controls. In the early days of electrical recording, rarely more than one or two microphones were used, and the signals were normally routed to a single output channel. (The terms "line out" and "output bus" are also used and refer to the main signal outputs of the system.) The system was simple, consisting of no more than a few volume controls, or faders, some kind of signal level metering, and a few switches for routing the program to the recording machines. Audio transmission systems used in the motion picture industry were more complex from their inception because of the need for recording dialogue, sound effects, and music at different times, ultimately mixing them into a single composite sound track.

Mixing consoles must be designed for the application at hand. Such activities as sound reinforcement, radio broadcasting, television broadcasting, motion pictures, video post-production, as well as sound recording, all have their specific creative procedures, and the consoles chosen for those applications have been customized for those operations. This chapter will cover the evolution of consoles used in the recording industry, noting how the complexity of the console has increased over the years to fit the creative and musical demands at hand.

Before audio transmission systems are covered in detail, a number of basic elements and concepts will be discussed: equivalent input noise, symbol conventions, patch bays, matching and bridging of loads, operational amplifiers, input circuitry, and active combining networks.

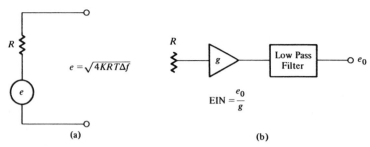

**Figure 11-1.** Equivalent input noise (EIN). (a) Representation by an ideal (noiseless) resistor in series with a noise voltage source. (b) Measurement of EIN.

## 11.2 BASIC CONCEPTS

### 11.2.1 Equivalent Input Noise (EIN)

Any audio transmission system is limited in dynamic range by noise at low levels and distortion at high levels. The maximum signal-to-noise ratio in a properly designed and operated system is always established at its input. There is a limit to how low the noise floor of the system can be, and it depends on the parallel combination of the resistance of the input transducer (microphone) "looking" into the input resistance of the first stage of amplification. This combination determines the *thermal noise* level of the input circuit, which is noise due to the thermal agitation of the molecular structure of the resistances themselves. The thermal noise voltage at the input is given by the equation:

$$E = (4kTR\Delta f)^{\frac{1}{2}} \tag{11-1}$$

Here, $k$ (Boltzmann's constant) is $1.38 \times 10^{-23}$ joules per kelvin; $T$ is the temperature in °K; $\Delta f$ is the bandwidth over which the measurement is made; and $R$ is the parallel resistance combination. Typical values are: $T = 300$°K (80°F), $R = 300$ ohms, and $\Delta f = 20$ kHz (normal audio bandwidth). These values yield a thermal noise of about 0.3 microvolts rms, some 130 dB below a reference of 1 volt. This calculation represents a theoretical ideal, and practical devices will not approach this value closer than about a decibel.

With dynamic microphones, this relationship is established at the console's input; with capacitor microphones, it is established at the high-impedance amplification stage, which immediately follows the capacitor element within the microphone case itself.

Figure 11-1 shows details of EIN measurement. Many manufacturers use A-weighting in presenting their measurements, and of course the reference resistance must be noted if noise ratings are given in microvolts. Often the readings are converted to power and the results expressed in dBm. Values in the range of −126 to −129 are common.

### 11.2.2 Symbol Conventions

There is no universal set of standards in the audio industry for symbol conventions in laying out block diagrams for consoles. To a large extent, individual manufacturers rely on their own conventions, but an experienced engineer can usually make the transition from one flow diagram to another. Some typical representations are given in Figure 11-2:

An *amplifier* is universally shown as in Figure 11-2(a). A simple triangle usually indicates fixed voltage gain, while a variable resistance, as shown in (b), indicates that the gain is adjustable.

A *fader* or volume control is normally shown as in (c) or (d) in the figure; they may be grouped, or ganged, as shown in (e).

A *panpot* is normally shown as a one-in/two-out configuration, as given in (f).

A rectangle normally indicates a signal processing block, such as an *equalizer* or *filter*, as shown in (g). The function is always indicated.

A *termination*, or *load resistor*, as required by some amplifiers, is shown in (h). These are not found in many modern console flow diagrams.

*Wire connections* are normally as shown in (i).

Various symbols are used to indicate *tie points*, *reference* points, and *abbreviated connections* between devices. Some of these are shown in (j).

A *transformer* is shown in (k). These are normally used to produce a balanced signal, or to accept a balanced signal from an external source.

*Meters* are normally indicated as shown in (l).

### 11.2.3 Patch Bays

Most large consoles have comprehensive patch bays (the terms jack field or jack bay are often used) to allow convenient rerouting of signals, or to remove a defective component from the signal flow path. The basic conventions are shown in Figure 11-3. The wiring shown in (d) is referred to as a "normal," indicating that the signal normally flows through. A patch cord inserted into either jack will interrupt the signal flow, enabling it to be fed to another device and then routed back into the other jack, or elsewhere.

### 11.2.4 Matching and Bridging Concepts

In earlier console design, it was customary to load each amplifier with a resistance equal to the nominal output impedance of that amplifier. In so doing, the amplifier output voltage was quite dependent on loading, and this made it imperative for each active device to "look into" the correct load if levels were to be properly maintained throughout the console. Traditionally, 600 ohms was the nominal termination.

During the 1960s, this design principle gave way to the bridging concept, in which all amplifier output impedances are low and all input impedances are high. This ensures is that a large number of loads may be placed across a single amplifier without causing a significant voltage drop.

There is, however, a curious holdover from the old 600-ohm days. In many console signal flow diagrams, signal voltage levels are given in dBv. Levels in dBv are referred to 0.775 volts, which is the voltage that will produce a reference power of 1 milliwatt when applied across a load of 600 ohms. Furthermore, many consoles can produce their

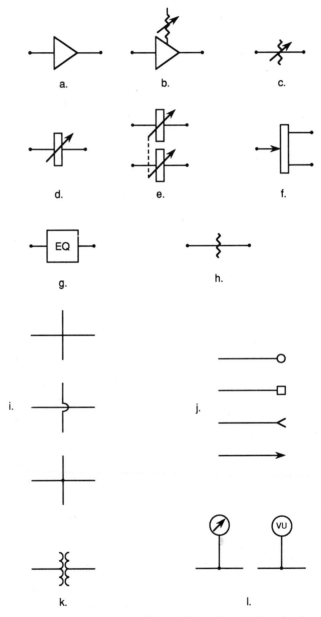

**Figure 11-2.** Symbol conventions. (a) Amplifier; (b) amplifier with variable gain; (c and d) fader or volume control; (e) grouped faders; (f) panpot; (g) signal processing block; (h) termination resistance; (i) wire connections; (j) tie points; (k) transformer; and (l) meters.

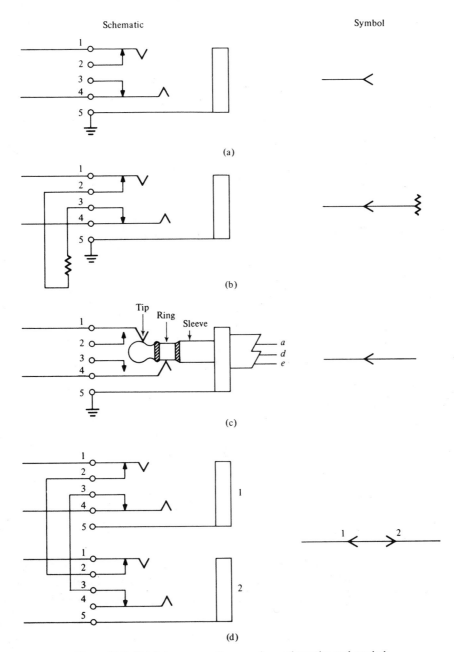

**Figure 11-3.** Patch bay conventions; various schematics and symbols.

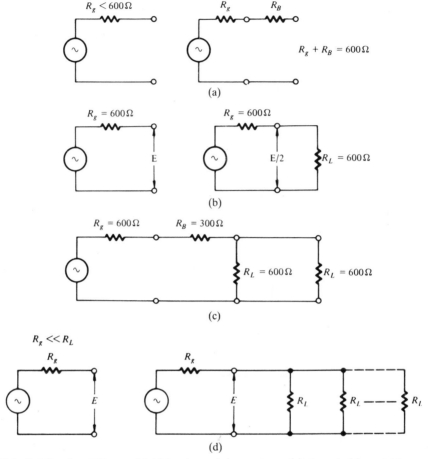

**Figure 11-4.** Details of matching and bridging transmission systems. (a) through (c), matching system. (d) Bridging system.

rated output voltage level across a 600-ohm load, in which case the voltage level in dBv will have the same numerical value as the power level in dBm.

In a matching system, any amplifier with an internal resistance less than nominal needs to have an additional resistance, $R_B$, added in series, as shown at Figure 11-4(a). When an amplifier is loaded with a matching resistance, as shown in (b), the output voltage will be halved. If multiple loads are to be fed by a single amplifier, it is necessary, as shown in (c), to use an added resistor, $R_B$, in order to maintain a 600 ohm load. By comparison, in a bridging system, as shown in Fgure 11-4(d), $R_g$ is much less than $R_L$, and many loads in parallel may be placed across an amplifier with no adverse effect.

## 11.2.5 Operational Amplifiers (Opamps)

*Opamps* provide a convenient and flexible means of signal routing and processing, and are used in most console designs today. The term *operational amplifier* derives from the

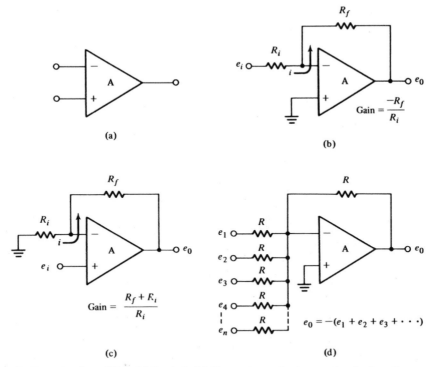

**Figure 11-5.** Operational amplifier. (a) Symbol. (b) Connection and gain equation for inverting operation. (c) Connection and gain equation for noninverting operation. (d) Connection at a combining amplifier of unity gain.

role these devices play in performing analog mathematical operations, such as addition, subtraction, multiplication, and division, as well as the functions of integration and differentiation in calculus.

The basic representation of the opamp is shown in Figure 11-5(a). Ideally, it should have the following characteristics; infinite gain, infinite input impedance, and zero output impedance. Actually, the gain of a typical opamp is in the range of 100 to 110 dB; its input impedance is in the range of 10 megohms (10,000,000 ohms); and the output impedance is in the range of a few ohms. These are "sufficiently close" to infinity and zero to enable us to make some simplifying assumptions and to establish the gain of the opamp purely in terms of the external resistances, $R_i$ and $R_f$, which are used in conjunction with it.

Figure 11-5(b) shows the opamp configured as an inverting amplifier. Note that the ratio of external resistances determines the gain. The version shown in (c) is non-inverting, and the version shown in (d) enables a number of signals to be combined with virtually no interaction between them.

## 11.2.6 Electronically Balanced Input Circuits

Many consoles today use electronically balanced input circuits as an alternative to the more expensive transformer input. Such a circuit is shown in Figure 11-6. Here, both

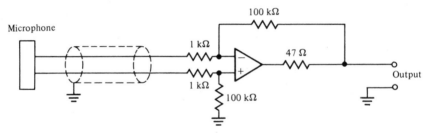

**Figure 11-6.** Balanced differential input circuit using operational amplifier.

signal leads from a microphone feed directly to the opamp inputs through 1000-ohm resistances, making a total input impedance of 2000 ohms as seen by the microphone. Both input leads are balanced with respect to ground. In other configurations, the input circuit can be made variable over a wide range, providing immunity to overload due to the virtual ground summing points at the opamp inputs.

### 11.2.7 Active Combining Networks

Figure 11-7(a) shows the physical details of an active combining network. The versions shown in (b) and (c) are among the many which may be used as abbreviated representations in console flow diagrams. The crossbar arrangement shown in (b) is probably the most useful in that it indicates, by the small circles, exactly which inputs are available at which outputs. The gain of an active combining network is generally set to unity so that the signal may be fed directly to the bus output fader and then to the line output amplifier.

### 11.3 AN EARLY STEREO CONSOLE

The first console to be discussed is typical of recording technology as it developed with two-track stereo tape recording during the early 1950s. Details are shown in Figure 11-8. Here we see the division of the console into three clear sections: input, output, and monitor. Essentially, the console provided for perhaps up to twelve inputs, each of which could be panned into a pair of stereo busses. Monitoring was switchable between the stereo output busses and the return from the stereo tape recorder. Normally, such a console would be used in conjunction with an external talkback system for studio communication and slating (adding take numbers and the like to both tape channels). Such basic designs as these are still in use today and are normally referred to simply as *stereo mixers*.

### 11.4 AN EARLY FOUR-CHANNEL STEREO CONSOLE

During the early 1960s, most record companies had three- or four-channel recording capability on half-inch magnetic tape. At that stage in the evolution of recording it was customary to monitor each recorded channel with its own dedicated loudspeaker. Thus, it was common in those days to see three or four loudspeakers located in front of the

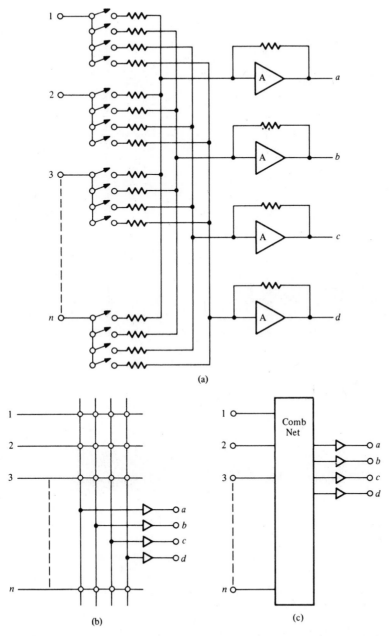

**Figure 11-7.** Combining networks. Representations shown (a through c) are equivalent.

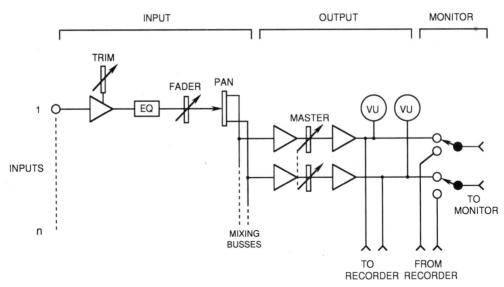

**Figure 11-8.** Signal flow diagram of a simple stereo recording console.

console over the control room window. Details of a four-channel console are shown in Figure 11-9. Note again that the console can be broken down into input, master, and monitor sections. The term normally used to describe this basic console design is *split configuration*.

The increased track capability gave the producer and engineer some flexibility in rebalancing soloists, bass lines, or other critical musical elements at a later time, thus setting into motion the demand for even more track capability.

A typical input section included switchable microphone/line so that both low-level and high-level input signals could be accommodated. This was followed by a relatively simple in-line equalizer and then the input fader. There were normally as many reverberation (echo) send channels as there were main outputs, and the reverberation send could be either pre- or post-fader. The normal application here is post-fader, so that the amount of reverberation remains consistent with the input signal it is applied to. The pre-fader reverberation send would be used for special effects, such as creating the illusion that an input signal might be fading into the distance, as it were, as the input fader was reduced.

In the output section, submaster faders adjust the level sent to the four-track recorder. Normally, the reverberation return was directly into the booster amplifiers just ahead of the ganged master output faders. In other applications, the reverberation returns could be crosspatched so that the reverberation from a signal originating at the left might be heard coming from the right.

Tape recorders of the day provided the rudiments of overdubbing (via Ampex Sel-Sync), so that new tracks could be added, or altered, in synchronism with the remaining tracks. Such activities required substantial repatching of the console and were cumbersome.

The monitor section was normally switchable between the bus outputs and the outputs from the recorder. Mixdown to two-channel stereo was generally not done in the studio control room, but rather in a post-production remix room.

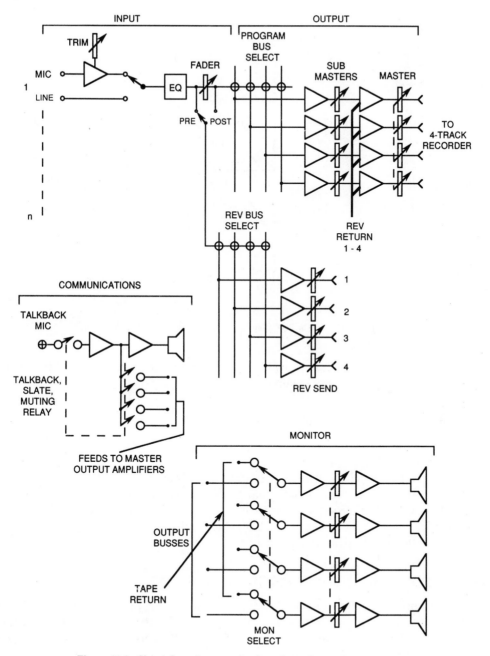

**Figure 11-9.** Signal flow diagram of a four-channel recording console.

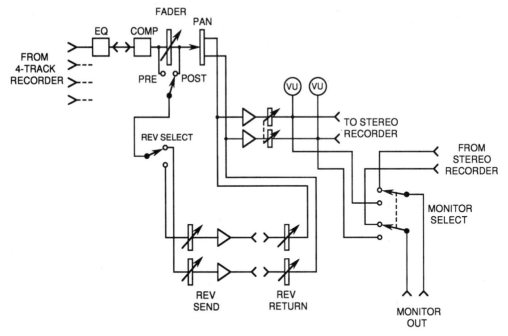

**Figure 11-10.** Signal flow diagram of a four-channel remix console.

The communications function provided studio talkback, as well as slating directly onto tape through the output booster amplifiers.

## 11.5 A FOUR-CHANNEL REMIX CONSOLE

The four-channel recording made on the previously discussed console was generally remixed into two-channel stereo on a console dedicated to that purpose. Typical details are shown in Figure 11-10. The four-track feeds could be individually equalized and compressed, or subjected to further signal processing via patching points. Reverberation could be added to tracks that were left "dry" during the original recording. Again, pre- or post-fader reverberation sends were available, and the reverberation return could be panned into the stereo array at any position.

## 11.6 A MODERN SPLIT CONFIGURATION CONSOLE

The advent of the Beatles and other immensely successful pop/rock groups during the 1960s pointed the way for multitrack expansion in order to accommodate new musical requirements. The shift to multitrack went first to 8, then to 16, and finally to 24-track capability. The new consoles differed from their predecessors in many ways, among them:

1. The need for more signal processing capability in each input module. More flexible equalization, filtering, and noise-gating have become commonplace.

2. Pairwise (odd–even) bus selection, with panning between the pair. This allows output busses to be treated as stereo pairs, if need be.
3. Return to two-channel monitoring. Beyond four channels, it is difficult to accommodate a monitor loudspeaker for each output bus.
4. Simplified console routing and switching for the all-important musical requirements of overdubbing and laying in new tracks over previous ones.
5. The need for more auxiliary send busses to facilitate headphone monitoring in the studio.
6. Use of the main recording console for mixdown purposes and other post-production activities.

Figures 11-11 through 11-13 show the operating controls for a large but relatively straightforward 24-bus console. The architecture of the console from input to output will be discussed, with reference to the corresponding signal flow diagrams shown in Figures 11-14 through 11-16. Capital letters are used to relate the controls with corresponding elements in the flow diagrams.

### 11.6.1 Input Module

Normally, this console would be supplied with 36 input modules, each contained in a single strip. For ease of illustration, the module is shown divided into three sections, but the reader should understand that the three sections, indicated as (a), (b), and (c) in Figure 11-11, are all in a single line, with (a) at the top, (b) in the middle, and (c) at the bottom.

Beginning with Figure 11-11(a), the control labeled +48 (A) engages phantom powering for capacitor microphones. The trim control (B) adjusts the gain of the input amplifiers so that the level can be optimized through the module. Control LI (line input, C) switches the input from microphone to high-level line input. During recording operations, the output of a synthesizer or other electronic instrument might be fed in at this point, while during mixdown the output of a multitrack recorder would be fed back into the console at this point.

Control D, marked $\phi$ (Greek phi, indicating phase), inverts the polarity of the signal input. (Its function is not shown in Figure 11-14.) This function is useful in correcting for miswired cables, as well as optimizing both direct-in and microphone signals, which often are not of the same polarity.

Control E engages the 100-Hz high-pass filter (useful for reducing rumble or other low-frequency noise), and control F engages the six-knob equalizer. Note the flexibility of the equalizer; both low-mid and high-mid frequencies can be selected, and both can be boosted or cut. HF and LF transition frequencies are fixed, but both can be boosted or cut.

The six auxiliary feeds are shown in Figure 11-11(b) and are indicated in Figure 11-14 at N. AUX sends 1 through 4 can be switched either pre- or post-fader, while 5 and 6 are post-fader only. Normally, in studio monitoring over headphones, the musicians prefer to hear the signal pre-fader, so that any running level changes by the engineer will not

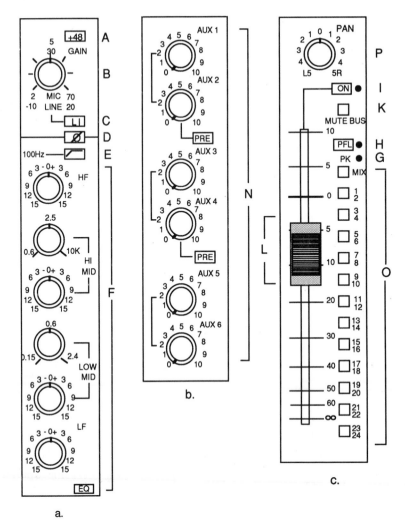

**Figure 11-11.** Physical view of input module of a modern split-configuration console. (a) Upper portion. (b) Middle portion. (c) Bottom portion. (*Data courtesy Soundcraft*)

alter the signal they are hearing. AUX 5 and 6 would normally be used for reverberation send.

The jumpers indicated at M in Figure 11-14 are internally adjustable so that the pre-fader position can be taken either before or after the equalizer.

Figure 11-11(c) shows the remaining functions in the input module. G is the peak indicator, a light-emitting diode (LED) which illuminates when the signal level is within 6 dB of overload. If it blinks on a continuous basis, it is a warning to the recording engineer to reduce the input level to the module via the trim control B.

Functions H, I, J, and K are all related to muting, unmuting, and "soloing" the input signal. PFL indicates "pre-fader listen," and that function, engaged by the PFL control

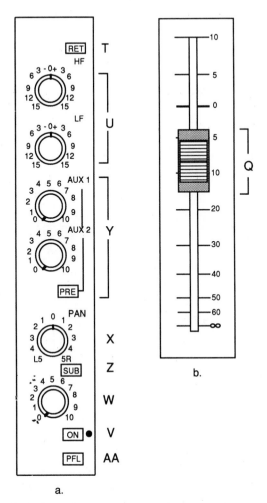

**Figure 11-12.** Physical view of output module of a modern split-configuration console. (a) Upper portion. (b) Bottom portion. (*Data courtesy Soundcraft*)

(H), mutes the console's monitor section, letting the engineer hear only the signal present in the module. This is a very useful diagnostic function that enables the engineer to isolate problems such as noise, defective microphones, unwanted signal leakage, and the like. Normally, the PFL function is non-destructive; that is, it does not affect any of the output signals that are being routed to tape recorders. It may be engaged at any time without creating problems in this regard. (Note comments later regarding the "solo in place" function, SIP.)

The fader L adjusts the signal level through the input module and is the engineer's primary means for adjusting all relative levels during the recording and remix processes. The panpot P is used to set the relative levels which are to be sent to odd–even pairs of output busses.

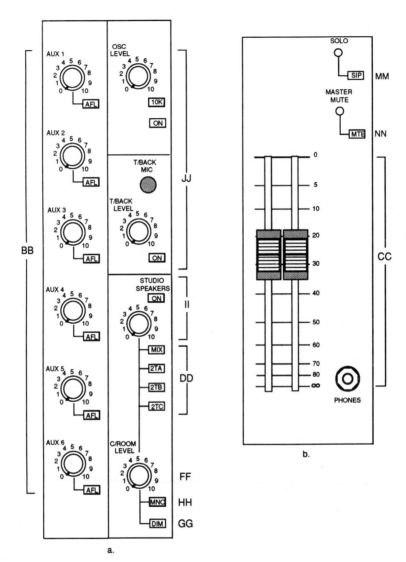

**Figure 11-13.** Physical view of master/monitor module of a modern split-figuration console. (a) Upper portion. (b) Lower portion. (*Data courtesy Soundcraft*)

Bus selection is made via the array of small buttons shown at O. Normally, the engineer will route a given input only to a single output bus. For example, if a signal is to be sent only to track 1 of the multitrack recorder, the engineer will select the button marked 1–2 and adjust the panpot to its far left position. Note that the module can be routed to any or all of the 24 busses, as well as to the MIX bus pair, indicated by L and R at position O in Figure 11-14.

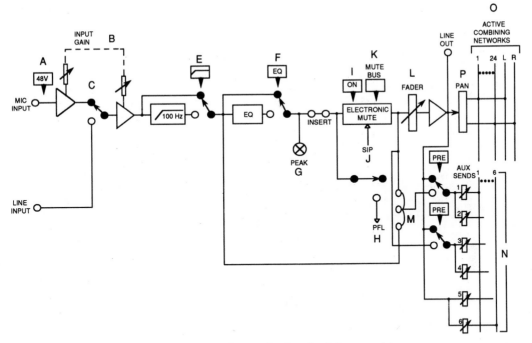

**Figure 11-14.** Flow diagram for Soundcraft input module.

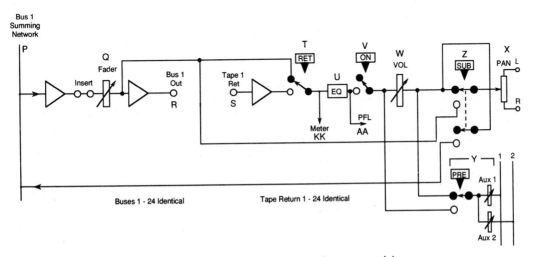

**Figure 11-15.** Flow diagram for Soundcraft output module.

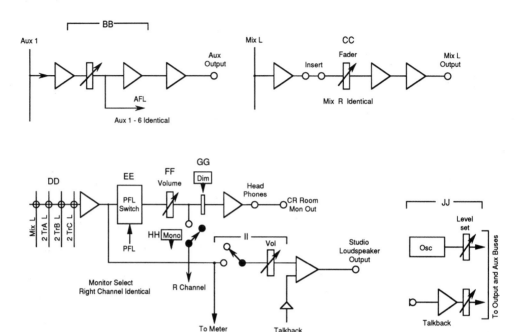

**Figure 11-16.** Flow diagram for Soundcraft master/monitor module.

## 11.6.2 The Master (Group) Module

In a 24-track console there are 24 master modules, and the output of each will normally feed directly to the corresponding input of the multitrack recorder. Figure 11-12 shows the layout of a master module, and Figure 11-15 shows the corresponding signal flow diagram.

The primary input to the module is the corresponding group, or bus, active combing network, shown at P. This signal is fed to the master fader Q, where the level is adjusted for optimum modulation of the corresponding channel of the multitrack recorder (R).

The return from the multitrack recorder is at point S, and the switch T is used to engage either the bus output or the corresponding tape playback return. A simple two-knob equalizer is shown at U, and the on/off switch for the master module is shown at V. A small rotary fader is shown at W and is used to set the group level to the panpot X which feeds directly to the L and R MIX busses for normal two-channel mixdown.

AUX inputs 1 and 2 can be engaged in the master module, as shown at Y, with either pre- or post-fader send. These are useful for either headphone monitoring (during recording) or reverberation send (during mixdown).

The control labeled SUB, shown at Z, is used to route the group output bus directly to the L and R MIX busses and to reroute the output of the rotary fader back into the corresponding group combining network. This function is not essential to the normal operation of the console, but it does provide added flexibility during certain remix operations.

### 11.6.3 The Output/Monitor Module

The physical layout of the output/monitor module is shown in Figure 11-13, and the corresponding signal flow is shown in Figure 11-16. The controls indicated at BB are the outputs of the six AUX busses, from which points the feeds are made to the headphone monitor amplifiers or the reverberation devices. AFL indicates "after fader listen" and is a means for the engineer to hear exactly what is being fed to the studio musicians for headphone monitoring or reverberation send.

The L and R mix busses are controlled by faders CC and are fed to the two-track stereo recorder.

The monitor select switch, shown at DD, lets the engineer choose to monitor from the stereo busses or from one of three two-track recorder returns. EE is the switching logic for the PFL and AFL functions, and FF is the control room monitor level control. GG is a "dimmer" switch, which reduces the monitor level conveniently so that the engineer can communicate with people in the control room without having to reset the monitor level control. HH ties the two stereo channels together in mono, while II engages the studio loudspeakers and level control.

The controls JJ inject the engineer's and producer's talkback and oscillator signals into all group and AUX busses. The oscillator signals are used for recorder alignment and for setting playback reference levels.

Metering points in the console are indicated at KK and LL in Figures 11-15 and 11-16.

In Figure 11-13(b), the solo-in-place (SIP) function is shown at the top (MM). When engaged, this function lets the engineer listen to the PFL signal during multitrack recording, panned between the stereo loudspeakers as it appears in the monitor mix. It is important to note that this function *cannot* be used during stereo mixdown, inasmuch as it derives its SOLO signal via the panpots feeding directly to the L and R busses. In the parlance of the trade, this kind of solo-in-place function is termed "destructive." Many consoles are of similar design, and the engineer is advised to check out this function carefully before using Solo-In-Place.

Finally, control NN provides a muting function for all input modules which have their MUTE BUS control (K) engaged.

## 11.7 EVOLUTION OF THE IN-LINE CONSOLE

The in-line console design is widely used today for multitrack recording. In terms of layout, it effectively does away with the Master section of the console, integrating that function into the input modules. As a result, overall console size can be reduced, albeit with much more complexity. The essential building block of an in-line console is the input/output (I/O) module, which provides for signal input and bus assignment, as well as monitoring from the multitrack recorder.

In-line consoles may take many forms, depending on the manufacturer's priorities, but the I/O module essentially provides two modes of operation. Figure 11-17 illustrates typical multitrack application. In this mode, the CHANNEL path routes the input signal (A) directly to the desired recording bus with only a level set (B) and panpot (C) in the

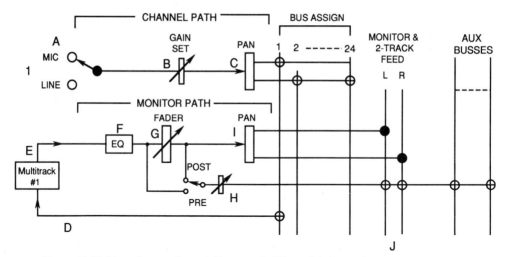

**Figure 11-17.** Flow diagram for an inline console I/O module in multitrack recording mode.

path. The aim here is simply to make the bus assignment to the multitrack recorder and ensure that the correct recording level is attained. The bus (D) is fed to the multitrack recorder, and the return from the recorder is brought back at E into the MONITOR path.

The monitor path provides equalization and filtering (F), level set (G), pre- and post-AUX feeds (H), and panning (I) into L and R monitoring busses. In this manner, input signals to the multitrack tape recorder can be kept free of any signal processing, while the monitor path provides the engineer with considerable flexibility in monitoring the signal and experimenting with any degree of signal processing, such as equalization, reverberation, and dynamic range manipulation. It is possible to make a multitrack recording and a "rough" two-track recording at the same.

The other mode of operation of the I/O module is shown in Figure 11-18. Here, the signal is introduced at (K). The equalizer/filter combination (L) has been switched into the channel path, as have the main fader (M) and the AUX sends (N). The signal is then assigned via the panpot (O) and bus selectors. At this point the signals can be reassigned to new tracks on the multitrack recorder (P, Q, R, and S), or routed directly to a two-track recorder via the L and R busses.

The switching of equalizers and faders between monitor and channel paths is often labeled "Swap" on the console and is accomplished with the arrangement shown in Figure 11-19. As a rule, the large fader, filter, equalizer, and any other signal processing element, are all individually switchable between the monitor and channel paths.

An in-line console may have any number of inputs, and those inputs can be assigned to any or all of the output busses. However, the first 24 inputs would have dedicated returns from the 24-track recorder, and all playback from the multitrack recorder would be via the I/O modules. Outside of its unique I/O modules, the monitor/communication functions of the in-line console are very much like that of many split configuration consoles.

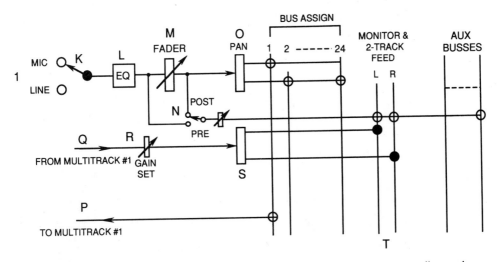

**Figure 11-18.** Flow diagram for an inline console I/O module in alternate recording mode.

Figure 11-20 shows the complexity of a typical I/O module for an in-line console. The signal to the channel path is introduced at A. The controls shown at B, C, D, and E can be switched between the channel and monitor paths. Panning is shown at F, and bus assignments are made at G. Auxiliary sends are shown at H, and the bus output is shown at I. The feed to the multitrack recorder is at J, and the multitrack return is shown at K.

## 11.8 GAINS AND LOSSES IN CONSOLE ARCHITECTURE: GOOD ENGINEERING PRACTICE

Modern consoles are relatively easy to operate in terms of maintaining proper signal levels from input to output. Essentially, the procedure for making a multitrack recording

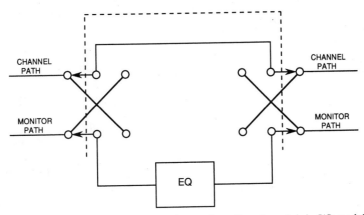

**Figure 11-19.** Circuit diagram for transfer, or "swap" mode switch in I/O module.

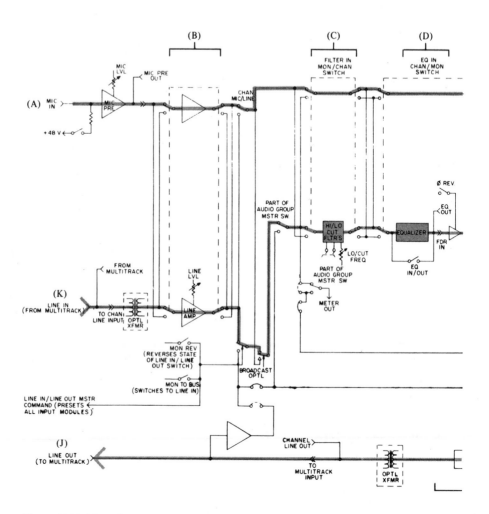

**Figure 11-20.** Flow diagram for an inline console. (*Data courtesy Quad-Eight*)

is to set the input level via the microphone trim potentiometer on the input module while the input fader is set at its −10 dB position. The output bus or group fader is normally set to its full position. The "zero level" on the bus output meter (shown at point KK in Figure 11-15) corresponds to the chosen alignment fluxivity level on the tape recorder, and the engineer can then reliably set levels, as read on the meter, for appropriate modulation of the tape. The reason for setting the input fader at its −10 dB position is to allow room for routine level adjustment, in either direction, during the course of recording operations.

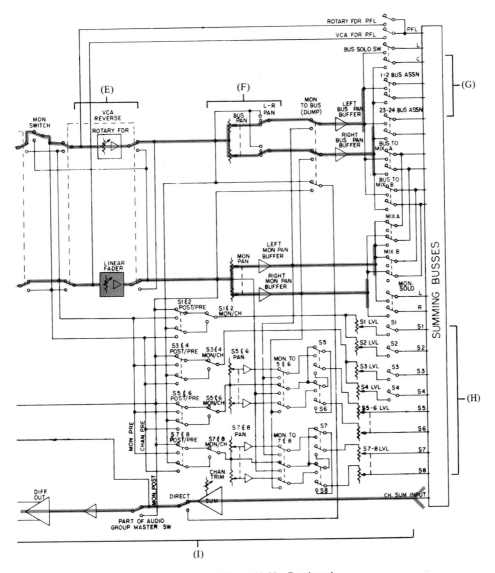

**Figure 11-20.** Continued.

There are two important factors the engineer should know regarding the zero indication on the bus meters: the electrical headroom in the console that exists above that reference level, and the tape modulation corresponding to zero reference level. In most consoles there is at least 20 dB of headroom above the zero reading on the meter, so there is the assurance of a clean signal being delivered to the tape recorder. But *how much* signal should be delivered to the tape recorder is another matter. In analog tape recording, the reference fluxivity on the tape is normally about 12 dB below the maximum output (MO) of the tape, corresponding to total harmonic distortion of about 3%. Under these

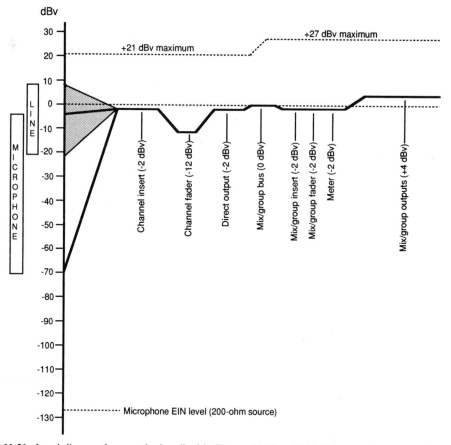

**Figure 11-21.** Level diagram for console described in Figures 11-14 to 11-16. The normal range of microphone and line input levels is shown at the left of the diagram; these would be adjusted using the trim control on the input module. Levels indicated by the bold lines represent average signal levels. Note that headroom above average levels is at all times in excess of 20 dB. Note also that once operating level has been established at the input, further level changes are kept to a minimum. (*Data courtesy Soundcraft*)

conditions, it is best to maintain bus levels of about zero on the meters, with occasional peaks indicating +3 or +4 above that point. In digital recording, it is customary to align the recorder so that zero on the bus meters corresponds to levels of −15 or −20 dB, relative to full modulation of the digital recorder. In this case, the digital recorder and the console will reach their overload points at the same point. Some engineers prefer a slight lead factor, perhaps 3 or 4 dB, so that the recorder will overload slightly ahead of the console.

The normal operating levels in a typical console are shown in Figure 11-21, which shows the straight-through relationship between a single input routed to a single output track. For multiple inputs being routed to a single output, as in the case of remix operations, the trimmers must be readjusted downward approximately 3 dB for each doubling of inputs, according to the following equation:

**Table 11-1. Suggested Level Reduction for Multiple Inputs**

| Number of inputs | Relative mix level (dB) |
|:---:|:---:|
| 1 | 0 |
| 2 | −3 |
| 3 | −4.8 |
| 4 | −6 |
| 5 | −7 |
| 6 | −8 |
| 7 | −8.5 |
| 8 | −9 |
| 9 | −9.5 |
| 10 | −10 |

$$\text{Level reduction} = 10 \log N \qquad\qquad (11\text{-}2)$$

where $N$ is the number of combined inputs per output channel. Table 11-1 shows these values for $N$ from 1 to10. If this level reduction is not made, then the level in the stereo mix busses just ahead of the ouput faders will be higher than normal, thus requiring that those faders be set lower than normal. This would in effect reduce the normal headroom capability in the mix busses, creating some risk of signal overload.

As a general rule, engineers should always be on the lookout for faders that are continuously operating below the halfway point on the console. This is usually a good indication that signal level is too high at some point earlier in the signal chain. Many problems do not occur at the start of a recording session, but develop insidiously as the session progresses. Musicians sometimes play louder as the session gets underway, and the first reflex of the engineer is to pull down the input faders. The logical thing to do of course is to retrim the input preamplifiers. Experience is a good teacher here, but it is very useful to observe experienced engineers at work.

## 11.9 STUDIO INTERFACE

The recording console is the central control for a large array of input, output, and external signal processing functions. We must be just as careful with levels external to the console as we are with those within the console. This section discusses the subsystems external to the console.

### 11.9.1 Input Functions

*Microphones.* Balanced input is essential because of the extremely low signal voltages associated with microphones. Three-pin XL-type connectors are universally used, with pin 1 ground and the audio signal between pins 2 and 3. Standard poling of the connector

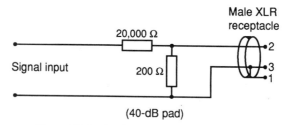

**Figure 11-22.** A microphone simulation circuit.

is such that a positive-going pressure at the microphone will cause a positive-going voltage at pin 2. For purposes of initial console calibration and checkout it is useful to have a circuit such as that shown in Figure 11-22, which places a 40-dB pad in the output of an oscillator to simulate the output of a microphone. For example, a voltage input of 0.7 volts will be reduced to 7 millivolts, which is the output signal of many capacitor microphones when placed in a sound field of 94 dB $L_P$. The circuit is useful in checking out losses in long microphone cables as well.

**Direct Instrument Pickup.**   In popular recording, it is customary to make direct-in connections with many electronic instruments. This ensures complete acoustical isolation of the instrument, where that may be desirable. Figure 11-23 shows some of the ways direct inputs can be made. In many cases, the signal from the instrument's pickup can be inserted directly into a microphone input. However, where there is additional processing of the signal via the instrument's integral equalizer, effects generator, or the like, the direct-in connection will have to be made from a line level output jack on the instrument's

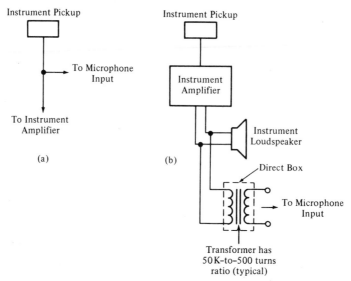

**Figure 11-23.** Direct instrument pickup. (a) From pickup transducer. (b) From loudspeaker.

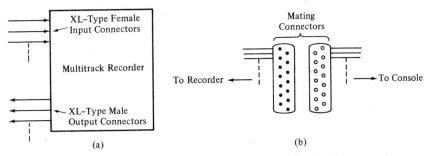

**Figure 11-24.** Recording loop. (a) Individual connectors. (b) Multiple connectors.

amplifier, or possibly via a direct box connected to the instrument's loudspeaker leads. Caution must be observed at all times, since "hot chassis" problems could lead to various hums and buzzes, or, at worst, to electrical shock.

### 11.9.2 The Recording Loop

The recording loop is shown in Figure 11-24. It is a unity gain loop, with the return signal from the recorder at the same level as the input signal. With multichannel recorders, there can be dozens of three-conductor cables lying around, and it is difficult to keep equipment neat and orderly. Many studio complexes wire their multichannel recorders so that inputs and outputs are grouped into multipin connectors, with up to 8 or 12 channels in a single connector. Such an arrangement facilitates moving and reconnecting the recorders.

Normally, the output busses of the console are balanced, with maximum output capability of +24 dBv. Monitor return points in the console are often unbalanced and may have maximum input level capability quite a bit less than 20 dBv. Caution is advised, and the engineer should ensure that the maximum recorded level on tape will not overload these inputs.

### 11.9.3 The Reverberation Loop

Figure 11-25 shows a typical reverberation loop. Many consoles do not have metering on their various AUX send busses, and the recording engineer must carefully determine the maximum drive signal available. Level controls on the reverberation devices should be set so that the system can operate without internal clipping or overload. Usually, there is an indicator, perhaps a light-emitting diode (LED) that will show this condition. It is important that the reverberation device, whatever its type, be operated at the highest "safe" level, so that the full signal-to-noise capability of the unit is attained.

The reverberation return signal is often fed back into a pair of input modules with the input switches set for line input. Reverberation return signals are normally mixed into the main signal path at a level low enough to ensure that the self-noise of the reverberation system will not be a problem. Acoustical reverberation chambers tend to be noisier than mechanical or digital devices, so special care should be taken with those systems. Time

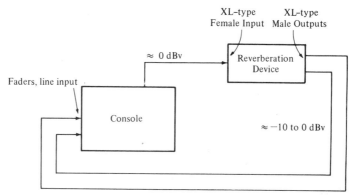

**Figure 11-25.** Reverberation loop.

delay devices are often used in conjunction with reverberation devices, and the foregoing comments apply there as well.

### 11.9.4 Limiters and Compressors

If a single channel is to be limited or compressed, the compressor may be patched into the input module itself at any convenient line level point before the fader, as shown in Figure 11-26. The engineer may want to have the compressor ahead of, or after, the equalizer section of the module. The reason is that the dynamics of the compressor are highly dependent on the spectral content of the program. The decision is basically whether it is better to compress a signal that has already been equalized, or is it better to equalize a signal that has already been compressed. The experienced engineer will know the difference and choose accordingly; the young engineer will soon learn through experimenting. This matter will be discussed this further in the section covering signal processing.

For stereo signal compression, it is necessary to use a compressor whose gain functions track precisely in the stereo mode. Such devices will be patched in the console's output section, preferably ahead of the master faders. The compressors must be capable of handling fairly high signals at their inputs, and delivering undistorted outputs in the +20 dBv range.

### 11.9.5 Loudspeaker Monitoring

The monitoring system is shown in Figure 11-27. In addition to the monitor level control on the console, the monitor amplifier may have input level controls. Since most power amplifiers can be driven to full output by an input signal of only about 0.7 or 1 volt, it is clear that the monitor signal from the console to the amplifier will be quite low most of the time. Many studio operators prefer to calibrate the playback level in the control room so that a reading of zero on the meter will, for a reference setting of the monitor level control, produce an acoustical level of 85 dB $L_P$, or some other convenient level,

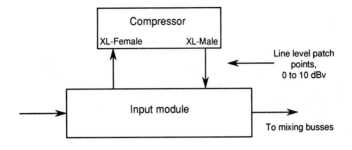

a.

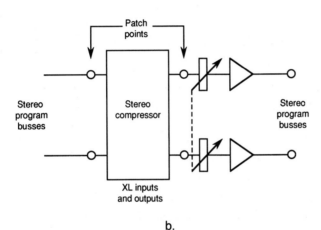

b.

**Figure 11-26.** Location of compressors/limiters. (a) Compression on one signal. (b) Stereo compression on composite signal.

in the control room. The main value in this is that it enables the same playback level to be duplicated easily in other studios.

### 11.9.6 Headphone Monitoring in the Studio

At least one pair of AUX busses in a recording console should be dedicated to headphone monitoring in the studio. The nature of much popular and rock music demands that players be able to hear each other when separated by considerable distance in the studio, and headphone monitoring is the accepted way of doing this. Figure 11-28 shows details of this.

There are some useful variations here. In many studios, each player is given a small junction box for the headphones that contains a passive level control, enabling each player to adjust monitoring levels over a useful range.

With only two channels of headphone monitoring available, the signal has to be a "best fit" for all the musicians present. Some will want more of the bass line, while others will

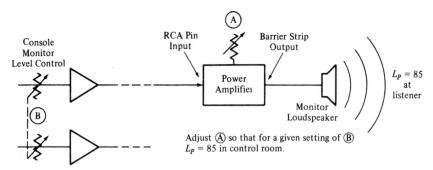

**Figure 11-27.** Monitor system calibration.

want less of it. More to the point, a vocalist will undoubtedly want to hear the vocal line with reverberation, while others in the studio may not. The only way around this problem is to provide multiple monitoring AUX sends (up to 6) and providing each player with a separate mixing panel, usually mounted on the music rack. This is expensive, and it may require a lot of setup time, inasmuch as many musicians are at a total loss at "dialing in" their own mix.

There are no easy answers. Let it just be said that headphone monitoring remains, in many ways, an afterthought in modern studio recording.

## 11.10 CONSOLE AUTOMATION

Console automation dates from the early 1970s. The early systems were tape-based and encoded fader positions through sampling and multiplexing on a pair of spare tracks on the multitrack recording. Any changes in the mix involved toggling new data between the two tracks, and cumulative errors were bound to occur as positional data was repeatedly reformatted and rerecorded. Figure 11-29 shows functional details of such a system. At the heart of the system was the VCA (voltage-controlled amplifier), which

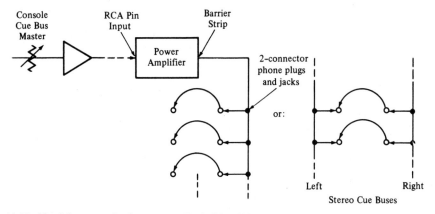

**Figure 11-28.** Headphone monitoring system. Typical headphone sensitivity is 94 dB $L_P$ for 1 milliwatt input.

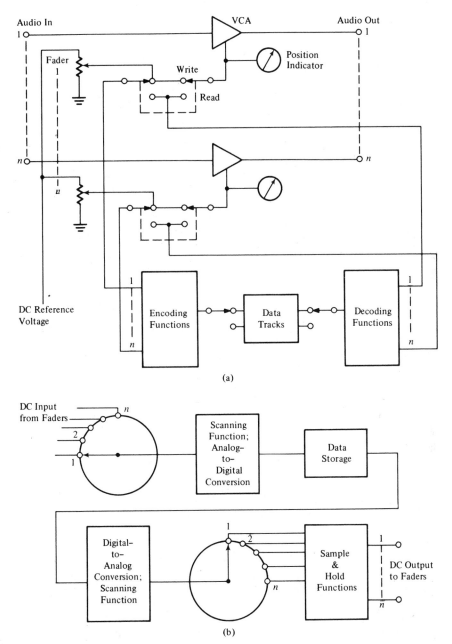

**Figure 11-29.** Early console automation. (a) Basic flow diagram for automated control of levels. (b) Detail of sample-and-hold. (c) Details of a typical data track. Each biphase "word" controls a single gain or switching function.

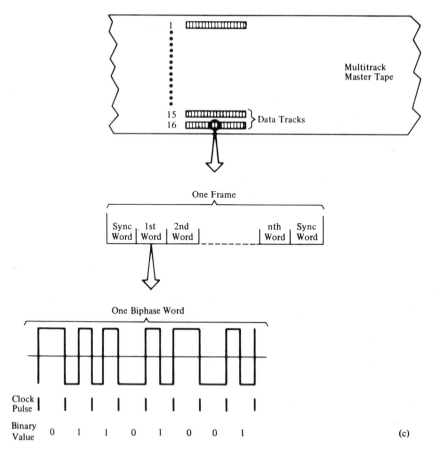

Figure 11-29. Continued.

was used to control signal levels in both normal and automated operation of the faders.

Those days are long gone; modern automation systems are computer-based and afford the user greater flexibility and accuracy. The new systems make use of SMPTE time code, which is recorded on a single track on the multitrack tape. Fader positional data is not stored on the tape, but rather on a floppy disk in the associated computer. As many changes in position as desired may be made, with no accumulation of errors.

There are two operational approaches; one uses VCAs, while the other makes use of moving faders. In the VCA approach, the engineer manipulates the faders as in making a normal mixdown. That positional information is stored, and on replay the VCAs are accessed directly by the system, while the faders remain stationary. The position indicator, shown in Figure 11-29(a), lets the engineer know the status of each VCA. In the moving fader approach, the faders actually move during the automated replay procedure, letting the engineer see directly the status of each fader. The moving fader approach to automation is intuitively more satisfying to the engineer, but the approach is generally more costly because it involves critical servomechanisms to move the faders quickly and accurately.

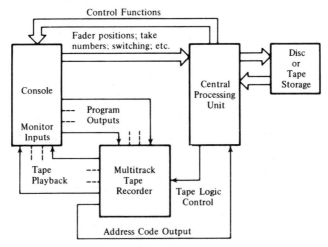

**Figure 11-30.** Flow diagram for an asynchronous console automation system.

Current console automation systems are available with a wide array of options, including subgroup control, enabling a single fader, during the "write" process, to control a number of faders. Thus, a complicated mixdown can be vastly simplified so that it may only involve a few faders. Other console functions may be automated as well, including muting, panning, and equalizer control. Multiple mixdowns may be made and stored; they may be merged or updated at any point. Figure 11-30 shows the basic layout of a modern console automation system.

## BIBLIOGRAPHY

1. J. Borwick (ed.), *Sound Recording Practice*, Oxford University Press, New York (1987).
2. J. Eargle, *The Microphone Handbook*, Elar, Plainview, N.Y. (1982).
3. J. Frayne and H. Wolfe, *Sound Recording*, Wiley, New York (1949).
4. W. Jung, *IC OP-AMP Cookbook*, H. Sams, Indianapolis (1974).
5. J. Woram, *Sound Recording Handbook*, H. Sams, Indianapolis (1989).
6. J. Woram and A. Kefauver, *The New Recording Studio Handbook*, Elar, Commack, N.Y. (1989).
7. *Motion Picture Sound Engineering*, prepared by the Research Council of the Academy of Motion Picture Arts and Sciences, D. Van Nostrand, New York (1938).

# 12

---

# SIGNAL METERING AND OPERATING LEVELS

---

## 12.1 INTRODUCTION

The various meters associated with consoles and tape recorders are the means by which the recording engineer establishes and maintains proper transmission and recording levels. This chapter examines the various kinds of metering that are useful to the engineer, and discusses analog tape fluxivity references and their relationship to metering.

## 12.2 DYNAMIC RANGE, HEADROOM, AND OPERATING LEVELS

The dynamic range of an audio transmission path is the spread between the highest and lowest signal levels that can be effectively accommodated. The limit at high levels is the onset of some specified amount of distortion, while at low levels the limit is the A-weighted noise level of the system. As we have seen, microphones may exhibit dynamic ranges in excess of 120 dB, and typical signal paths through a console may be even greater. The recording medium itself is the weakest link in the system. Without noise reduction, analog tape recorders have dynamic ranges of the order of 68 to 72 dB, unweighted. Current digital recorders have dynamic ranges slightly greater than 90 dB, unweighted.

The recording engineer has the job of fitting the signal into the medium in the most effective way. This means that he must hold the average signal level as high as possible, while still allowing sufficient room for peak signals. Figure 12-1 shows the relation between normal operating level and the extremes the medium can be expected to handle. The region between normal operating level and peak capability is referred to as *headroom*.

Obviously, the greater the headroom allowance, the more accurately the peak signal can be accommodated by the recording medium. However, if too much headroom is desired, the overall signal level may be held too low, and the noise floor of the medium may intrude.

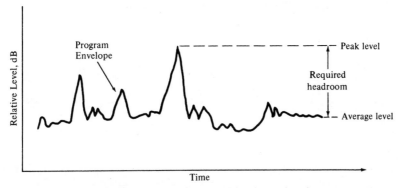

**Figure 12-1.** Illustration of peak level, average level, and headroom in a long-term program envelope.

Each recording medium has a maximum permissible signal level that can be accommodated, and there is normally an *alignment level,* which is some 9 or 10 dB below this point. Average program levels are usually lower than the alignment level by an amount depending on the program nature itself.

## 12.3 THE VU (VOLUME UNIT) METER

The traditional method of metering in a 600-ohm system is the VU meter. In its basic form the VU meter registers zero on its scale when the voltage corresponding to one milliwatt in a 600-ohm load is applied (0.775 V). In its normal application in recording, a 3600-ohm resistor is placed in series with the meter so that its zero level reading corresponds to +4 dBv (1.23 V). The appearance of the VU meter face is shown in Figure 12-2.

The ballistics, or dynamic action, of the VU meter is such that it will reach its full deflection in about one-third of a second, as shown in Figure 12-3. This characteristic is roughly the inverse of the ear's judgment of loudness as a function of signal duration (see Figure 2-2), and much of the continuing popularity of the VU meter comes as a result of its correlation with the loudness of full level signals. The fallback time of the VU meter is about one-third of a second.

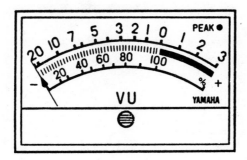

**Figure 12-2.** Face of a standard VU meter. (*Courtesy Yamaha*)

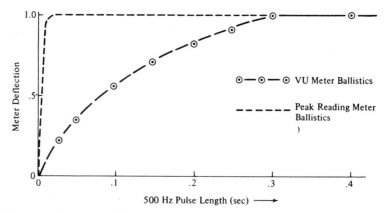

**Figure 12-3.** Response of meters to 500-Hz pulsed signals. Below about ⅓ second the response of a VU meter does not indicate maximum level. By comparison, a peak program meter gives a more accurate account of shorter pulses.

## 12.4 THE PEAK PROGRAM METER (PPM)

Figure 12-3 also indicates, by the dashed line, the ballistics of a typical PPM. These devices are electronic, whereas the VU meter is normally a passive device. The PPM reaches its full deflection in about 10 msec, and as such it tends to read overall higher levels, as compared to the VU meter, when the two are calibrated to the same steady-state signal.

There are several versions of the PPM. The form preferred by the BBC (British Broadcasting Corporation) is shown in Figure 12-4. The rather simple meter face has seven markers, all equally spaced by 4 dB intervals. Zero dBv normally produces a reading at marker 4. The rise time of the meter is 10 msec, and the fallback time is about 3 seconds, making the meter quite responsive to sudden transient signals, while providing the engineer sufficient time to observe them.

The various PPMs have been standardized by the IEC (International Electrotechnical Commission) and their respective scales are shown in linear form in Figure 12-5. All versions have a rise time of 10 msec. Types I and IIb have fall times of about 13 dB per

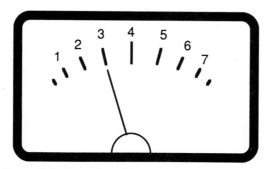

**Figure 12-4.** Illustration of the BBC peak program meter.

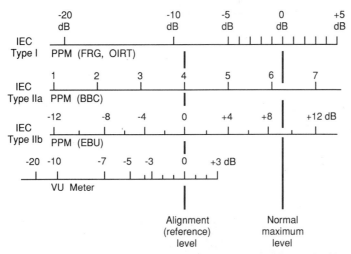

**Figure 12-5.** Comparison of scales and calibration points on VU and various PPMs. (*Data after Thiele (3)*)

second. The scales are aligned to show their normal calibration to a steady-state signal of +4 dBv.

## 12.5 RESPONSE TIME, LEAD FACTOR, AND TAPE CALIBRATION LEVEL

If a VU meter and a Type IIa PPM meter are fed a +4 dBv signal, they will both read zero, but on program material the two meters will not necessarily track each other. In general the PPM meter will read higher by a factor of 6 to 10 dB, depending on the transient nature of the program. This difference is sometimes referred to as *lead factor*.

Given the same magnetic tape stock, we would expect an engineer in the United States (using VU meters) and an engineer in Germany (using Type IIa PPMs) to record the same kind of program material at nearly the same levels on the tape. However, using their respective meters, the German engineer will notice that levels are reading some 6 to 8 dB higher than his American counterpart. If both meters were calibrated to the *same* tape fluxivity, the tendency would be for the German engineer to record the same program some 6 to 8 dB lower than the American engineer!

The answer to this problem is simply for the German engineer to calibrate his tape recorder so that it records at a higher level for a given steady-state input signal. This is the case, and it has been for some decades. Table 12-1 shows the various reference tape fluxivities that have been used over the years. Note that the DIN (Deutsche Industrie Normen) standards have always been in the range of 6 dB higher than the corresponding U.S. standards.

Taking the original Ampex tape alignment level as a reference, the DIN 360 nWb/m was 5.8 dB higher, just about equal to the lead factor between the PPM and the VU meter on speech program. When the U.S. elevated level was introduced to take advantage of the newer high output tapes, the DIN standard was raised so that the two reference levels remained about 6 dB apart.

### Table 12-1. Reference levels for magnetic recording

| Fluxivity (nanowebers/meter) | Description |
|---|---|
| 185 nWb/m | Old Ampex reference level (0 dB) |
| 200 nWb/m | "Rationalized" reference level (+0.68 dB) |
| 250 nWb/m | New U.S. elevated level (+2.6 dB) |
| 360 nWb/m | Old European (DIN) level (+5.8 dB) |
| 510 nWb/m | New European (DIN) level (+8.8 dB) |

## 12.6 NEW ELECTRONIC METERS

Today, we see a variety of bargraph meters in consoles. These are, for the most part, designed by the console builders and may or may not conform to any accepted standard as regards sensitivity and ballistics. Nevertheless, these meters can be quite useful, provided the engineer studies the operating manual carefully. More to the point, there are many meters that superficially look like VU meters. On steady-state input signals, they may perform like VU meters, but performance on dynamic program material may be significantly different.

## 12.7 PEAK, AVERAGE, AND RMS VALUES OF WAVEFORMS

Figure 12-6 shows several waveforms, along with indications of their peak, rms, and average values. The VU meter is an average reading instrument, and a sluggish one at that. Most PPMs, even with their 10-mec rise time, do not respond quickly enough to register single high-level peaks. A waveform such as that shown at Figure 12-6(a) will be indicated by a VU meter some 13 dB lower than its actual peak value. Such are the problems with metering that have given rise to so many standards.

## 12.8 DIGITAL RECORDER ALIGNMENT

Unlike analog tape recorders, digital recorders are quite clean up to a point at which they go into hard signal clipping. It is customary to align them so that +4 dBv at the console's output is set to a recording level some 20 dB below full recording capability. This requires that the console's output capability be at least +24 dBv to ensure that the console will not clip before the recorder does. The meters on the digital recorder are normally driven from the analog-to-digital converters, so that even an instantaneous signal that reaches full recording level will be noted as such. In a sense, the meters on the digital recorder are PPMs *par excellence*, catching peaks which might easily get by the best traditional PPMs!

Under these alignment conditions, the VU meters may be making occasional forays into the +3 region, or perhaps hitting the pin at the right edge of the meter on occasion, while at the same time the digital meters are indicating signals within 4 or 5 dB of maximum. Here, the lead factor between the two meters can be as high as 15 dB.

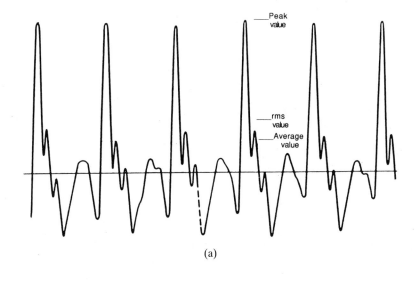

(a)

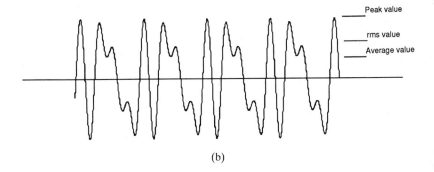

(b)

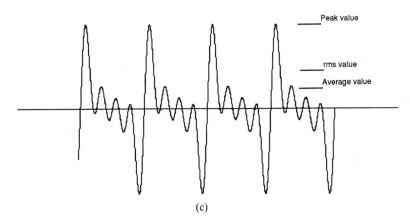

(c)

**Figure 12-6.** Peak, rms, and average values of various program waveforms. (a) Trumpet at 400 Hz. (b) Synthesized tone (first four harmonics). (c) Same harmonics as in (b), but with polarity reversed in 2nd, 3rd, and 4th harmonics. Note that peak value depends on phase relationships between harmonics.

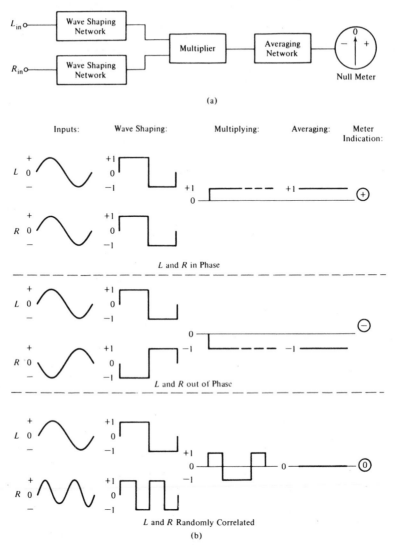

**Figure 12-7.** Details of a stereo correlation meter. (a) Schematic diagram. (b) Action of meter for three signal conditions: in-phase, out-of-phase, randomly correlated.

## 12.7 STEREO METERING

### 12.7.1 Correlation Metering

In addition to metering levels in a pair of stereo channels, the recording engineer needs to know the precise phasor relationship between them, and the *stereo correlation* meter is a convenient way of observing this. Details are shown in Figure 12-7. Positive correlation indicates a preponderance of in-phase program, while negative correlation indicates a preponderance of out-of-phase information.

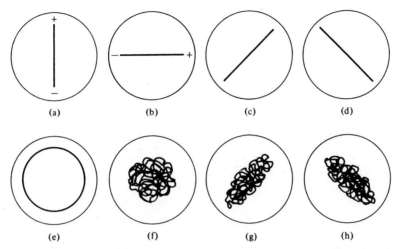

**Figure 12-8.** Stereophonic oscilloscope patterns. (a) Left only. (b) Right only. (c) Left and right in same polarity. (d) Left and right in opposite polarity. (e) Left and right at phase angle of 90°. (f) Normal stereo program. (g) Stereo program with significant monophonic components of same polarity. (h) Stereo program with significant monophonic components of opposite polarity.

### 12.7.2 Oscilloscope Patterns (Lissajous Figures)

Instantaneous visual monitoring of stereo program has always interested the engineer. While the correlation meter provides a time-averaged view of the stereo program, oscilloscope viewing provides an instantaneous picture.

An oscilloscope is a test instrument that provides viewing of two inputs simultaneously by means of lateral and vertical deflection of an electron beam aimed at a phosphorescent surface. Normally, the oscilloscope is used to observe waveforms, and in this mode the waveform to be viewed is introduced into the vertical input while a linear sweep signal, synchronized to one period of the wave form, is introduced into the horizontal input.

For stereo viewing, the sweep signal is disabled, and the stereo signals are connected directly to the vertical and horizontal inputs. The patterns that are observed are known as Lissajous figures. A variety of inputs are shown in Figure 12-8. In (a) the left channel only is shown connected to the vertical input; in (b) the right channel only is connected to the horizontal input. In (c) equal in-phase signals are fed to both inputs, and in (d) equal out-of-phase inputs are shown. In (e), equal inputs with a 90° phase shift between them are applied to the two inputs. The pattern shown in (f) is typical of a normal stereo program with little common information between the channels; the pattern appears to be contained roughly within a circular envelope. The pattern in (g) is that of a stereo program contain strong in-phase, or center phantom, information. The pattern shown in (h) is for a stereo program containing common out-of-phase information.

### 12.7.3 Sum and Difference Metering

Many broadcast engineers prefer to have a sum–difference option in stereo metering, since this give important information regarding the RF modulation of the signal. Generally,

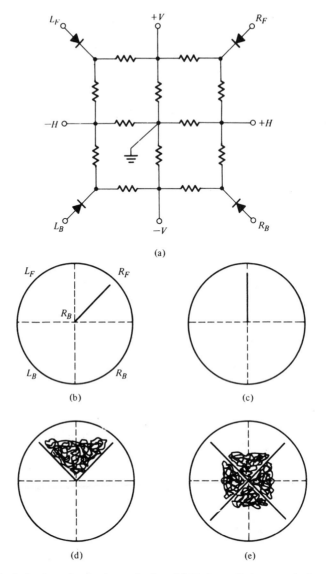

**Figure 12-9.** Method of visual quadraphonic monitoring. (a) Resistor–diode network shown. The four signal inputs are indicated as $L_F$, $R_F$, $L_B$, and $R_B$. The inputs to the balance oscilloscope are shown as $+H$ and $-H$ for horizontal and $+V$ and $-V$ for vertical. (b) Response to a single $R_F$ signal. (c) Response for a signal panned between the front pair of channels is shown. (d) View of stereo program presented to the $L_F$ and $R_F$ channels. (e) Normal quadraphonic program.

the difference signal will be about 6 to 8 dB lower than the sum signal. This is highly program-variable, but in no case should the difference signal be consistently higher than the sum signal. Sum–difference meters are calibrated by feeding the matrix only a single stereo channel. Under this condition, both meters should read the same.

## 12.8 QUADRAPHONIC METERING

A metering system for quadraphonic program material that makes use of a resistor–diode network and a balanced input oscilloscope is shown in Figure 12-9. A unique aspect of this display is that it provides a vector representation for individual signals in their assigned directions around the listener.

### BIBLIOGRAPHY

1. G. Ballou (editor), *Handbook for Sound Engineers*, H. Sams, Indianapolis (1987).
2. J. Borwick (ed.), *Sound Recording Practice*, Oxford University Press, London (1987).
3. N. Thiele, "Three-level Tone Signal for Setting Audio Levels," *J. Audio Engineering Society*, vol. 33, no. 12 (1985).
4. J. Monforte, "A Dynamic Phase Meter for Program Material," *J. Audio Engineering Society*, vol. 36, no. 6 (1988).
5. H. Tremaine, *The Audio Encyclopedia*, H. Sams, Indianapolis (1969).
6. J. Woram and A. Kefauver, *The New Recording Studio Handbook*, Elar, Commack, N.Y. (1989).

# 13

## MONITOR LOUDSPEAKERS

### 13.1 INTRODUCTION

To a large extent, today's high-level monitor loudspeakers had their origins in motion picture technology that began in the late 1920s. Subsequent development of high-frequency (HF) compression driver and horn systems during the 1930s gave us an art that has remained largely unchanged in its fundamental aspects for more than half a century. Recent years have seen remarkable developments in areas once thought to be the domain of consumer high fidelity, and it is now possible to design monitor loudspeakers using direct radiator components that have high output capability with reliability and low distortion. The base of measurement has broadened substantially in the last decade, and we now find monitor loudspeaker designs that have been refined in areas scarcely thought of earlier.

Of course there is no single philosophy of monitor loudspeaker design, and different approaches seem to favor different musical requirements. There are, however, certain performance attributes that all recording engineers would agree are important. It is the ranking of these attributes and system requirements that leads us in different directions, according to our respective monitoring needs.

Figure 13-1(a) shows a signal flow diagram for a typical monitor loudspeaker system. The dividing network contains low-pass, band-pass, and high-pass sections, that divide the program spectrum so that each transducer in the system receives only those frequencies intended for it. Level controls, which are optional, provide some degree of adjustment of the system to the environment. Photographs of typical monitors in several power classes are also shown. There are many loudspeakers labeled as monitors by their manufacturers, when in fact they may not generally be used as such. Let the buyer beware.

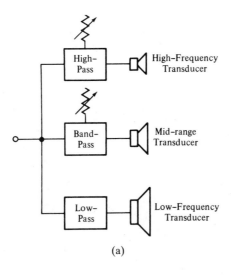

(a)

(b)

**Figure 13-1.** Typical recording monitoring loudspeakers. (a) Signal flow diagram for a three-way system. (b) A three-way "bookshelf" monitor. (c and d) Details of two-way coaxial monitors. (e) A two-way monitor using a large format HF compression driver-horn combination. (*Photographs courtesy JBL, UREI, and Tannoy*)

**Figure 13-1.** Continued.

## 13.2 MONITOR LOUDSPEAKER REQUIREMENTS

### 13.2.1 Flat Frequency Response

Two aspects are important: axial response and power response. Axial response is measured in the free field along a given direction, or axis, from the loudspeaker. The data usually presented is measured along the principal (0°) axis of the system. Power response is a measure of the total power radiated by the system as a function of frequency. In the ideal system, both axial and power response are assumed to be flat, or constant with frequency.

**3.2.1.1 Axial Response**  Figure 13-2 shows the on-axis response of two typical monitors. These measurements are referred to a distance of 1 meter, and the power applied to the systems is nominally 1 watt. Both measurements are made in so-called *half-space*; that is, the loudspeakers were placed close to a large reflecting boundary, thus simulating their normal flush mounting conditions in the front walls of the recording control room. Tolerances of ±3 or 4 dB are common.

Loudspeaker sensitivity is generally defined as the on-axis $L_P$ for 1 watt nominal power input, referred to a distance of 1 meter. Values in the range of 87 to 94 are common.

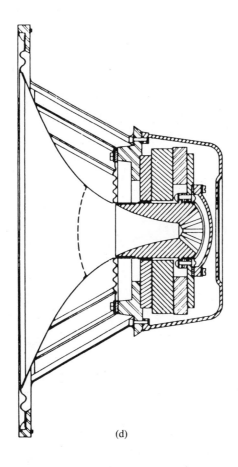

(d)

**Figure 13-1.** Continued.

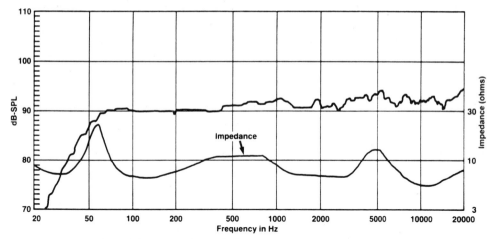

**Figure 13-2.** On-axis frequency response of typical three-way monitor systems. (*JBL data*)

Relatively flat on-axis frequency response is important in that it describes the nature of the first arrival sound at the recording engineer's ears. The flatter it is, the more natural the impression of instrumental timbres.

**3.2.1.2 Power Response** A convenient, but indirect, measure of a system's power response can be shown by its −6 dB beamwidth plots, as indicated in Figure 13-3. The system shown in (a) exhibits reasonably controlled coverage, as indicated by the fairly constant angle between its −6 dB points relative to the on-axis value above 1000 Hz. The system shown in (b) is somewhat more irregular in this regard.

The system shown in (a) would be a good choice for use in a monitoring environment in which wall reflections were significant. The system shown in (b) would best be used in an environment relatively free of reflections, or at fairly close-in positions to the engineer and producer.

Another indication of a system's power response can be determined from its directivity index (*DI*) (see Section 1.8.1). Figures 13-4(a) and (b) show the *DI* plots, respectively, for the two systems whose beamwidths are shown in Figure 13-3. For systems with flat on-axis response, the inverse of the on-axis *DI* curve is a relative measure in dB of the system's power response.

The higher the *DI* of the system, the less it tends to excite room reflections, for a given on-axis sound pressure. The directivity factor (*Q*) and *DI* of a loudspeaker system can roughly be approximated from a knowledge of the −6 dB horizontal and vertical beamwidth values by the following equations:

$$Q = \frac{180°}{\arcsin \left[ (\sin \alpha/2)(\sin \beta/2) \right]} \tag{13-1}$$

$$DI = 10 \log \frac{180°}{\arcsin \left[ (\sin \alpha/2)(\sin \beta/2) \right]} \tag{13-2}$$

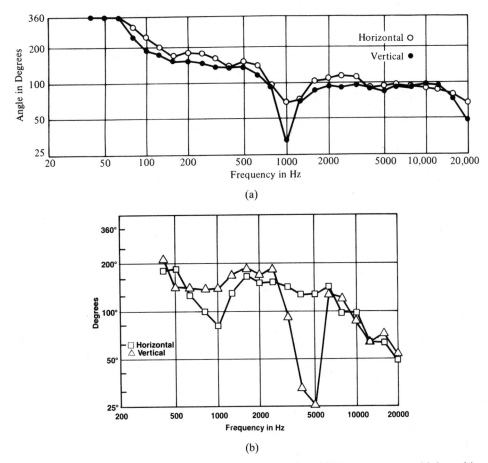

**Figure 13-3.** Beamwidth plots (−6 dB) for typical monitor systems. (a) Two-way system with horn-driver HF section. (b) Three-way bookshelf system. (*JBL data*)

where α = nominal −6 dB horizontal coverage, and β = nominal −6 dB vertical coverage.

The following equation relates the loudspeaker's 1-watt, 1-meter sensitivity, its *DI*, and its efficiency:

$$\text{Sensitivity} = 109 + DI + 10 \log (\text{efficiency}) \qquad (13\text{-}3)$$

When sensitivity and *DI* are known, the system efficiency can readily be determined. Most monitor systems are, in the mid-band range, no more than about 1% efficient.

## 13.2.2 Wide Power Bandwidth

It is relatively easy to design systems with flat on-axis response and smooth power response. It is far more difficult to design a system, however, that can deliver constant

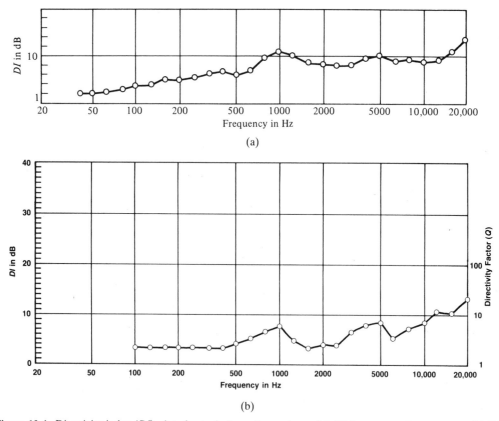

**Figure 13-4.** Directivity index (*DI*) plots for typical monitor systems. (a) *DI* for two-way horn system. (b) *DI* for three-way bookshelf system (*JBL data*)

acoustical output power over its entire frequency range at the highest levels. *Power bandwidth* is a measure of how well a system can do this.

As a rule, a monitor system can deliver far more output at mid frequencies than it can at very low and very high frequencies. Insofar as most musical program material does not make great demands at the frequency extremes, relative to mid-band, this may not be a problem. However, certain kinds of music—synthesizers, for example—can tax the output capabilities of many otherwise adequate systems at the frequency extremes.

Figure 13-5 shows the maximum allowable electrical input power to a two-way monitor system with a 380-mm (15-inch) low-frequency (LF) transducer and horn loaded HF transducer. Note that at frequencies from about 30 Hz up to 1 kHz the system can accommodate power input of 150 watts. Above that frequency, the maximum input to the HF part of the system must be progressively rolled off in order to accommodate the requirements of the HF compression driver. In terms of acoustical power output, the same system, under the input conditions shown in Figure 13-5, will yield the response shown in Figure 13-6.

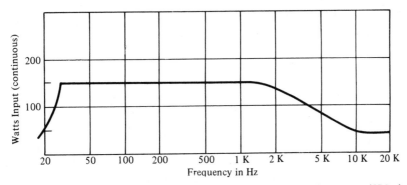

**Figure 13-5.** Maximum electrical input for a monitor system versus frequency. (*JBL data*)

In general, musical requirements exhibit a somewhat rolled-off HF acoustical spectrum (see Section 2.6), so that system limitations at high frequencies are not often a problem. Low-frequency requirements can be considerable, depending on the program source. Organ recordings, for example, can be quite demanding if playback at high levels is desired.

The power bandwidth of a system can be extended by designing it around multiple components, especially at the frequency extremes. In general, three- and four-way systems will have greater power bandwidth than two-way systems designed around similar components.

### 13.2.3 Time Domain Response

In the last fifteen years, time domain response of monitor loudspeakers has become an important attribute. It is a measure of the relative time dispersion between the different components in a multiway system as a function of frequency. Blauert and Laws (6) have indicated a threshold below which relative delays over the frequency band cannot be readily detected. This threshold is shown in Figure 13-7, along with the delay plots of several monitor loudspeakers.

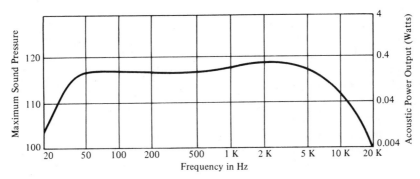

**Figure 13-6.** Maximum acoustical output for the system whose electrical input limits are shown in Figure 13-5. Sound pressure is calculated for a reverberant space with a total absorption of 18.6 m² (200 ft²). (*JBL data*)

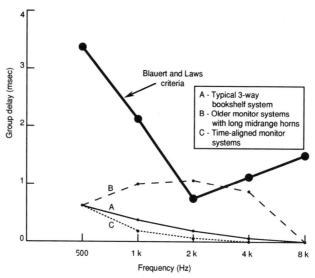

**Figure 13-7.** Blauert and Laws thresholds for audibility of group delay (heavy curve). A, typical bookshelf monitor system; B, older monitor systems with long midrange horns; C, time-aligned monitor systems.

Most systems in use today fall well below the Blauert and Laws threshold. Some systems, such as the UREI Time Align series, minimize the residual error through passive delay correction networks. Only older monitor designs making use of relatively long midrange horns will exhibit delay response that falls above the Blauert and Laws threshold.

### 13.2.4 Low Distortion and System Reliability

In the typical recording studio, monitor loudspeakers may be subjected to quite high input power. It is essential that they be robust and able to withstand occasional electrical abuse. For this reason, we normally find high-level monitor systems designed around HF compression driver and horn combinations, since these components can exhibit electrical-to-acoustical conversion efficiencies on the order of 15 to 20%. In normal system designs, these devices may be padded down (reduced) in drive level so that they rarely receive input powers exceeding 10 to 15 watts, even when monitoring at very high levels.

LF systems for high-level monitoring are generally designed around ported enclosures, inasmuch as these designs can result in greater output capability in the 30 to 40 Hz range than can sealed LF systems. Figure 13-8 shows the relation between port output and cone output in a properly designed ported LF system. At enclosure resonance, the LF transducer exhibits minimum excursion, and therefore will produce relatively low distortion. LF output is maximized from the port openings through Helmholtz resonance action of the enclosure. Below the enclosure resonance frequency, the system's response rolls off at the steep rate of 24 dB per octave. It is thus important to filter the program input below that point so that very low frequencies do not contribute to needless cone

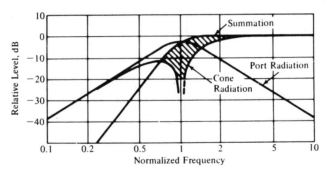

**Figure 13-8.** Relative acoustical contributions of port and cone in a ported system. (*Data after Benson (5)*)

excursion. By comparison, a sealed system rolls off below enclosure resonance at the rate of 12 dB/octave.

Typical plots of system distortion are given in Figure 13-9. Here, the input power has been set for the same output level of 100 dB $L_P$ as measured at 1 meter. At outputs in this range and lower, the second harmonic distortion in the bookshelf system is generally lower at high frequencies than it is in horn systems. However, at higher levels, this advantage quickly goes away as the power limitations of the HF transducer in the three-way system are reached. In these measurements, the HF transducer in the three-way system was a 25-mm (1-inch) diameter dome device.

Power ratings of monitor loudspeakers are generally conservative estimates. Average program ratings assume that only occasional peaks, perhaps no more than 3 or 4 dB greater, will be common. It is well known, however, that many loudspeakers can routinely handle short program peaks some 8 to 10 dB higher than average levels, provided that the mechanical limits of the individual transducers are not exceeded and that thermal limits of the transducer are not exceeded. It is always better to be safe and to overdesign a monitor system than it is to drive a marginal system to its limits.

Dynamic compression of LF transducers is common when they are overdriven for significant periods of time. Figure 13-10 shows what may happen here. Because of overdrive, the voice coil temperature has risen considerably and the dc resistance has risen. As a result, the transducer draws less power from the amplifier and its sensitivity has dropped. As subtle as this may appear in the graph, the effects are readily heard by recording engineers and producers.

## 13.2.5 Stereo Imaging

The requirements for producing stereo phantom images were discussed in detail in Section 2.3. It is assumed that conditions of symmetry exist and that the listener is positioned on the plane of symmetry between the loudspeakers. Structural and acoustical symmetry in the monitoring environment has a great deal to do with this, as does symmetry in the monitor loudspeakers themselves.

Most manufacturers of monitor loudspeakers provide them in matched left-right pairs that are mirror images of each other. Where a given monitor design is symmetrical about its own vertical axis, then a single model will suffice, since the vertical in-line array is inherently mirror imaged in the horizontal plane.

Where attention has been paid to all aspects of physical and acoustical symmetry in the monitoring space, then reasonable imaging can be expected over a listening area that will allow both producer and engineer to hear program panning assignments with analytical accuracy.

It is worth stressing again the ephemeral nature of phantom images in stereo for all but listeners located precisely on the plane of symmetry between the loudspeakers.

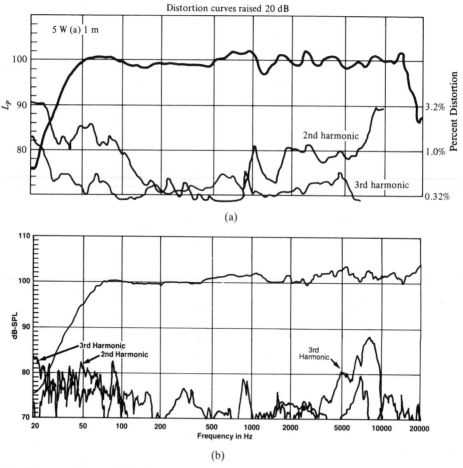

**Figure 13-9.** Distortion characteristics of monitors. (a) Fundamental, 2nd and 3rd harmonic distortion measured at a distance of 1 meter with level set at 100 dB $L_P$ for a two-way system with horn HF. (b) Fundamental, 2nd and 3rd harmonic distortion measured at a distance of 1 meter with level set at 100 dB $L_P$ for a three-way bookshelf system. Distortion components have been raised 20 dB for ease of reading. (*JBL data*)

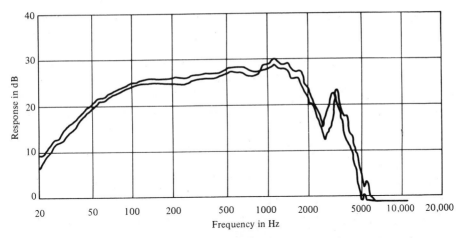

**Figure 13-10.** Dynamic compression for a 380 mm (15-inch) LF transducer driven at 1 watt (upper curve) and 100 watts (lower curve). Curves have been overlaid, taking into account the 20 dB difference in power levels. (*JBL data*)

## 13.3 CHOOSING THE RIGHT MONITOR DESIGN

### 13.3.1 Pop/Rock Requirements

Most studio installations are largely dedicated to popular and rock recording, and it is generally recommended that two- or three-way designs using compression driver–horn HF elements be specified. Such systems usually have power sensitivities of 93 to 95 $L_P$, 1 watt at 1 meter, and continuous input power ratings of 300 watts are common. Under these conditions, a single system can deliver direct sound field values of $L_P$ of 113 at a distance of 3 meters. A pair of such loudspeakers can deliver $L_P$ of 116, due to doubling of acoustical power. Such monitoring levels are certainly possible in the modern recording studio, but prolonged operation is not common, nor is it recommended.

Response down to 35 Hz is usually sufficient in the studio, since few instruments go lower than this. One exception is the kick drum in a modern drum set, with the microphone placed close to the drum head.

If extended LF response is felt to be necessary, then a set of one or more subwoofers may be installed in the control room. These usually take the form of 360-mm (18-inch) LF transducers mounted in large ported enclosures tuned to 20 or 25 Hz.

Many high-level monitoring systems will benefit from biamplification, as shown in Figure 13-11. In biamplification, the low-frequency and high-frequency sections of the monitor loudspeakers are each driven by separate amplifiers, with the dividing network placed ahead of the amplifiers. Intermodulation distortion is minimized, and amplifiers generally can be used at lower average powers than can a single full-range amplifier.

### 13.3.2 Requirements for Classical Recording

Most classical recording is monitored at levels approximating those of the ensemble itself as heard at "front row" locations in a concert hall. Some producers and recording

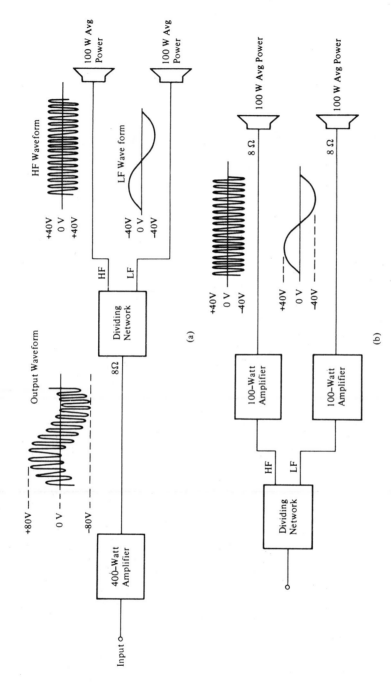

**Figure 13-11.** Principle of biamplification. In normal amplification (a), a single amplifier must handle a voltage swing large enough to ensure that both HF and LF signal components can pass through without distortion. In this case, that requirement is ±80 volts. In biamplification (b), two amplifiers are used, and the signal components are separated before the amplifiers. While producing the same HF and LF output as demonstrated at (a), the biamplified system requires that each amplifier handle a voltage swing of only ±40 volts. This difference represents a 4-to-1 ratio (6 dB) in amplifier power requirement.

engineers prefer higher levels, since that will allow them to hear balance problems, intonation problems, noises, and the like, more easily.

Most classical recording is normally done on location, and this means that the monitoring environment has to be improvised, often rather quickly. Portable loudspeakers are necessary, and they are usually standard models, often drawn from the consumer high-fidelity catalog.

Recent trends in classical recording emphasize very low distortion at moderate monitoring levels, and, above all, accuracy in stereo imaging. It is not uncommon to see three- or four-way designs, often with sealed LF sections, used for these purposes. After all, the classical producer is often aiming his product at the audiophile, and it is natural that he choose a monitor design which is typical of what the target consumer may have in his home.

The sonic texture of some highly regarded audiophile loudspeaker systems may be generally quite different from those of the normal compression driver high-level monitor systems. In particular, the audiophile loudspeaker may exhibit less "edginess" in full string ensemble textures than will the typical compression driver system. The output limitation of the audiophile loudspeaker may not be a significant factor, considering the moderate acoustical level requirements for monitoring classical recording.

### 13.3.3 So-called Near-field Monitoring

Near-field monitoring is a misnomer that refers to monitoring over small loudspeakers placed on the meter bridge of the modern console. A better term is *direct-field* monitoring, since these small loudspeakers are usually no more than a meter or so away from the recording engineer. The real value in these monitors is not their placement in the direct field, but rather that they pose both output level and bandwidth limitations on what is heard by the engineer and producer. To this extent, they give a more or less accurate impression of what the typical consumer might hear in his automobile, or over a small home stereo system.

A variety of small two-way systems with 150- or 200-mm (6- or 8-inch) diameter LF transducers have been used for such purposes, and particular designs are apt to fall in and out of favor relatively quickly. This is not dismiss them lightly, because such monitoring is important. Many such systems do exhibit remarkably flat direct field response, but with LF limitations imposed by their small-diameter transducers.

### 13.3.4 Headphone Monitoring

Many classical recording engineers and producers feel quite comfortable and assured in their work while monitoring over headphones. The advantages of this are good acoustical isolation from noises and acoustical problems in the control room area, and the ability to hear program defects quite readily. It is strongly recommended, however, that loudspeakers be used for making initial balance settings.

**Table 13-1. General characteristics of various classes of monitor loudspeakers**

| System description | Number of elements | Diameter of LF element (mm) | Sensitivity (1 W at 1 m) | Program power rating (watts) | Uses |
|---|---|---|---|---|---|
| "Mini-monitor" | 2–3 | 150–200 | 86–89 | 50–100 | Near field |
| Broadcast monitor | 2–3 | 200–300 | 89–93 | 100–150 | Moderate levels at moderate distances |
| Various high-end consumer models | 3–4 | 300–380 | 86–91 | 150–300 | Classical, at moderate distances and levels |
| Single LF, compression driver systems | 2–3 | 380 | 93 97 | 200–400 | Pop/rock |
| Dual LF, compression driver systems | 2–3 | 380 | 95–99 | 250–500 | Pop/rock |

### 13.3.5 Comparison of Various Monitor Designs

Table 13-1 presents averaged data on various types of monitor loudspeakers, which will be useful to the recording engineer in making monitor choices.

## 13.4 MONITOR SYSTEM EQUALIZATION

### 13.4.1 Background

Even when careful attention has been paid to environmental acoustical details, and when the monitors themselves have been designed for the smoothest possible power response, there may be some irregularities in acoustical response at the recording engineer's listening position. While these may be negligible, they are often carefully neutralized through the use of one-third octave equalization. At the same time, the overall system response may be shaped to match a given contour. The general aim here is to match monitoring responses throughout a given studio complex, and, indeed, to match them with other recording locations far removed. This is a noble goal, and one not always met.

### 13.5.2 Hardware Considerations

It is common to equalize monitor systems by the method shown in Figure 13-12. Here, a pink noise generator (PNG) is placed ahead of the monitor channel equalizer, and overall response is measured by means of a real time analyzer (RTA) with its microphone placed at the listening position. The RTA then shows, by rapid scanning, the acoustical response on one-third octave intervals. The equalizer is then adjusted so that the overall time-averaged response of each monitor channel matches a given contour.

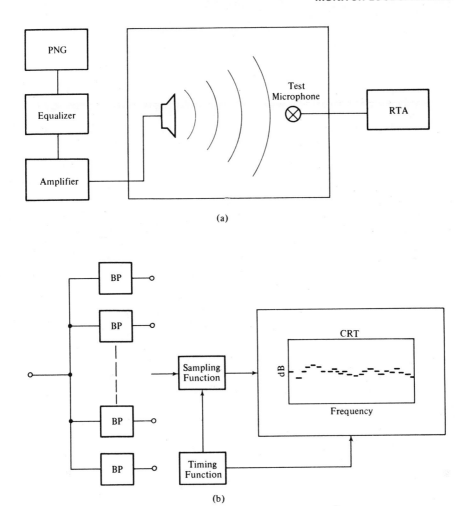

**Figure 13-12.** Instrumentation for equalization. In (a) a pink noise generator is fed into each monitor channel. Pink noise exhibits equal power in each third-octave band, and the equalizer is adjusted so that the desired response contour is matched. A real-time analyzer (RTA) is used to measure the response (b). The RTA consists of multiple third-octave bandpass sections that are sequentially scanned and presented as a continuous level display versus frequency.

Figure 13-13 shows some of the contours that have been used in sound system equalization. In general, there is a continuing preference for flatter monitor systems, and the contour shown at Figure 13-13(d) is quite common.

The equalizers used for this purpose should be of minimum phase design; that is, they should produce the minimum amount of phase shift consistent with their amplitude characteristics.

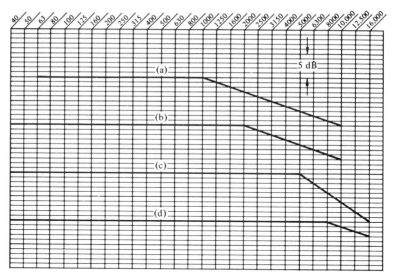

**Figure 13-13.** Suggested system equalization contours. Curve *a* is used widely in sound reinforcement equalization. Curve *b* is used in motion picture systems. Curves *c* and *d* have been used in recording control room equalization, with a general preference for *d*. Tolerances of ±1.5 dB can generally be met above 200 Hz in control rooms, while tolerances of +2, −4 can be met below 200 Hz. In well-designed rooms, smoother response can be expected below 200 Hz.

# BIBLIOGRAPHY

1. "Symposium on Auditory Perspective," *Electrical Engineering*, pp. 9–32, 214–219 (January 1934).
2. *Acoustics Handbook*, Hewlett-Packard Applications Note 100 (November 1968).
3. G. Augspurger, "The Importance of Speaker Efficiency," *Electronics World* (January 1962).
4. G. Augspurger, "Versatile Low-Level Crossover Networks," *db Magazine* (March 1975).
5. J. Benson, "Theory and Design of Loudspeaker Enclosures," *AWA Technical Review*, vol. 14, no. 1 (August 1968).
6. J. Blauert and P. Laws, "Group Delay Distortion in Electroacoustical Systems," *J. Acoustical Society of America*, vol. 63, no. 5 (May 1978).
7. M. Collums, *High Performance Loudspeakers*, Pentech Press, London (1978).
8. L. Beranek, *Acoustics*, pp. 313–322. McGraw-Hill, New York (1954).
9. M. Engebretson, "Low Frequency Sound Reproduction," *J. Audio Engineering Society*, vol. 32, no. 5 (1984).
10. J. Eargle, "Equalizing the Monitoring Environment," *J. Audio Engineering Society*, vol. 21, no. 2 (1973).
11. J. Eargle, "Requirements for Studio Monitoring," *db Magazine*, (February 1979).
12. J. Eargle, and M. Engebretson, "A Survey of Recording Studio Monitoring Problems," *Recording Engineer/Producer*, vol. 4, no. 3 (1973).
13. C. Molloy, "Calculation of the Directivity Index for Various Types of Radiators," *J. Acoustical Society of America*, vol. 20, pp. 387–405 (1948).
14. C. Davis and G. Meeks, "History and Development of the LEDE Control Room Concept," Preprint number 1954; paper delivered at the AES Convention, Los Angeles, 1982.
15. D. Smith, D. Keele, and J. Eargle, "Improvements in Monitor Loudspeaker Design," *J. Audio Engineering Society*, vol. 31, no. 6 (1983).
16. *Loudspeakers*, an anthology of articles appearing in *J. Audio Engineering Society*, 1953 to 1983.

# 14

## CONTROL ROOMS AND THE MONITORING ENVIRONMENT

### 14.1 GENERAL REQUIREMENTS

The modern recording studio control room must provide space for recording equipment, operators, producers, musicians, and occasional visiting VIPs. It must provide good sight lines into the studio, and acoustical leakage from the studio or any associated isolation booths into the control room must be acceptably low. Air handling in the control room must be efficient and quiet. In addition to these requirements, the space must satisfy its own special acoustical requirements in terms of sound absorption and reflection.

Modern trends in decor have reversed earlier notions of the control room as a confined "recording booth," and today we commonly see designs which are esthetically pleasing as well as efficient in the utilization of limited space.

For many applications, the space just described may not be absolutely necessary, and for remote recording the engineer is indeed fortunate if a typical living room environment can be found, or simulated.

Before describing in detail the variety of monitoring rooms used throughout the industry, this chapter will study a few basics having to do with loudspeaker boundary relationships in rooms and the acoustical treatments that are often used in monitoring spaces.

### 14.2 LOUDSPEAKERS AND BOUNDARY RELATIONSHIPS

Figure 14-1 shows the basic nature of a reflected acoustical image at a rigid surface. The reflection acts as an additional sound source, and its effect at the listener will be modified by the off-axis relationships between the primary radiator and the reflecting surface. At low frequencies, the reflected image will be strong because those frequencies are relatively nondirectional. At high frequencies, the reflection will be less, because those frequencies are not directed at the wall by the primary radiator.

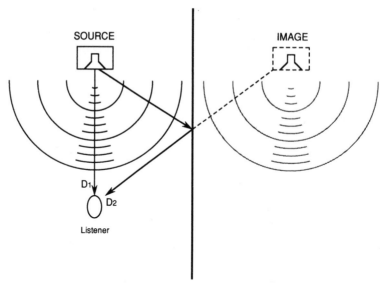

**Figure 14-1.** Relation between a sound source, a primary reflection, and the listener.

Figure 14-2 shows in section view the rather complex case of a loudspeaker suspended above the control room window. This method of mounting loudspeakers was typical in the industry up to the early 1970s, and as can be seen there are two primary images and one secondary image. The secondary image is significant only at low frequencies, but the primary images may be significant at mid frequencies. The images are all spaced apart,

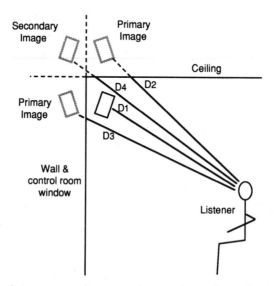

**Figure 14-2.** Relation between a sound source, primary and secondary reflections, and the listener.

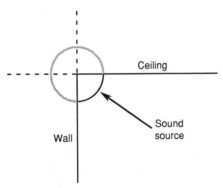

**Figure 14-3.** Minimizing reflections by placing a loudspeaker directly at a boundary.

and this means that they will all arrive at the listener within a time interval of a few milliseconds. The effect at low and mid frequencies will be reinforcements and cancellations in response, while the effect at high frequencies may be entirely negligible.

High-frequency reflections off the ceiling are easy to damp out; a layer of sound absorptive material will take care of them. But there is no easy way to absorb the low-frequency reflections.

Now, if the loudspeaker is mounted at the intersection of a wall and the ceiling, as shown in Figure 14-3, the locations of the reflected images are nearly coincident with the primary radiator itself. As a result, there will be minimal interference due to differing path lengths.

### 14.2.1 Low-Frequency Pressure Doubling

If the low-frequency output of a radiator in free space is measured and assigned a reference value of 0 dB, as shown in Figure 14-4(a), the output of the loudspeaker at low frequencies will increase by 6 dB when it is placed against a single large reflecting surface (shown in (b)). The reason for this is that the reflected image is virtually coherent with the primary source, and the two will add vectorially to produce double pressure, a 6-dB increase in level. (Another way to explain the phenomenon is to view the new boundary condition in terms of producing an increase in directivity index as well as mutual coupling between the primary and secondary images. Both effects contribute 3 dB.)

Subsequent doubling of the images, as shown in (c) and (d), will increase low-frequency level by 6 dB per doubling, resulting in an increase of 18 dB for the radiator if it is placed at the intersection of three perpendicular planes. In practice, this translates into very boomy bass, and unless a loudspeaker has been specifically designed for corner location, it is usually best not to put it there. Thus, the very steps that promote smooth bass response free of peaks and dips often make for too much bass!

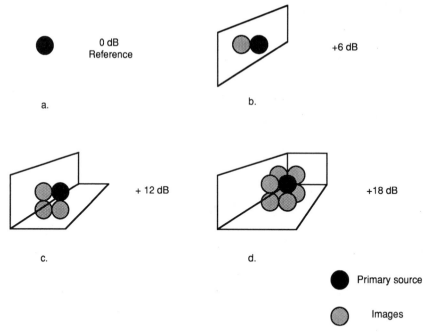

**Figure 14-4.** Pressure doubling through successive "halving" of radiation solid angle. (a) Loudspeaker in free space ($4\pi$ steradians). (b) Loudspeaker in half-space ($2\pi$ steradians). (c) Loudspeaker in quarter-space ($\pi$ steradians). (d) Loudspeaker in one-eighth space ($\pi/2$ steradians).

## 14.3 WAYS OF CONTROLLING REFLECTIONS

Essentially, reflections must be controlled, not eliminated. The acoustical designer normally goes about the task by providing the following treatments in a listening room:

a. *Bass traps.* A bass trap is a broadband absorber of low frequencies, and such an absorber is not small. In general, the absorber must be at least one-quarter wavelength in physical depth at the lowest frequency at which it is intended to be effective, and it must have an adequate amount of surface area. Effective absorption at 100 Hz requires a trap about 0.8 meter (32 inches) deep. Often we see large portions of the side and back walls of control rooms configured as bass traps.

Bass traps are used to provide smooth room response free of low-frequency standing waves, and in the process, substantial amounts of low-frequency acoustical power will be absorbed. Rooms so treated may need a large number of low-frequency loudspeakers to generate the desired low-frequency sound pressure levels.

b. *Controlled mid- and high-frequency absorption.* At these frequencies it is desirable that the balance between direct and reflected sound at the listening position be about equal.

c. *Diffusion of reflected sound.* The mid- and high-frequency sound that is reflected should be well diffused. Two treatments that are widely used are shown in Figure 14-5. Irregular surfaces, often made up of stones of random shape, provide reasonable

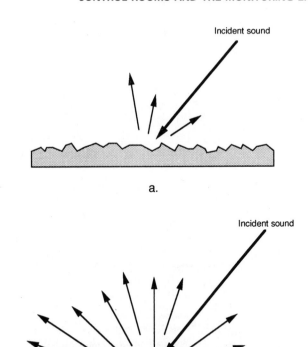

**Figure 14-5.** Diffuse reflections. (a) From a rough surface. (b) From a quadratic residue diffusor.

diffusion in all directions and are adaptable to modern decor. The quadratic residue diffusor (3, 7) provides excellent diffusion in one plane over a fairly large frequency range, depending on the size of the diffusor and the dimensioning of its many cells.

## 14.4 CONTROL ROOM DESIGN PHILOSOPHIES

At one time, it was generally thought that absorptive and diffusive surfaces should be randomly disposed around the control room. Designs since the late 1970s have favored an approach that keeps the front of the control room relatively absorptive, while the rear of the room is reflective in specific ways.

The live-end, dead-end (LEDE) design has its analytical basis in the measurement of the early reflection patterns in the control room (2, 4). While earlier versions of the LEDE design specifically called out absorptive surfaces in the front half of the room and reflective surfaces in the rear, a more analytical definition of the concept states the following requirements:

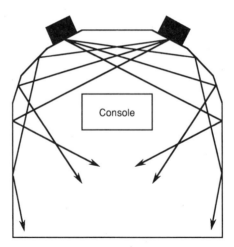

**Figure 14-6.** Specular reflection of short wavelengths from the front boundaries of a control room.

1. Early wall and ceiling reflections in the control room should be some 12 dB below the direct sound from the monitor loudspeakers heard by the engineer.
2. Strong reflections from the rear of the control room should occur at least 15 msec later than the arrival of direct sound from the monitors and be about 6 dB above the diffuse sound field level.
3. The sound decay in the control room, after initial reflections, should be smooth.

In practical listening terms, what this means is that the direct sound heard by the recording engineer will be free of peaks and dips in amplitude caused by strong early-arriving side wall and ceiling reflections. Reflections from the rear of the room will not be heard as such because of the precedence effect (see Section 2.3.4.). However, since they arrive via a number of paths, their acoustical summation should be relatively smooth. The listener will thus appreciate the uncolored direct field response of a reflection-free environment, but without the excessive deadness and oppressiveness often associated with such environments. An additional aspect is that early reflections in the studio, such as might occur between an instrument and the floor, or other nearby boundary, will be perceived before any reflections in the control room itself.

The LEDE control room must be deep enough, front to back, to accomplish its goals, and many monitoring rooms are too small to satisfy this requirement. In such spaces it is customary to use a combination of broadband reflective and absorptive materials in the back portion of the space.

The notion of a "reflection-free zone" around the console has been voiced by a number of control room designers, and Figure 14-6 shows graphical description of the concept. Specular (mirror-like) reflection is shown here, and that assumes that sound reflects the way light does. As discussed in Section 1.6, sound that strikes any surface is absorbed, transmitted and reradiated in a complex way. Sound wavelengths that are quite small relative to the reflecting surface may reflect in specular fashion, with the angle of incidence being virtually equal to the angle of reflection. But sounds of longer wavelength tend to

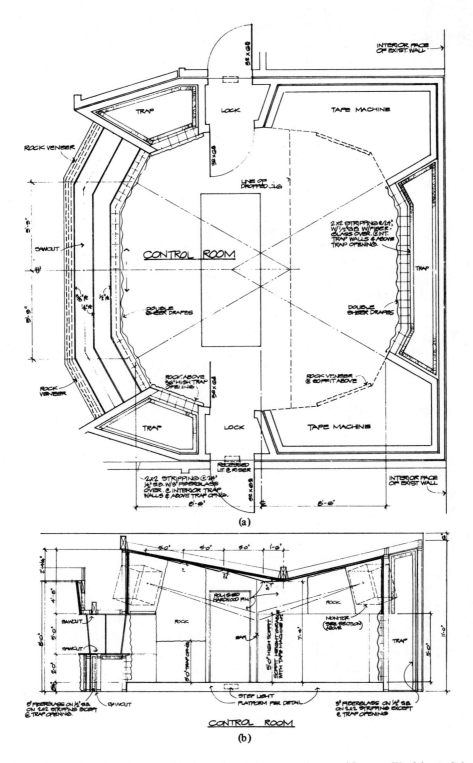

**Figure 14-7.** Plan (a) and section (b) views of a modern control room. (*Courtesy Westlake Audio*)

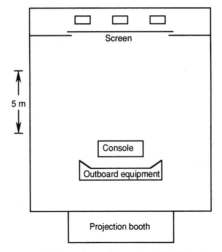

**Figure 14-8.** Plan view of a typical dubbing theater.

diverge, or diffract, as they reflect from the surface. Thus, the reflection-free zone must be carefully described in terms of wavelength, and many designers do not do this.

## 14.5 EXAMPLES OF MONITORING ROOM DESIGNS

Figure 14-7 shows horizontal and vertical section views of a recording control room with a working area that is roughly square. Provision is made for a rear pair of monitor loudspeakers as well as the traditional front pair. Note the positioning of bass traps along the back center wall and the two frontal sections adjacent to the window looking into the studio. The ceiling detail itself functions as a bass trap. Note that the physical depth of the bass traps is in the range of 1 meter, indicating that these would be effective in absorbing bass frequencies down to about 86 Hz. In general, such a room would produce about equal amounts of direct and reflected sound at the principal monitoring position. The monitors are soffit-mounted, that is, flushed into the architectural detail, looking down on the monitor space. The rear corners provide generous space at floor level for tape recorders.

Figure 14-8 shows a plan view of a monitoring space as used in the motion picture industry. The form is that of a small theater, and the room is normally called a dubbing theater. The facility is used to record the final balance of dialogue, sound effects, and music in motion pictures. The room is rather large, compared with most monitoring spaces, and the seating is normally limited to 50 or 60 persons. While the room may have a reverberant signature characteristic of a small public theater, the use of highly directive monitor loudspeakers (three behind the screen) generally ensures that the balance of sound at the mixing console consists equally of direct and reflected components.

At the other end of the spectrum is the MIDI room, shown in Figure 14-9. Often called a keyboard room, such spaces are used by musicians as they assemble tracks played

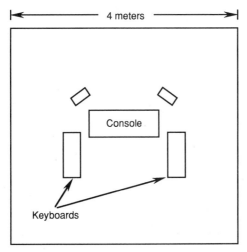

**Figure 14-9.** Plan view of a small MIDI room.

on synthesizers via the MIDI (musical instrument digital interface) code. Performing and monitoring can take place in the same room, since the audio feed from the instruments is entirely electrical. These spaces are often on the small side, and there is often little acoustical treatment. Standard consumer loudspeakers with low directivity are often used for monitoring, and this again indicates that the listener receives equal amounts of direct and reflected sound.

The "universal theme" in the monitoring environments discussed here is the equal balance between direct and reflected sound at the prime monitoring position, which Augspurger (1) discusses in detail. Even when unlikely spaces are pressed into duty as monitoring spaces, as in typical remote recording activities, the conditions most satisfying to the engineer and producer are those in which direct-to-reverberant fields are nearly equal.

## 14.6 TIMBRAL RELATIONSHIPS BETWEEN LARGE AND SMALL MONITORING SPACES

If traditional measurement methods are used, the matching of monitor equalization between large and small rooms does not normally result in the two spaces "sounding the same," even when identical loudspeaker models are used. Staffeldt (8, 9) has determined that a better match of timbre (sound quality) will result if the systems are equalized so that the same spectrum is produced at the input of the ear canal. This requires an artificial head for making measurements instead of the usual single microphone or microphone array.

This has long been a matter of concern in the film industry, where the final product is heard in typical theaters as well as in the living room via videotape transfers and laserdiscs.

# BIBLIOGRAPHY

1. G. Augspurger, "Loudspeakers in Control Rooms and Living Rooms," Proceedings of the AES 8th International Conference, "The Sound of Audio," Washington, DC, 3–6 May 1990 pp. 171–178.
2. C. Davis and G. Meeks, "History and Development of the LEDE Control Room Concept," preprint number 1954; paper delivered at the AES Convention, Los Angeles, 1982.
3. P. D'Antonio and J. Konnert, "The Reflection Phase Grating Diffusor: Theory and Application," *J. Audio Engineering Society*, vol. 32, no. 4 (1984)
4. D. Davis and C. Davis, "The LEDE Concept for the Control of Acoustic and Psychoacoustic Parameters in Recording Control Rooms," *J. Audio Engineering Society*, vol. 28, no. 9 (1980).
5. F. Everest, *Acoustic Techniques for Home & Studio*, TAB Books, Blue Ridge Summit, Pa. (1973).
6. H. Olson, *Acoustical Engineering*, D. Van Nostrand, New York (1957).
7. M. Schroeder, "Progress in Architectural Acoustics and Artificial Reverberation: Concert Hall Acoustics and Number Theory," *J. Audio Engineering Society*, vol. 32, no. 4 (1984).
8. H. Staffeldt."The Subjectively Perceived Frequency Response in Small and Medium Sized Rooms," *J. Society of Motion Picture and Television Engineers*, vol. 91, no. 7 (1982).
9. H. Staffeldt, "Measurements and Prediction of Timbre of Sound Reproduction," *J. Audio Engineering Society*, vol. 32, no. 6 (1984).

# 15

## EQUALIZERS AND FILTERS

### 15.1 INTRODUCTION

Equalizers and filters are among the oldest signal processing devices in recording. The technology goes back to early telephony in the 1800s, when equalizers were used to make the output of a transmission system "equal" to its input. The term has remained in recording and broadcasting as a description of any device that alters the frequency response of a transmission channel in any way.

A filter is a special kind of equalizer that removes a portion of the audio spectrum. In some disciplines, however, the term filter is used almost synonymously with equalizer.

### 15.2 BASIC TYPES OF EQUALIZERS

Figure 15-1 shows the family of curves for a three-knob equalizer that was popular in early motion picture recording, mainly for dialogue equalizing. The need for equalization arose from the practice of recording dialogue at various distances from the actors, depending on the nature of the scene. Some degree of equalization was required if the sound was to remain consistent. The controls were marked LF, MF, and HF; the LF and HF controls provided both cut and boost action, while the MF control provided two sets of midrange boost contours. The controls could of course be used together, with the net response being the sum of all three sections. By way of terminology, the HF and LF boost and cut action are called "shelving," inasmuch as the response remains on a plateau, a shelf, as it were, in the range over which it has been boosted or cut. Most boosting action at the frequency extremes is of this sort; however, the cut action can be a constant rolloff, as typified by the high- and low-pass filter response shown in Figure 15-5. Early equalizers such as the one described here were very often passive devices, with insertion losses in the range of 12 to 15 dB. Later designs were usually active, with integral amplifiers that provided unity gain through the equalizer when no equalization was switched in.

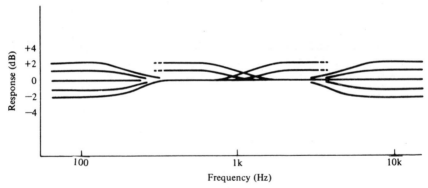

**Figure 15-1.** LF, MF, and HF characteristics for a dialogue equalizer used in motion picture sound recording.

A later development was the so-called program equalizer, which was normally used to correct for response problems in full-range program material. Typical curves are shown in Figure 15-2. These devices were rather large and were normally mounted in a rack outboard to the console. The midrange boost action in this filter is termed "peaking," while the high and low sections provide shelving boost and cut functions.

A still later development was the graphic equalizer, as shown in Figure 15-3, which provided reciprocal action (peak and dip) across the frequency range. The name derives from the fact that the positions of the operating controls follow the frequency response contour that the device produces.

The parametric equalizer is of relatively recent design, and its name derives from the fact that three parameters of equalization (frequency selection, boost or cut, and bandwidth, or "$Q$," control) are all independently variable. A typical parametric equalizer will have three or four sections, with adjacent ones overlapping in their frequency coverage. Figure 15-4 shows the basic parameters as well as typical composite frequency

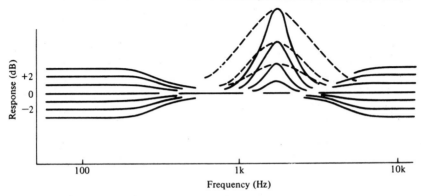

**Figure 15-2.** Family of curves for a program equalizer. Functions include HF and LF shelving actions for boost or attenuation. Variable peaking is available at selected midrange frequencies, and the bandwidth of the peaking action is variable.

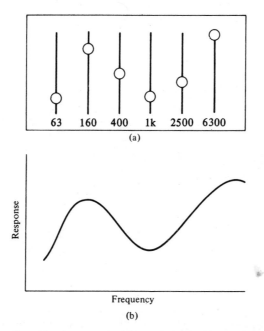

**Figure 15-3.** A graphic equalizer. For the control positions shown in (a), the frequency response shown in (b) takes on a form resembling the positions of the controls.

response curves which can be produced. Like the graphic equalizer, the parametric equalizer can produce reciprocal sets of curves.

## 15.3 FILTERS

There are basically three types of filters in general use today: high-pass, low-pass, and band-reject. Figure 15-5 shows families of high- and low-pass filter settings, as well as a typical notch filter setting. The rolloff slopes of typical high- and low-pass filters are normally in the range of 18 dB per octave.

Filters are generally used to remove noise, such as rumble or hiss, from older recordings. If a discrete frequency has marred a recording, a notch filter can often be used to remove it, at least partially. Many notch filters are capable of upwards of 60 dB action precisely at the design frequency, but that full action is often accompanied by unwanted coloration of the remaining signal.

In some cases, the use of filtering represents the lesser of evils, and there are far better methods of removing noise from a recording, will be discussed in Chapter 18.

## 15.4 CREATIVE USES OF EQUALIZERS FILTERS

Most applications of equalizers and filters today are creative rather than remedial, and the following short list details some of these uses.

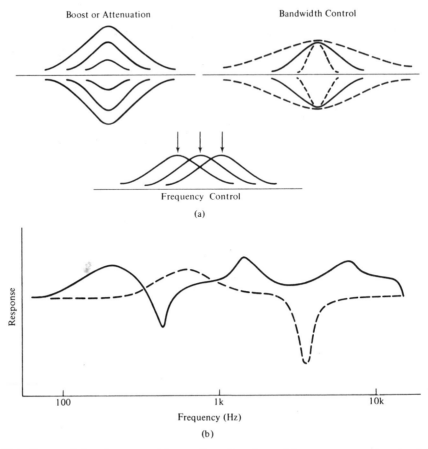

**Figure 15-4.** Characteristics of a parametric equalizer. Functions of boost or attenuation, bandwidth, and frequency selection are shown in (a). Typical composite equalization curves are shown in (b).

*Fullness* may be added by boosting frequencies in the 100 to 300 Hz regions. The effect is probably most useful on normally weak instruments, such as the acoustic guitar and celesta. No more than 4 to 6 dB should be used.

A recessive sound can be made to *project* more if a broad peak is added in the 800 Hz to 2 kHz region. Again, no more than 4 to 6 dB should be enough.

The *articulation transients* of many instruments may be heightened by emphasizing the appropriate frequency region. For example, a bass viol exhibits fundamental frequencies in the 40 to 200 Hz region and significant overtones (harmonics) up to about 2 kHz. The sound of the player's fingers on the strings is nonharmonically related to the actual tones produced by the strings, yet they are often equally important in defining the musical line. Adding a broad peak in the 1 to 2 kHz range will delineate them. Similarly, the transients of fingers against the strings of an acoustical guitar can be heightened by boosting in the 2 to 4 kHz range.

*Crispness* in percussion instruments can be heightened by a high-frequency shelving

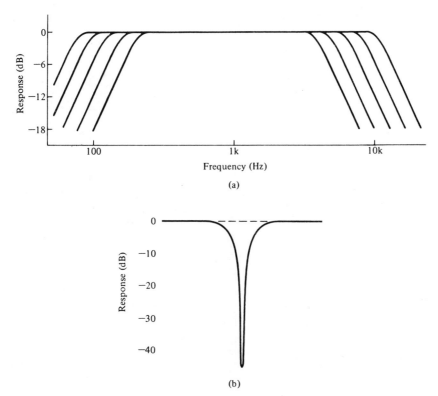

**Figure 15-5.** Filters used in recording. (a) Typical response curves for high and low pass filters. (b) A typical notch filter. Adjustment of the notch frequency and depth is customary.

boost above 1 or 2 kHz. Bongo and snare drums often benefit from this. Again, the less equalization, the better; 4 to 6 dB should suffice.

*Proximity effect* may be reduced by using a *shelving cut* action. The exact frequency below which the action should be effective will depending on the microphone pattern and the operating distance.

Several caveats are in order:

a. Boosting and peaking should be done sparingly, if at all, on metal-to-metal transients. The high-frequency output from the instruments is already considerable, and adding more is simply courting tape saturation or overload in subsequent analog transfer operations.
b. Never use equalization as a substitute for better microphone placement. This is a habit that can easily grow out of laziness into sloppiness.
c. Do not boost too many tracks of a multitrack recording in the same frequency range. To do so makes for an unbalanced spectrum that is musically unsatisfactory. In pop-rock recording the goal should be a fairly uniform spectrum from 50 Hz to about 8 kHz during full ensemble passages.

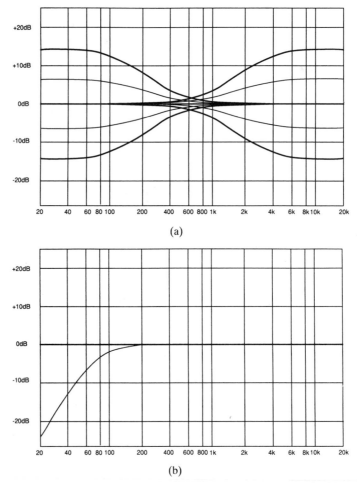

(a)

(b)

**Figure 15-6.** Typical console input equalization curves. (a) HF and LF shelving action. (b) High-pass (100 Hz) action. (c) Parametric peak and dip, continuously variable. (d) parametric bandwidth control (continuously variable). (*Courtesy Soundcraft*)

## 15.5 CONSOLE INPUT EQUALIZERS

Modern consoles have comprehensive equalizers in their input modules, and this suffices for nearly all equalization tasks facing the engineer for both recording and remix sessions. Such equalizers are small, with markings that are often difficult to read. The controls are generally concentric, which further confuses the markings. Engineers who work at a particular console are urged to learn the equalizers thoroughly.

Some consoles have three-section parametric equalizers, and whether parametric or not, most console equalizers are usually reciprocal. Figure 15-6 shows several families of curves that are typical of console input equalizers.

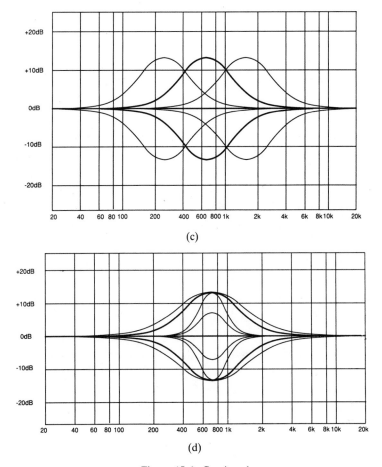

(c)

(d)

**Figure 15-6.** Continued.

## 15.6 PHASE AND AMPLITUDE RELATIONSHIPS IN EQUALIZERS

Most of the equalizers in use today are of the *minimum phase* type; that is, they introduced the minimum amount of phase shift that can be associated with a given amplitude change. As such, both phase and amplitude are reciprocal, and the "undoing" of a given amount of boost, by passing the signal once again through a complementary dip, will "undo" the phase shift as well. This is shown in Figure 15-7, where both amplitude and phase shift are shown for a response peak (a) and a complementary response dip (b).

Phase shift of the signal is related to relative delay or advancing of the signal in time by the equation:

$$\text{Relative delay} = \frac{-d\phi}{d\omega} \tag{15-1}$$

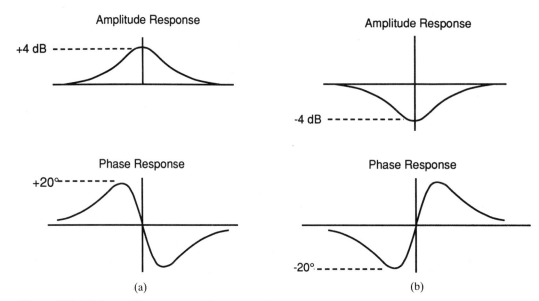

**Figure 15-7.** Minimum phase response of equalizers. (a) Amplitude and phase response for peaking action of 4 dB. (b) Amplitude and phase response for dipping action of 4 dB.

Relative delay is expressed here as minus the rate of change of phase with respect to frequency; $\phi$ is the phase shift in radians and $\omega$ is the angular frequency, $2\pi f$. In the example of Figure 15-7, the maximum phase shift for the amplitude boost of 4 dB is 20°. For a 1-kHz signal, 360° represents one period, or a time interval of 0.001 second. The effect of the phase shift would be to add $(20/360)(0.001)$ second, or an additional delay of $5.5 \times 10^{-5}$ second, to the 1-kHz signal.

## 15.7 ISO PREFERRED FREQUENCIES

The ISO (International Standards Organization) has a preferred list of frequencies for subdivision of the octave into equal percentage intervals. The most common series is one-third octave division, and these intervals are based on the tenth root of ten, or $10^{0.1}$. This value is equal to 1.259, which is very nearly equal to the cube root of two (1.26), and thus derives the familiar third-octave series of frequencies.

Another series is based on the twentieth root of ten, or $10^{0.05}$, and this results in a series of one-sixth octave intervals.

One decade (10-to-1 ratio) of the one-sixth ISO numbers is given in Table 15-1, along with the rationalized, or rounded-off numbers in everyday use for one-sixth, one-third, and one octave intervals.

Most modern equalizers with fixed frequency selection use ISO preferred numbers from either the one-sixth or one-third octave series. Those who are familiar with graphic equalizers will note that the frequencies chosen are almost always taken from one of the above series and are uniformly spaced within the series.

**Table 15-1. ISO preferred frequencies for one-sixth and one-third octave division**

| ISO frequency | One-sixth octave | One-third octave | One octave |
|---|---|---|---|
| 100 | 100 | 100 | 100 |
| 112.2 | 112 | | |
| 125.9 | 125 | 125 | |
| 141.3 | 140 | | |
| 158.5 | 160 | 160 | |
| 177.8 | 180 | | |
| 199.5 | 200 | 200 | 200 |
| 223.9 | 224 | | |
| 251.2 | 250 | 250 | |
| 281.8 | 280 | | |
| 316.2 | 315 | 315 | |
| 354.8 | 355 | | |
| 398.1 | 400 | 400 | 400 |
| 446.7 | 450 | | |
| 501.2 | 500 | 500 | |
| 562.3 | 560 | | |
| 630.9 | 630 | 630 | |
| 707.9 | 710 | | |
| 794.3 | 800 | 800 | 800 |
| 891.3 | 900 | | |
| 1000 | 1000 | 1000 | |

## BIBLIOGRAPHY

1. Ballou, G. (ed.), *Handbook for Sound Engineers*, H. Sams, Indianapolis (1987).
2. J. Borwick, *Sound Recording Practice*, Oxford University Press, New York (1987).
3. J. Woram, *Sound Recording Handbook*, H. Sams, Indianapolis (1989).
4. J. Woram and A. Kefauver, *The New Recording Studio Handbook*, Elar, Commack, N.Y. (1989).

# 16

## COMPRESSORS, LIMITERS, AND NOISE GATES

### 16.1 INTRODUCTION

This chapter will discuss the various methods of automatic signal amplitude control that are used to contain the dynamic range of recorded music within specified limits. Until very recent times, the various recording mediums had dynamic range capabilities that often fell short of the musical requirements placed on them. This necessitated both technical and musical decisions regarding how and when to alter recorded levels so that both soft and loud passages could be accommodated.

Even when the medium can contain the musical program without compromise, there are many home playback environments in which the allowable dynamic range is further limited by noise at one end and amplifier power capability at the other. The automobile, of course, imposes even narrower limits on dynamic range.

While an experienced recording engineer can "ride gain" on a program manually, things can get out of hand in short order when much is going on. In broadcast work, there are times when no engineer is on duty. And there must always be the assurance that average levels, fed from a wide variety of program sources, will be the same, or nearly so. There is also the overriding requirement in broadcasting that the absolute maximum signal modulation level should not exceed allowable legal limits.

This chapter will discuss various means of broadband signal level control, in addition to discussions of specialized tools for operating on specific portions of the audio spectrum.

### 16.2 THE COMPRESSOR

#### 16.2.1 Signal Flow Diagram

Figure 16-1 shows a block diagram of a compressor. The direct path between input and output is through a VCA (voltage-controlled amplifier) whose control voltage is determined

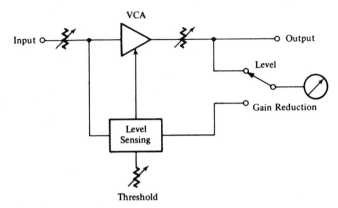

**Figure 16-1.** Functional diagram of a compressor.

through signal processing in the side chain at the bottom of the figure. Program level is sensed, and a dc voltage is produced that lowers the gain of the VCA as the input signal increases.

Some compressors have input and output faders, as shown here. The input fader, since it is ahead of the side chain, will determine the amount of signal going to the side chain, thus determining the amount of gain reduction. The output fader acts only as a final gain adjustment for the device. The meter is switchable between the signal output and the side chain so that the engineer can read either the actual output signal level or the amount of gain reduction at a given time (this function is normally calibrated in dB).

### 16.2.2 Gain Curves

Figure 16-2 shows a gain curve for a compressor. The diagonal line running from lower left to upper right represents the constant gain of a normal amplifier. For each input signal increase in dB, there will be a corresponding output signal increase, and the line thus has a slope of unity.

A compressor operates very much like a linear amplifier at low signal levels, but when a predetermined threshold is reached, the compression action takes over and the overall gain is reduced. The point on the gain curve where the compression action begins is called the threshold of compression. (Some engineers refer to that point on the curve as the "knee.")

The compression ratio is related to the slope of the gain curve in the region of compression. In the figure, the gain curve has a slope of 2-to-1; that is, for each signal increase of 2 dB at the input, the output will only increase by 1 dB. For a 4-to-1 compression ratio, an increase of 4 dB at the input will result only in an output increase of 1 dB.

### 16.2.3 Attack and Release Actions

The reader should understand that, during compression action, the actual gain through the compressor is constantly varying, just as though an engineer was constantly

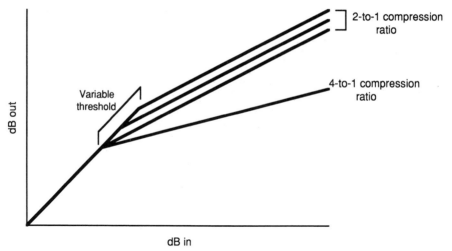

**Figure 16-2.** Gain curves for a compressor.

manipulating a gain control on the console. Such changes cannot be made instantaneously, nor should a previous gain setting be suddenly altered, otherwise the action will be quite obvious to the ear, and ultimately unsatisfactory. The gain changes performed by a compressor must be fast enough to catch sudden program peaks (attack time), but slow enough to allow a gentle return to the previous setting when a peak has passed (recovery time).

The effects of attack and recovery time are illustrated in Figure 16-3. The input signal envelope suddenly switches to a higher value at $t_1$, which is in the range of compression. The gain of the compressor is rapidly reduced, and the compressed output signal drops accordingly, after a slight amount of overshoot. When the signal returns to its original value at $t_2$, the gain of the compressor is restored to its original value. Note that both attack and release times are not instantaneous; the attack time may be fairly fast, but the recovery time is relatively slow.

Many compressors have external adjustments for both attack and release time, while other models have both functions fixed internally. Attack times are normally in the range of 100 msec to 1 msec, while recovery times vary from 0.5 sec to about 2 or 3 sec. While a very fast attack time would seem to be desirable, it often comes with the penalty that it can be heard as such. Many newer compressors have advanced circuitry that enables sudden inaudible gain changes to be made. A *zero-crossing detector* can be used ensure that the gain change is made at the instant the audio signal has a value of zero, thus minimizing the audibility of the gain change as such. For special applications, some compressors slightly delay the main signal path through the VCA portion of the compressor, while allowing the side channel to operate on the undelayed signal. If this is done carefully, the command from the side chain telling the VCA to lower its gain actually comes *before* the program signal itself, thus avoiding any overshoot when the program peak occurs.

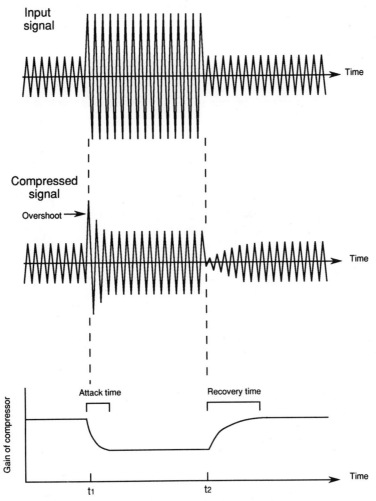

**Figure 16-3.** Effect of attack and release on gain of compressor.

## 16.3 THE LIMITER

Basically, a limiter is a compressor that has a built-in compression ratio of 10-to-1 or higher, and relatively fast attack and recovery times. The high compression ratio ensures that the program signal, once the threshold of limiting has been attained, will not increase substantially.

Limiters are most often used to prevent accidental overload of transmission channels. For example, a limiter is the last signal processing element in a broadcast system, its chief function being that of preventing inadvertent overmodulation of the transmitter. LP records are often mastered with a dedicated high-frequency limiter in the circuit that prevents the system from going into curvature overload, which is the inadvertent cutting of a signal that cannot be properly traced by the spherical-tipped playback stylus. While

**Figure 16-4.** Photograph of a limiter-compressor. (*Courtesy UREI*)

compressors are often used to do some quite audible things to the program, limiters are normally designed not to be heard as such.

The "de-esser" is a special kind of limiter in which the side chain analyzes the high-frequency spectrum, producing a control voltage that acts to reduce the effect of overly bright sibilant sounds, as produced by many singers and announcers. Rather than reducing the entire signal when a sibilant sound appears, these devices normally reduce the signal in the 6 to 8 kHz range appropriately.

Some commercially available compressors have a range of variable settings large enough that a single unit can be used as both compressor and limiter. Such a model is shown in Figure 16-4.

## 16.4 CONTROL FUNCTIONS ON COMPRESSORS AND LIMITERS

Some operational suggestions for setting up and using compressors and limiters are given in the following.

*Input level control.* This control is of limited usefulness, since it basically interacts with the threshold control. If more compression is desired, it is best to get it by readjusting the threshold control.

*Threshold control.* For a fixed signal input setting, advancing the threshold control will cause the device to go into compression at progressively lower input signal levels. This is a critical adjustment and should be set so that the onset of compression will occur just as the signal is tending to become too loud or prominent in the program context at hand.

*Compression ratio.* This control determines the departure from natural dynamic relationships that exist in the program input signal. Low compression ratios will not materially detract from natural program dynamics; high compression ratios can sound quite unnatural. An experienced ear is required in making this setting.

*Attack time.* The general rule here is to use as short an attack time as possible without having it become audible as such. In fast-moving music, short attack times may be more appropriate than in slower music.

*Release time.* This is perhaps the most subjective adjustment of all. It should be set so that there is no "breathing" or "pumping" audible in the program, due to modulation of the program's noise floor by too-rapid gain changes.

*Output level control.* This control merely sets the signal level which feeds subsequent devices.

*Metering.* The meter normally has two functions. One of these indicates the output program level, and this is useful in determining the maximum level through the device. The other function lets the engineer know how much gain reduction is employed at any given instant. Good engineering practice, and good taste, dictate that there should be no more than necessary.

*Stereo ganging.* Many compressors can be ganged together to act in unison on stereo program. This ensures that there will be no inadvertent image shifting due to uneven gain shifts between the stereo channels. In this mode, both VCAs are controlled by the same voltage.

## 16.5 APPLICATIONS OF COMPRESSORS AND LIMITERS

In recording, compressors have many uses, including the following:

a. A performer who tends to move toward and away from the microphone produces a wide variation in level. A properly adjusted compressor can smooth out much of this variation, producing a recorded track that can be more easily processed later. Vocalists are apt to the be most problematic in this regard. The compressor should be inserted ahead of the input fader so that the engineer has wide control of overall level. The choice of compression ratio is a matter of taste; in general it should be low as possible, while still accomplishing the desired purpose.

b. Variations in the output of an electric bass can easily be smoothed by the application of gentle compression, thus providing an even and solid bass line. If the recovery time is long compared with the natural decay rate of the instrument, then the original character of the instrument will be preserved.

c. In the preceding example, if the recovery time of the compressor is fast compared with the natural decay rate, then the sound of the instrument will be transformed into a sustained, organ-like sound, exhibiting little of the instrument's natural decay characteristic (see Figure 16-5.)

d. A similar effect can be obtained by applying heavy limiting with as short a recovery time as possible to cymbals. *Heavy limiting* implies that the input signal is always above the limiting threshold, so that the program will appear at a fixed output level. The effect is bizarre and is reminiscent of cymbal tracks played backwards.

e. Voice-over compression is a method of causing background music or effects to diminish in level when an announcer speaks, allowing the level to return to normal when the announcer quits speaking. This is a special arrangement in which the signal to the side chain is derived, not from the signal to be compressed, but rather from the announcer's signal. Details of this are shown in Figure 16-6.

f. Program compression. In many broadcast operations there is the need for long-term program compression in which programs from many sources need to be fairly well matched in overall loudness and consistency. This is a tall job for many compressors, in that the signals should ideally be first adjusted to the same reference level before

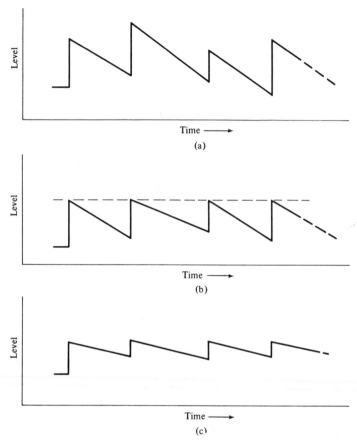

**Figure 16-5.** Typical application of a compressor. (a) Envelope of a bass played pizzicato (plucked). (b) Effect of gentle compression on envelope. (c) Effect of fast recovery time on envelope of compressed signal.

compression takes place. There are special compressors (some including low-signal expansion to duck out noise) that address these specific problems, and they should be considered for these special applications.

## 16.6 NOISE GATES AND EXPANDERS

In many kinds of multitrack recording the dynamic range of a given track may be fairly small, perhaps no more than 15 to 20 dB. Sounds picked up that are below this range may in a sense be regarded as noise and can only be a nuisance during later operations. Such noises might include page turns, rustling sounds, and of course leakage from other instruments. Ideally, we would like for the microphone to be open when program is present, and closed when program is not present. A device known as a noise gate can do this fairly well.

Operation of the noise gate is shown in Figure 16-7. The gain curve is shown in (a).

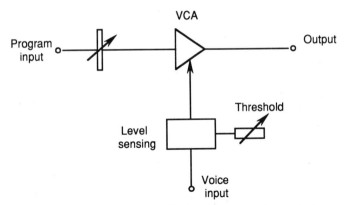

**Figure 16-6.** Use of a compressor in "voice over" application. Compressor lowers background music only when the announcer talks.

The device acts as a unity-gain amplifier at high levels, and this is indicated by the diagonal line with slope of unity. As the input level is lowered, the gating threshold is reach, and the gain of the amplifier is reduced, thus lowering the level of any noise in the input channel. Both the gating threshold and the range of gating are adjustable, as are attack and release times.

The noise gate is a signal expander; it is the inverse of a compressor because its output level range will always be greater than the input range. Some models of noise gates provide for external gating, and this allows one signal to be gated on and off by another for special effects. One of the most notable designs is the Allison Kepex (keyable program expander).

## 16-7 DYNAMIC CONTROL IN THE CONSOLE

Many newer consoles have noise gates and other gain control functions built into the input modules, so that the engineer has to do relatively little patching of outboard devices into the input module. The location of the gain control module in the signal flow structure is critical. In some cases, it is best if located ahead of the equalizer, while in others it will function better if it is after the equalizer. The switching arrangement shown in Figure 16-8 can be used to accomplish this without external patching.

The engineer should be aware of the differences in performance that this switching can make. For example, assume that an input signal from a vocalist has occasional low-frequency "popped p's" resulting from breath sounds at the microphone. If the signal is to be compressed, the low-frequency sounds may drive the compressor into operation, when the effect on the music would not be appropriate. It would clearly be best to remove the low-frequency disturbance first, and then apply compression.

In another example, assume that a vocalist is "well behaved" in the "popped p" department, requiring only gentle compression to maintain a good overall level. In this case, any amount of equalization may be used following the compressor, with no effect on the compression as such.

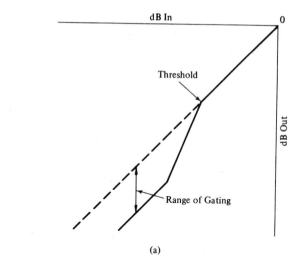

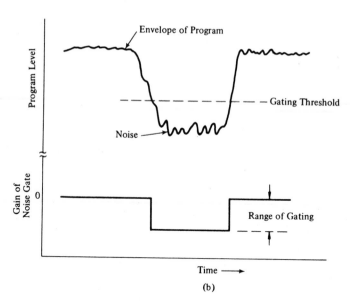

**Figure 16-7.** The noise gate. (a) Typical gain curve. (b) Effect of gating action on program envelope.

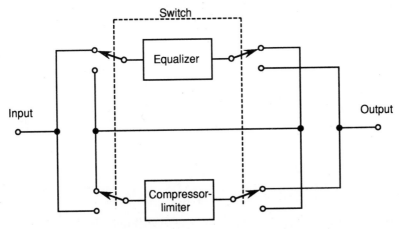

**Figure 16-8.** Diagram for a switch that reverses the positions of equalizer and compressor in a console.

## BIBLIOGRAPHY

1. W. Aiken and C. Swisher, "An Improved Automatic Level Control Device," *J. Audio Engineering Society*, vol. 16, no. 4 (1968).
2. J. Borwick (editor), *Sound Recording Practice*, Oxford University Press, New York (1987)
3. D. Connor and R. Putnam, "Automatic Level Control," *J. Audio Engineering Society*, vol. 16, no. 4 (1968).
4. J. Woram, *Sound Recording Handbook*, H. Sams, Indianapolis (1989)

# 17

## REVERBERATION AND SIGNAL DELAY

### 17.1 INTRODUCTION

Acoustical reverberation chambers, often referred to as "echo" chambers, date from the 1930s and were used primarily for special effects in motion picture production. Their introduction into the mainstream of recording dates from the late 1940s. The early systems were monophonic, and natural stereo perspectives were difficult to achieve, even with a pair of mono chambers. During the late 1960s, digital hardware was developed that would ultimately simplify reverberation generation, and electronic signal delay (often called "time" delay) devices became commonplace.

The first natural-sounding digital reverberation systems were developed during the 1970s, and today there are many excellent devices that have benefited from lower-cost hardware as well as advanced internal programming. Delay techniques have also spawned a variety of other signal processors, such as pitch and tempo regulators and various modulating schemes for producing chorus effects. These will be discussed in the following chapter.

This discussion will begin with an analysis of acoustical reverberation chambers.

### 17.2 ACOUSTICAL REVERBERATION CHAMBERS

#### 17.2.1 Analysis

As discussed in previous chapters, the relationships between direct sound, early reflections, and the reverberant sound field are essential in conveying a sense of ambience in a recording. Under many recording conditions, there may be insufficient natural reverberation, and the engineer must resort to artificial methods. Consider first a "target" auditorium with the following characteristics:

$$V = 16,500 \, m^3$$

$$S = 5000 \text{ m}^2$$

$$\bar{\alpha} = 0.2 \text{ (at 500 Hz)}$$

Then $T_{60}$ at mid-frequencies will be about 2.6 seconds.

The initial time gap between the receipt of direct sound and the first side reflections will depend on where a listener is seated in the auditorium, but in general we can relate it to the mean free path (MFP) in the room (see Section 1.11.7), which is calculated as

$$MFP = \frac{4V}{S}$$

From the room information given above, the equation gives a value of 13 meters for *MFP*, and this corresponds to a delay time of

$$T = 13/344 = 38 \text{ msec}$$

Let us compare these conditions with a typical small reverberation chamber with the same reverberation time at mid-frequencies:

$$V = 70 \text{ m}^3$$

$$S = 100 \text{ m}^2$$

$$\bar{\alpha} = 0.04$$

In this small chamber the MFP is about 3 meters, corresponding to an initial delay of 8 msec. Thus, if the output from the reverberation chamber is fed into a program channel, it will not convey the same sense of space as natural reverberation picked up in the model auditorium itself, because the onset of reverberation will be too soon.

The small chamber has another difficulty in its attempt to sound like the larger space, and that is its rather high Schroeder frequency (see Section 1.11.6). The Schroeder frequency for the auditorium is calculated as 25 Hz. For the reverberation chamber, the Schroeder frequency is 385 Hz.

What this tells us is that the auditorium will exhibit smooth response above 25 Hz, which is well below most musical fundamental frequencies. On the other hand, the signal from the reverberation chamber will show uneven response below 385 Hz, which is about G above middle-C on the piano keyboard. The ear will hear this quite clearly and tag it as artificial sounding.

The desired initial time delay gap can be created by delaying the signal from the reverberation chamber. During the 1950s and 1960s this was commonly done with a tape recorder running at 76 cm/sec (30 inches/sec). In recent decades this has been accomplished with digital signal delay devices.

For the most part, the Schroeder frequency problem was overlooked, and reverberation chambers were largely used with popular music, where the coloration could be either ignored, or possibly associated with the music itself. There is, however, a good but expensive solution for it. If a large diagonal vane is positioned in the room and rotated about once per minute, it will slowly redistribute the audible peaks and dips which result from the high Schroeder frequency, rendering the sound far more natural, insofar as the ear will have difficulty in "locking in" on a particular pattern of peaks and dips in response.

Thus, reverberation chambers are a legacy from the past. Few are built today, and most of the ones that are encountered today are 30 or more years old. During the 1960s, one of the most famous was the fire escape stairwell used by Columbia Records (now CBS Sony) at their studios at 799 Seventh Avenue in New York City. Their recordings of Johnny Mathis and Tony Bennett are testimony to its effectiveness. Another famous set of reverberation chambers dating from the mid 1950s can be found at the studios of Capitol Records in Hollywood.

### 17.2.2 Construction Details and Sound Pickup

Figure 17-1 shows details of a typical reverberation chamber. It was customary to locate these facilities in the basement or other remote areas. The boundaries were made of cinder block, or other rigid material, and finished with a coat of fine plaster. In order to prevent moisture from taking its toll, the plaster was usually sealed with varnish. The surface orientations were non-rectilinear, as can be seen.

While early chambers had one loudspeaker and one microphone, later ones were outfitted with two microphones so that a stereo pickup could be made. This was not stereo in the normal sense, but rather the pickup of two uncorrelated reverberation signals generated from a single source.

It is important for the microphones in the reverberation chamber to pick up as little direct sound from the loudspeaker as possible, and there are two ways this can be achieved. As shown in Figure 17-2(a), a figure-8 microphone can be oriented so that its null plane points at the loudspeaker, minimizing direct sound pickup. Alternatively, as shown in (b), a dipole loudspeaker can be used with its null plane pointed at the microphones. Another variation is shown in (c), which allows for stereo pickup from two program sources, as suggested by Davis (4). Here, a large reflective boundary is placed in the middle of a large chamber, with just enough space around it so that sound can pass from one side to the other. Stereo program is fed via the two loudspeakers, and the pickup from the two microphones is fed to the stereo busses. The leakage from one side of the chamber to the other provides a rich stereo spread of sound.

Bauer (1) describes stereo pickup in reverberation chambers through the use of coincident microphones. The technique produces a somewhat confined stereo image, with perhaps a bit too much center fill to it. In most applications of stereo reverberation, both producer and engineer are looking for more stereo spread than this technique can deliver. In MS format, however, coincident pickup in the reverberant chamber would allow the engineer some interesting options in that the amount of S component could be increased to widen the stereo image.

Most reverberation chambers have a fixed reverberation time, but it is possible to make a chamber variable in reverberation time by controlling the amount of effective absorption in the chamber. The method shown Fig. 17-2(d) is used by the Victor Company of Japan (6) and provides variable absorption by exposing more or less fiberglass through remote control. The range of reverberation time is shown in (e).

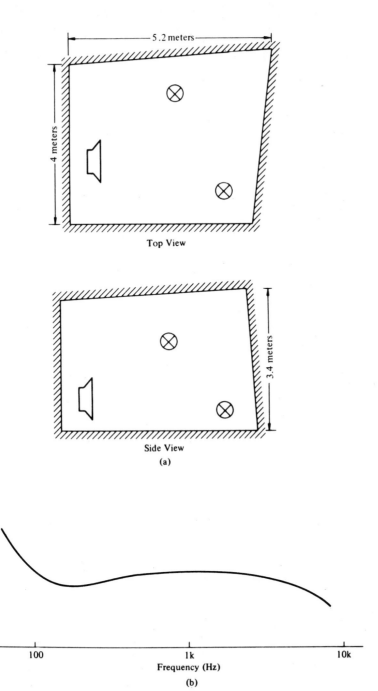

**Figure 17-1.** Details of an acoustical reverberation chamber. Plan and side views are presented in (a), and loudspeaker–microphone locations are suggested. Typical reverberation time is shown in (b). The dimensions are normally related to the cube root of 2, and this gives length, height, and width dimensions in the ratios of $1 : 1.25 : 1.6$ ($2^0$, $2^{1/3}$, $2^{2/3}$). The proportions provide for an even distribution of room modes at low frequencies. Reverberation chambers are typically finished in concrete or hard plaster, properly sealed and varnished. These materials provide an average absorption coefficient in the range of 0.02, enabling fairly long reverberation times to be developed in a relatively small space. It is customary to angle the walls slightly so that there will be no parallel surfaces.

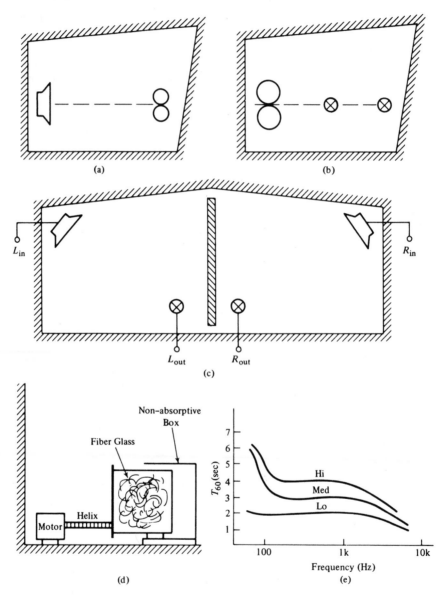

**Figure 17-2.** Applications of reverberation chambers. (a) Use of a figure-8 microphone with its null plane pointed at the loudspeaker to minimize pickup of direct sound. (b) Use of a dipole loudspeaker to minimize pickup of direct sound. (c) Stereo feed and pickup in reverberation chamber. (d) Varying the amount of absorption in the chamber, as done by the Victor Company of Japan. (e) Range of reverberation time provided by the method shown in (d).

## 17.3 MECHANICAL REVERBERATION SYSTEMS

The EMT model 140 reverberation plate became popular during the 1950s, and there are still many of them in use. It consists of a steel plate approximately 1 meter by 2 meters, tightly suspended in a metal frame. The plate is driven by a moving-coil transducer, and two piezoelectric transducers are used for stereo pickup. The plate is driven into transverse vibrational modes, with multiple reflections taking place at its boundaries. When properly tensioned, the plate exhibits high modal density, with especially good high-frequency response. Reverberation time can be varied over a wide range by moving a porous damping membrane closer to or farther away from the plate. Details of the plate and its response are shown in Figure 17-3.

The EMT-140 has the virtue of being adjustable to very short reverberation times and can thus be used to add density and richness to musical textures without the confusion of musical detail that longer reverberation times might cause.The unit is large and must be isolated acoustically. If it is not properly tensioned, there may be considerable variation in response from unit to unit. These difficulties have been largely overcome with the EMT-240, a device operating on similar principles but much smaller, using a very thin gold alloy foil instead of the steel plate. Its reverberation characteristics are shown in Figure 17-3(c).

For the most part, spring reverberators have been used in conjunction with electrical or amplified musical instruments such as guitars or organs. The success of such devices for recording has been very limited because of coloration due to insufficient modal density. A notable exception is the AKG BX-20. This device provides sufficient modal density through the use of a long, randomly structured spring that has been folded to occupy relatively little space, as shown in Figure 17-4. Two spring units are packaged in a single case, and the entire assembly can be transported without the need for readjustment. The reverberation time is variable through electromechanical regeneration (feedback) by means of the circuit shown in the figure.

## 17.4 DIGITAL REVERBERATION SYSTEMS

The principle of digital reverberation is shown in Figure 17-5. Analog signals are converted to a digital format, which enables them to be stored in a random access memory (RAM), to be recalled later and reconverted to analog form. The advantage in this method is that there is no signal degradation, regardless of program settings. By comparison, analog methods using charge-coupled devices introduce signal degradation proportional to the desired decay time.

Digital reverberation units are designed around a number of delay paths, which simulate the actual dispersion of sound in real spaces. Various delay settings can be chosen, as can spectral characteristics and a host of other factors. All models today are stereo; that is, there are two inputs and at least two outputs (some models have four outputs). Even if fed a monophonic input, the stereo models will produce uncorrelated output, similar to a reverberation chamber with one loudspeaker and two microphones for pickup.

A typical high-quality reverberation system today may offer the user control over many variables, such as the following:

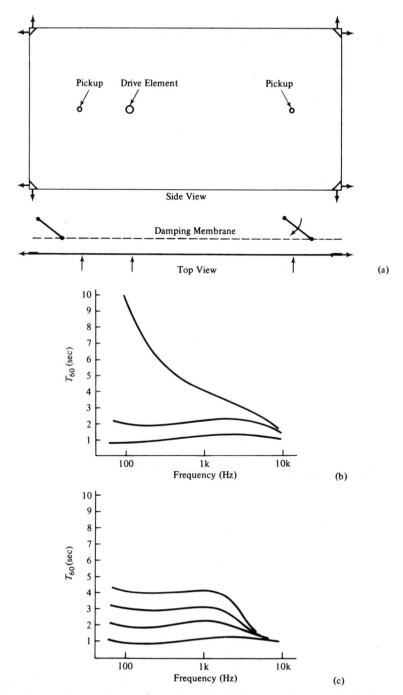

**Figure 17-3.** Reverberation plates. Mechanical details of the EMT-140 are shown in (a). Reverberation time can be adjusted as shown in (b). The EMT-240 produces the reverberation time characteristics shown in (c).

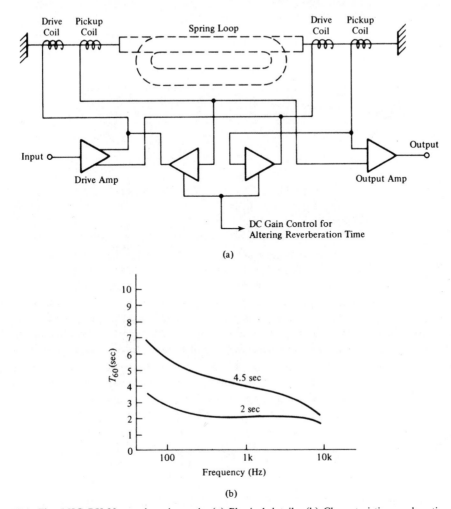

**Figure 17-4.** The AKG BX-20 reverberation unit. (a) Physical details. (b) Characteristic reverberation times.

*Program choice.*The user may choose among programs that are specifically modeled on physical spaces, such as concert halls, churches, small reverberation chambers, or even reverberation plates. Within each program there may be other options, such as simulated room size.

*Predelay.* This allows the user to delay the onset of reverberation, usually up to a value of 100 msec or so, in order to simulate the early time gap in a physical space.

*Pre-echo delays and level set.* This allows the user further flexibility in simulating early reflections.

*Low- and mid-frequency reverberation time.* These controls enable the user to select different decay rates for low and mid frequencies. The transition frequency between low and mid can also be chosen, giving the user flexibility in simulating spaces with specific absorption characteristics.

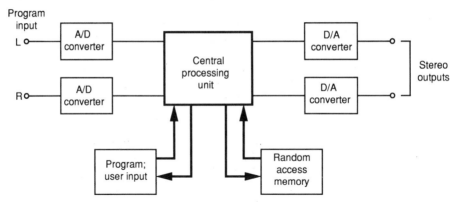

**Figure 17-5.** Functional diagram of a digital reverberation system.

*High-frequency rolloff.* This option lets the user determine the frequency above which the reverberant decay is quite rapid.

*Decay shape.* Normal decay is exponential, but other options may be useful. For example, the decay can be programmed to build up in level before it begins to decay. Such a program variation might be useful in pop or rock recording as a special effect.

*Mode density.* Some programs are calibrated directly in terms of room size, and increasing room size will increase modal density.

*Wet/dry mix.* Normally, the reverberant signal is fed back into the console and mixed into the program by the engineer. In some applications, the dry (unreverberated) signal can be balanced with the wet (reverberant) signal at the output of the reverberation unit.

Figure 17-6 shows a typical high-quality digital reverberation unit.

## 17.5 APPLICATIONS OF REVERBERATION AND SIGNAL DELAY

Figure 17-7 illustrates a typical stereo application of a reverberation unit. Only the reverberant signal processing is shown; in practice, the two resulting channels would mixed in with normal stereo program. $D_1$ through $D_3$ represent various delay times, and $R$ represents a mono-in, stereo-out reverberation device. Since a portion of the direct sound is fed to the left channel, localization will tend to be in that direction, as shown.

A more complex application is shown in Figure 17-8, where a similar approach is used to synthesize a quadraphonic reverberant sound field. Here, $D_1$ through $D_6$ represent progressively longer delay settings, so that the listener will localize direct sounds primarily at the left-front loudspeaker. The reverberant signal is not present in the left-front channel, and is progressively delayed to the remaining channels so that the sound field envelops the listener.

To a large extent, the complex relation between direct, early, and reverberant sound field components, as shown in Figure 17-9(a), can be simulated by the simpler approach, shown in (b), if attention is carefully paid to relative levels, timings, and source positioning. This is why the relatively simple schemes shown in Figures 17-7 and 17-8 work as well as they do.

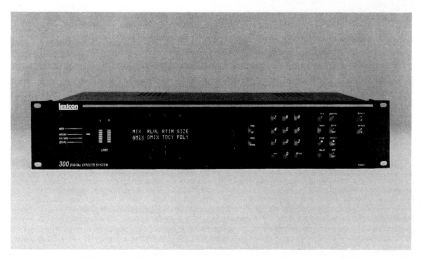

**Figure 17-6.** Photograph of a digital reverberation generator. (*Courtesy Lexicon*)

It is customary to use more than one reverberation device in complex mixdown activities. For example, reverberation added to percussion instruments would normally be shorter than that used with strings.

Many times, engineers are forced to work in venues that simply do not have long enough reverberation time for the program at hand. The standard studio technique of feeding the reverberation unit directly from the microphone signals via the AUX send

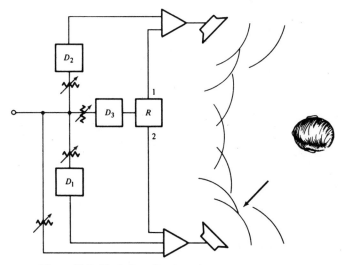

**Figure 17-7.** Typical application of stereo reverberation.

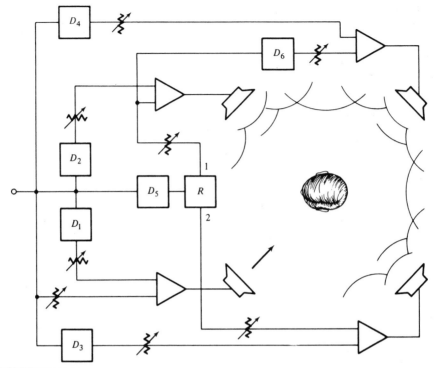

**Figure 17-8.** Typical application of quadraphonic reverberation.

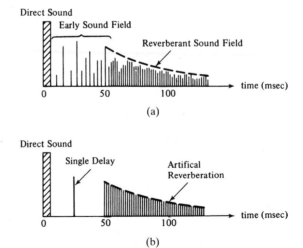

(a)

(b)

**Figure 17-9.** Simulation of early sound field. (a) The early sound field in an auditorium is quite dense. (b) A single delay preceding the onset of artificial reverberation can simulate the early field if timing, level, and direction are carefully adjusted.

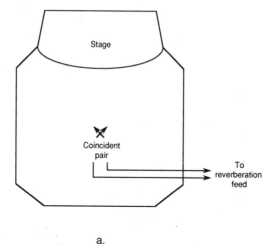

a.

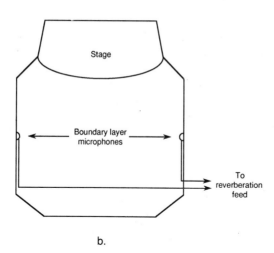

b.

**Figure 17-10.** Feeding reverberation generators from house microphones. (a) Use of a coincident pair. (b) Use of widely spaced boundary microphones.

busses may not be the best way to accomplish the job at hand. A far better general approach is shown in Figure 17-10. Two methods are shown that use the natural "mix" of sound in the hall to drive the reverberation device. The logic here is that the natural balance in the hall is proportional to the actual power output of the orchestra. In effect the engineer is simply livening the already present hall sound, and the result is likely to sound more natural than feeding the reverberation device with the overly "present" sound that comes directly from the microphones.

Much of the criticism of artificial reverberation in classical recording comes from the fact that it is not routinely handled in this manner.

## BIBLIOGRAPHY

1. B. Bauer, "Some Techniques Toward Better Stereophonic Perspective," *J. Audio Engineering Society*, vol. 17, no. 4 (1969).
2. B. Blesser and F. Lee, "An Audio Delay system Using Digital Technology," *J. Audio Engineering Society*, vol. 19, no. 5 (1971).
3. J. Borwick (ed.), *Sound Recording Practice*, Oxford University Press, New York (1987).
4. J. Davis, "Practical Stereo Reverberation for Studio Recording," *J. Audio Engineering Society*, vol. 10, no. 2 (1962).
5. M. Dickreiter, *Tonmeister Technology*, Temmer Enterprises Incorporated, New York (1989).
6. J. Eargle, "The Record Industry in Japan," *Recording Engineer/Producer*, vol. 5, no. 2 (1974).
7. J. Eargle, "Evolution of Artificial Reverberation," *Recording Engineer/Producer*, vol. 18, no. 2 (1987).
8. H. Meinema et al., "A New Reverberation Device for High Fidelity Systems," *J. Audio Engineering Society*, vol. 9, no. 4 (1961).
9. M. Rettinger, "Reverberation Chambers for Broadcasting and Recording Studios," *J. Audio Engineering Society*, vol. 5, no. 1 (1957).
10. J. Woram, *Handbook of Sound Recording*, H. Sams, Indianapolis (1989).
11. J. Woram and A. Kefauver, *The New Recording Studio Handbook*, Elar, Commack, N.Y. (1989).

# 18

---

# SPECIAL TECHNIQUES IN SIGNAL PROCESSING

---

## 18.1 INTRODUCTION

This chapter will discuss signal processing methods and techniques that do not so neatly fit into the subject areas of the three preceding chapters. Some of the techniques to be discussed are rather complex and may not be routinely accessible to the engineer; however, the engineer should know how they work and what useful things can be accomplished with them. The following techniques will be discussed: phasing, voltage controlled devices, out-of-band signal generation, pitch and tempo regulation, chorus generation, vocoders, advanced imaging methods, noise removal, and signal reconstruction.

## 18.2 PHASING (FLANGING)

Phasing is a technique from the 1960s. Originally, it was accomplished by feeding two tape recorders the same signal and combining their outputs. Any slight variation in the speed of one machine results in a small time difference between the two outputs, and the recombined signal exhibits comb filtering (see Section 9.7), which can be made to vary over a wide range.

The basic phasing process is shown in Figure 18-1. The term $T$ represents the fixed delay of each tape recorder, the time gap between record and playback heads. The term $\Delta t$ represents the difference in delay between the two machines and is the net value of delay that causes the comb filter response.

The value of $\Delta t$ can be varied electrically by driving one tape recorder with an external ac power source whose frequency can be shifted around 60 Hz. Another method of varying $\Delta t$ is for the operator to place a thumb on the flange of the tape feed reel, thus slowing it down. This practice has given rise to the term "flanging," which is synonymous with phasing.

The above techniques for phasing are cumbersome and introduce a fixed time delay into the signal path. So-called instant phasing is possible through the use of a delay whose total delay can be varied in small steps over a wide range, or through the use of a variable phase-shift network. These methods are shown in Figures 18-2(a) and (b). A similar effect can be produced with the Leslie rotating loudspeaker assembly, which is commonly used with electronic organs (Figure 18-2(c)). A pair of microphones located at slightly different distances from the loudspeaker will produce varying cancellations and reinforcements as a result of the rotation.

The sound of phasing is hard to describe. It is most effective on broad band program, such as cymbals and snare drum. It produces a bizarre "swishing" sound as the peaks and dips move up and down the spectrum. On vocal tracks, the effect often has a "disembodied and ghostlike" quality.

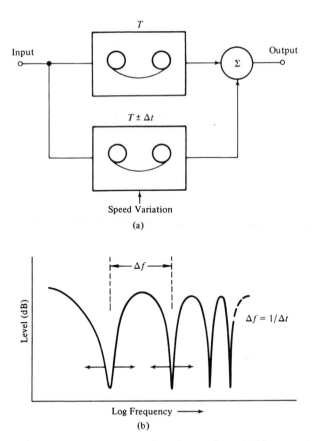

**Figure 18-1.** Principle of "phasing." Using two tape recorders as shown in (a), a speed variation is introduced into one machine, and their outputs are combined to produce the comb filter response shown in (b).

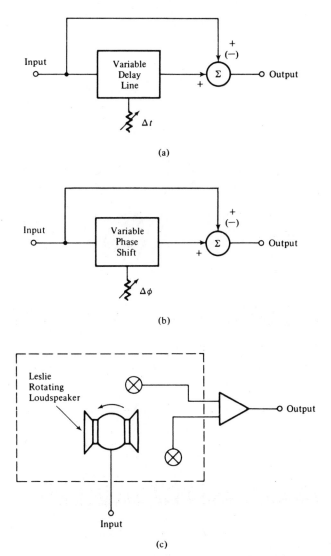

(a)

(b)

(c)

**Figure 18-2.** Alternate methods for phasing. (a) A variable delay line is used in place of the two tape machines shown in the previous figure. (b) Time delay has been replaced by variable phase shift. (c) Microphones are placed close to a Leslie rotating loudspeaker and the combined output of the microphones produces a random and constantly shifting pattern of reinforcements and cancellations.

## 18.3 VOLTAGE-CONTROLLED DEVICES

Many special studio effects are a direct outgrowth of the interface between electronic music synthesis and standard recording practice. The more useful of these techniques are voltage-controlled filters, voltage-controlled envelope shapers, and ring modulators.

Voltage-controlled filters take a number of forms, but one of the most common is a

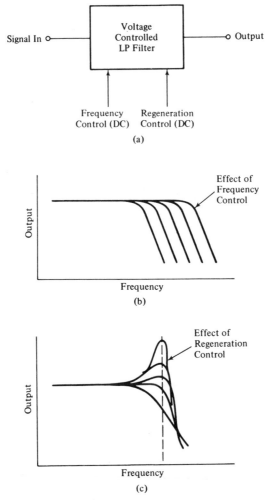

**Figure 18-3.** A voltage-controlled low-pass filter. (a) Basic scheme. (b) The effect of frequency control (with fixed regeneration). (c) The effect of regeneration (with fixed frequency).

low-pass filter, as shown in Figure 18-3. The cutoff frequency setting is controlled by one input and is variable over a large range. Another input controls regeneration or positive feedback, around the filter, enabling a response peak to develop at the cutoff frequency. Voltage-controlled filters were developed to add musical inflection to noise sources, oscillators, and other static ingredients of electronic music. Their careful use with instrumental timbres can result in unusual and interesting musical effects.

An *envelope shaper* is basically a voltage controlled amplifier with a detector (rectifier) ahead of the control signal input. This enables the envelope of one instrument to be superimposed on another instrument. In the example shown in Figure 18-4, the main signal input is a steady tone, while the control input is a percussive sound. The detector

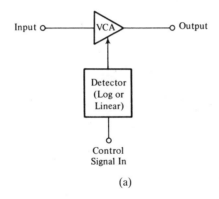

(a)

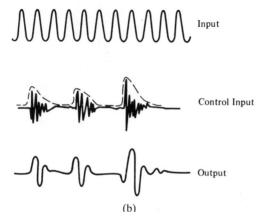

(b)

**Figure 18-4.** An envelope shaper. (a) The envelope of one signal can be detected and used to shape the envelope of another signal. (b) In this example, a steady signal is applied to the primary input, and an impulsive signal is applied to the control input. The output consists of the original input with the envelope of the control input signal.

extracts the envelop (dashed line) of the control signal and uses this to modulate the steady tone, giving it a percussive sound.

The *ring modulator* is simply a signal multiplier; its output is the instantaneous product of the two input signals. The simplest form of the device is shown in Figure 18-5. When two signals are multiplied, the product does not contain either frequency; rather, the sum and difference of the two frequencies are present. With complex waveforms at both inputs of a ring modulator, the output will be nonharmonically related to either input. Typically, if one input is in a normal musical pitch range and the other input in a very low-frequency range (5 to 20 Hz), then the output will retain some of the character of the first input, but with a severe "growl" to it.

With random inputs, the output bears no relation to either of the inputs. The effect is often reminiscent of shortwave radio reception, where many signals, voice-modulated as well as coded, intermodulate one another.

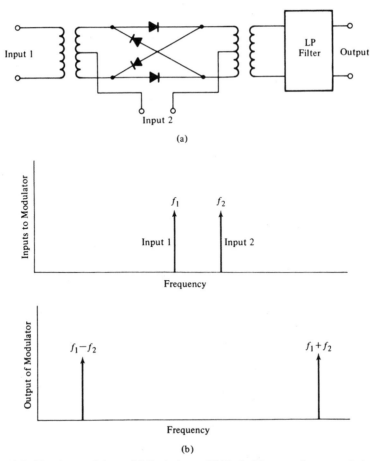

**Figure 18-5.** The ring modulator. (a) Basic form. (b) Typical input and output relationships.

## 18.4 OUT-OF-BAND SIGNAL GENERATION

It is possible to generate program-related signal both above and below the normal bandwidth of the signal at hand. The devices used for this are of comparatively recent development, and the effect is often very useful.

### 18.4.1 High-Frequency Generation

Many times, a given track on a multitrack recording may be inherently band limited. For example, a vocal track may not extent much beyond 4 or 5 kHz—and then only in the case of sibilant sounds. Any attempt to boost frequencies in the 8-kHz range will of course produce nothing; there is simply nothing there to boost. The same may apply at lower frequencies as well.

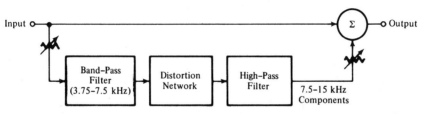

**Figure 18-6.** Out-of-band harmonic generation. A synthetic "top end" can be generated by distorting the octave between 3.75 and 7.5 kHz and filtering out the undesired low-frequency components.

The ear is relatively insensitive to pitch information at both the highest and lowest parts of the normal frequency range, and there are fairly simple methods for generating natural-sounding harmonic or subharmonic signals at the extremes of a program channel. Obviously, such techniques provide an effect that no amount of equalization can accomplish.

Figure 18-6 shows details of a circuit that generates an extra octave above 7.5 kHz. In this scheme, the octave between 3.75 and 7.5 kHz is used to produce a synthetic top octave between 7.5 and 15 kHz. The distortion network in the side channel can be adjusted both in the degree of distortion produced and the amount of this that is fed back into the main channel. The distortion network produces low-frequency components that, if allowed back into the main channel, would be quite audible. The purpose of the high-pass filter is to remove these components.

Such devices are used mainly on vocal tracks in pop-rock recording. Their use to modify full-range program is rather limited, inasmuch as an equalizer will do the job more easily.

## 18.4.2 Low-Frequency Generation

At the lower end of the frequency range, the task is somewhat more difficult. We want to *halve* the frequencies in the next-to-bottom octave to simulate the bottom octave. The dbx Company designed the "Boom Box" for this purpose. Details are shown in Figure 18-7. Subharmonic generation involves complex wave shaping, filtering, and gain control, as opposed to the relatively simple demands of high-frequency harmonic generation. The device has found wide application in discotheque work.

## 18.5 PITCH AND TEMPO REGULATION

One of the realities of normal recording processes is that changing the speed of a recording, fast or slow, will alter both pitch and playing time by reciprocal ratios. There is no simple analogy between sound recording and the motion picture art, where an adjustment of frame rate provides a totally satisfactory manipulation of the time domain in the form of fast or slow motion.

The problem with sound recording is that pitch and playing time are reciprocally related to the same variable—time: pitch has the dimension of cycles per unit time, while playing time has the dimension of time.

By only a slight stretch of the imagination, we can separate musical events into those that are perceived as unfolding in time, and those that are clearly perceived as functions of frequency. Elements of rhythm, the characteristics of vocal vibrato, and so forth, are clearly perceived as events in time. In fact, musical events that happen no more than 8 or 12 times per second can be clearly classified as time events. Events that occur more than, say, 20 to 25 times per second are perceived as having definite pitch and are clearly in the frequency domain. Those events between frequencies of 12 and 20 Hz fall into an indeterminate zone.

What we would like is some means of treating the time domain information (less than 12 Hz) as a series of "frames" to be duplicated or discarded at will, while leaving the frequency domain alone. This would provide us directly with a tool for tempo regulation; pitch regulation would follow naturally as a result of speeding up or slowing down a tempo-regulated recording by an amount equal to the reciprocal of that tempo regulation.

The means for accomplishing this is an extension of normal tape-editing techniques. In Figure 18-8(a) a tape recording has sections removed from it at regular intervals. The intervalic rate is low, not more than one or two times per second. If the edited recording shown in (a) is played at its original recorded speed, then the playing time will have been shortened by a factor of $(Y - X)/Y$. The pitch, of course, will remain the same. Stated another way, the tempo will have increased by a factor $Y/(Y - X)$. Now, if the recording is slowed down by a factor of $(Y - X)/Y$, the playing time will be restored to its original length, but the pitch will have been lowered by a factor of $(Y - X)/Y$. In this latter case, we have preserved the original tempo while we have lowered the pitch.

Attaching numbers to the process for greater clarity, let $X = 0.1$; then one-tenth of the tape is edited out and discarded at the established intervalic rate, and 0.9 becomes the factor by which the playing time will be shortened. (Recall that the tape is played back at its original recording speed.) We may say as well that the tempo has been increased by $Y/(Y - X) = 10/9 = 1.11$. Now, if the tape speed is slowed to 0.9 the original speed, the playing time will be restored to the original $(0.9)(1.11) = 1$, but in the process the pitch will have been lowered by a factor of 0.9.

Therefore, if we wish to *increase tempo or decrease pitch,* the editing process shown in Figure 18-8(a) must be used. The ratio $X/(Y - X)$ will determine the particular pitch or tempo rate desired.

If we want to *decrease tempo* (lengthen the playing time) or *increase pitch*, we must perform the editing procedure shown in Figure 18-8(b). Here, a duplicate of section X is inserted back into the recording at intervals of $Y$. The factor $X/(Y + X)$ now becomes the ratio by which pitch and tempo can be separately varied.

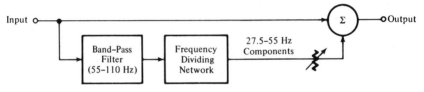

**Figure 18-7.** Details of the dbx "Boom Box". Generation of subharmonic components in the 55- to 110-Hz octave can add a synthetic low end to program material in which it may be missing.

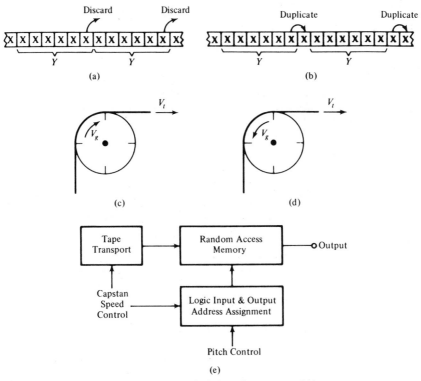

**Figure 18-8.** Details of pitch and tempo regulation.

## 18.5.1 Mechanical Systems

Making repetitive edits in a tape recording is a tedious process. An earlier mechanical process made use of a special tape transport that had a rotating playback head with gaps located at 90° intervals. The tape path around the head covered an arc of slightly less than 90° so that the tape was always in contact with one of the four magnetic gaps. The speeds of the tape and the gap, $V_t$ and $V_g$, respectively, could be varied separately. If $V_t$ is held constant, then the tempo will remain constant. Pitch can be lowered by a factor of $(V_t - V_g)/V_t$, as shown in Figure 18-8(c), or raised by the same factor by opposite rotation of the head, as shown in Figure 18-8(d).

For tempo regulation, $V_t$ is raised or lowered as desired to speed up or slow down the playing time. For maintaining constant pitch, the value of $V_t - V_g$ must always be equal to the original recording speed.

## 18.5.2 Electronic Systems

During the 1970s, digital technology simplified the process as shown in Figure 18-8(e). The block diagram is a direct analogy of the mechanical means shown at (c) and (d). The random access memory stores information corresponding to that contained in the

**Figure 18-9.** Photograph of a harmonizer. (*Courtesy Eventide*)

90° arc of tape in contact with the rotating head. $V_t$ is controlled directly, while $V_t \pm V_g$ is controlled by scanning the memory in either direction, as required.

### 18.5.3 Audible Artifacts in Pitch and Tempo Regulation

At the present state of the art, there are certain artifacts present when pitch and tempo regulation is employed. Since the technique, whether mechanical or electronic, results in unavoidable discontinuities (edits) in the otherwise smooth flowing program, there is a good chance that some of these will be audible. Much depends on the program material. For example, rapid-fire speech can undergo significant speeding up and still sound natural. On the other hand, music with long sustained passages may easily betray the cycling and recycling of delay line scanning.

The only dedicated devices for tempo regulation available today are targeted at special effects and advertising commercial production work, and in these applications they are excellent. It is difficult to imagine serious musical application of pitch and tempo regulation, but strange requests do come along and must somehow be met.

The basic quality of a pitch regulation system can be severely tested by feeding in a 500-Hz tone and listening to the output as the input signal is forward scanned (to raise the pitch), or reverse scanned (to lower the pitch). The engineer will hear small "blips" at the beginning of each scanning interval. These will be much less audible on music, but they are still there.

### 18.5.4 The Harmonizer

The term *harmonizer* describes a broad class of signal processors that provide pitch-shifted outputs, often more than one. Thus, it is possible in real time to create a version of the input at some fixed musical interval, either above or below the input. Figure 18-9 shows such a unit as manufactured by Eventide.

### 18.6 CHORUS GENERATORS

The purpose of a chorus generator is to take a single vocal or instrumental track and make it sound as if there is more than one performer. It is characteristic of any ensemble

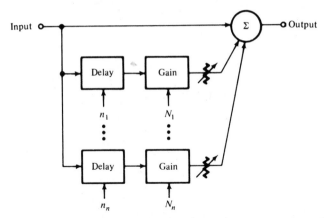

**Figure 18-10.** A chorus generator. Inputs $n$ and $N$ are random noise generators operating in the frequency range of 5 to 8 Hz. Four or five side channels of delay and gain are sufficient to produce a realistic chorus effect.

performing the same melodic line that there will be slight pitch, amplitude, and timing randomness among the players. These elements create a pleasing chorus effect and represent some of the natural advantage of a large performing group over a smaller one. The plan shown in Figure 18-10 provides a simulated chorus effect by combining a number of signals, each individually subjected to slight but random delay modulation for creating small pitch and timing randomness as well as randomness in amplitude (gain). The method cannot easily make a single voice sound like a large ensemble, but it can make a small group of voices sound like a much larger ensemble. Processors of this sort have been used extensively in electronic organs to create a natural ensemble effect.

Additional processing, not shown here, can result in multichannel output, providing spatial randomness as well.


## 18.7 VOCODERS

A vocoder is a *VOice CODER*, a complex signal processor that analyzes speech into its components and synthesizes it again out of these components. In the process of reconstructing speech from its components, substitutions can be made, and speech modulation can be added to a variety of musical or other non-speech sounds.

It has long been known that the basic information rate of speech is fairly low and that if speech were broken down into its basic components, it could be transmitted over quite narrow-bandwidth channels for subsequent reconstruction. The basic layout of a vocoder is shown in Figure 18-11. The spectrum filter banks detect the presence of speech signals in their respective bands, and that information is converted into a group of dc control signals. These filter banks are responsible for detecting the formants of speech, the vowel sounds such as "ah," "ee," "oh," and so forth. The pitch/excitation analyzer determines the fundamental frequency of speech and the presence of various "noise" components of speech, such as hisses, buzzes, and plosive sounds (b, p, d, etc.). Upon reconstruction,

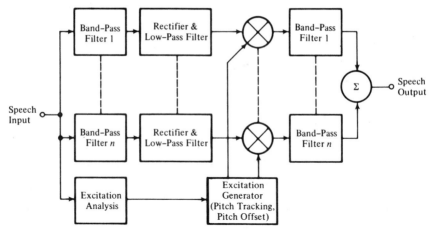

**Figure 18-11.** Basic diagram of a vocoder.

the fundamental is regenerated and the filter banks in the synthesizer portion of the system are gated according to the amount of signal originally present in each band. The excitation function restores the various noise components as required.

Depending upon how many band-pass filters there are and how sophisticated the pitch tracking and excitation functions are, vocoders can synthesize speech quite naturally. More recent embodiments of the vocoder allow a wide variety of effects useful in electronic music and recording. The more sophisticated systems contain many filter banks for more accurate analysis and synthesis of the vocal spectrum. In addition, the pitch/excitation function provides a pitch offset function that allows a man's voice to be transformed in pitch so that it may sound like a child's voice. Further, the pitch tracking may be replaced by an external source, thus enabling a wide band signal, such as an orchestra, to be speech-modulated!

## 18.8 IMAGING METHODS

### 18.8.1 Simple Image Widening

Many times, an engineer will be asked to make a previously recorded program "more stereo." What this generally means is to give a stereo recording more lateral spread, rather than to do pseudostereo treatment of a monophonic program. There are factors that might call for this. A stereo program may have been blended by mixing the two channels together somewhat; an engineer may simply have thought that the program had too much separation. Often, an engineer has had too heavy a hand on a center microphone (usually in picking up a soloist), and the resulting recording seems to be center heavy.

Borrowing a page from MS microphone circuitry, many of these problems can be fixed, or at least alleviated. The basic method is to slightly cross-feed the two channels with signals of opposite polarity. The setup shown in Figure 18-12 makes use of the polarity reversal switch in the console input modules to provide the cross-fed terms. Caution is

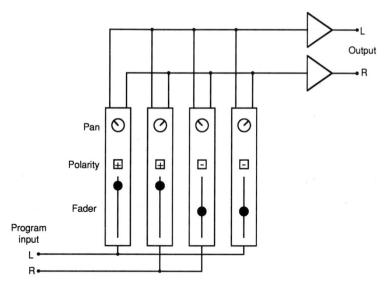

**Figure 18-12.** Basic console setup for cross-feeding opposite-polarity signals.

advised; do not use any more of the negative cross-feed terms than necessary, otherwise there will be too much negative polarity content in the resulting stereo program. As a practical matter, phantom center program can be reduced by no more than about 3 dB, while negative polarity terms will appear in opposite channels down some 10 dB in level. This will not impair separation of the left and right signals by any significant degree, and will, by the phasor relationships shown in Figure 2-4(e) give rise to left and right images slightly outside the loudspeaker base.

If a stereo program has been blended (by adding positive cross-feed terms), it is possible to use this technique to restore it to its previous condition, without the problems of remaining cross-fed negative polarity terms. Such a program could be represented by the following:

|  | *Left channel* | *Right channel* |
|---|---|---|
| *Original program* | $L + 0.7C$ | $0.7C + R$ |
| *Positive cross-fed terms* | $+0.3\,(0.7C + R)$ | $+0.3\,(0.7C + L)$ |
| *Blended program* | $L + 0.91C + .3R$ | $0.3L + 0.91C + R$ |
| *Negative cross-fed terms* | $-0.3\,(0.3L + 0.91C + R)$ | $-0.3\,(L + 0.91C + 0.3R)$ |
| *Signal summation* | $0.91L + 0.637C$ | $0.637C + 0.91R$ |
| *Normalizing factor* | $\times\ (1.099)$ | $\times\ (1.099)$ |
| *Final signal summation* | $L + 0.7C$ | $0.7C + R$ |

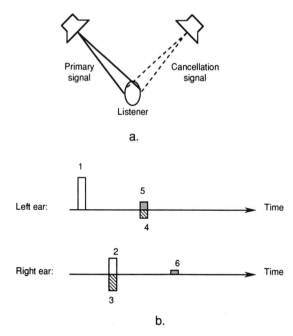

**Figure 18-13.** Producing images beyond the loudspeaker base. (a) Basic notion of crosstalk cancellation in the median plane. (b) Crosstalk cancellation by inverted delayed signals.

As can be seen, the original positive cross-fed terms have been removed in the blended program, and it has been restored to its original content.

### 18.8.2 Signal Delay Crosstalk Cancellation: Imaging Outside the Loudspeaker Base

Negative cross-fed terms between stereo channels tend to produce images that are slightly outside the loudspeaker base, but the effect is rather limited. A striking effect of localization outside the loudspeaker base can be produced through the cancellation of natural crosstalk terms, as they exist at the ears, and replacing them with new ones. As with all such out-of-bounds imaging, listener location is critical.

The method will now be described. Figure 18-13(a) shows a pair of stereo loudspeakers. Only the left loudspeaker produces a signal. It produces signal 1 at the left ear and a delayed signal 2 at the right ear. Now, we will add the same signal at the right loudspeaker, but delayed and inverted. It will be timed to arrive at the right ear at exactly the same instant the signal from the left loudspeaker arrives at the right ear, as shown at Figure 18-13(b). These new signals are called 3 and 4. Note that signal 3 effectively cancels signal 2 at the right ear; however, a later signal 4 will now be heard at the left ear. We continue the process with signals 5 and 6, and finally we are left with a residue signal 6 at the right ear, which does not get cancelled. We have gone far enough with the process from a practical point of view.

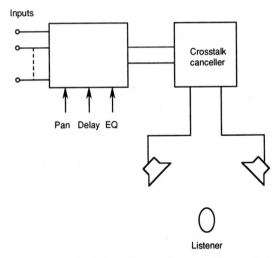

**Figure 18-14.** Basic flow diagram for crosstalk cancellation.

What we are left with is a situation in which the left stereo loudspeaker produces a signal primarily at the listener's left ear. The residue signal at the right ear is low enough in level to be ignored. By similar analysis, the right channel can be made to produce a signal predominantly at the right ear.

What we now have is essentially a spatial *binaural* system, but only for a listener precisely located on the median plane, or very close to it, and with a specified included angle between the loudspeakers. We can now play standard binaural recordings made with an artificial head (with due attention to equalization), and there will be heard a wide array of sound sources, many of them naturally positioned outside the loudspeaker base. Ambience in particular will seem to arrive over a large listening angle.

We can also take monophonic tracks and simulate their positions binaurally, using appropriate signal delay and equalization, and feed those signals to the crosstalk canceller. The loudspeaker listener positioned at the correct position will then hear those signals arrayed in space. It is possible, if all details are in place, for the listener to hear sounds clearly from far right and left. Signals originating from the back are also possible. In some cases, sounds can be heard with clear vertical position, due to the accuracy with which those sound sources are modified in frequency response by the pinnae of the ears on some artificial heads.

The flow diagram for the entire process is shown in Figure 18-14. It must be said that such an arrangement as this is quite complex and requires much dedicated equipment. Listening conditions are critical, and the effect works best in very well-damped listening spaces. Only in recent years has much of the necessary analysis and precise measurement of equalization requirements been made that will enable such systems to become practical.

Engineers are advised to check the monophonic compatibility of any stereo program material they have processed with the techniques discussed in this section, since the introduction of delays and polarity reversals between channels can often affect the monophonic summation in a profound way.

### 18.8.3 A Word to the Wise

As we move into the decade of the 1990s, we note that there are many schemes being offered to the professional user that purport to steer images well outside the loudspeaker base. All of these systems make use of the techniques discussed in this section, and some of them have not been well executed. There are often promises that are not kept, and the professional user should know those conditions under which these imaging methods will and will not work.

They work well only when phasor reconstruction can be controlled. This means that listeners must be at or near the plane of symmetry and that loudspeaker spacing must be carefully adjusted. Many times, the effect is excellent for closely spaced loudspeakers, such as a pair mounted at the sides of a television set. Here, the viewer is normally on the median plane and rarely strays from it. The close placement of loudspeakers also allows some degree of off-axis movement of the listener before phasor relationships are upset.

These systems are of virtually no use in the motion picture theater, because of wide spacing and included angular variation of loudspeakers, not to mention the requirement for satisfying all patrons.

## 18.9 NOISE REMOVAL AND SIGNAL RECONSTRUCTION IN OLD RECORDINGS

With the stunning success of the compact disc has come widespread reissue of older archival recordings. Because of the noise-free performance of the CD, many companies are transferring their old masters in an attempt to remove as much noise as possible, without doing any harm to the music. Some of those techniques will be discussed here.

### 18.9.1 Tick and Pop Removal

This technique is useful in transferring recordings from old disc sources. First, every attempt should be made to get a mint copy of the recording. Failing that, the record company should try to have new vinyl pressings made if the original metal molds can be located and appear to be in good condition. Unfortunately, not many of the old line record companies have kept their vaults in good order, and in recent years numerous original recordings have been scrapped under the assumption that previous tape transfers will be sufficient for all future needs.

If a good-quality pressing can be found, it should be carefully examined with a microscope to determine the best playback stylus for making the transfer. The smallest bearing radius that seems to play back smoothly should be used, and the bearing surface should contact a part of the groove that has not previously been worn. This requires a broad collection of removable stylus assemblies, which normally are used in conjunction with moving-magnet phonograph cartridges. Information on what is available here can be obtained from the few remaining manufacturers of phono cartridges.

The playback is transferred to tape. If manual de-ticking is to be done, then the transfer should be made to 38 cm/sec (15 inches/sec) tape. If digital processing is to be done,

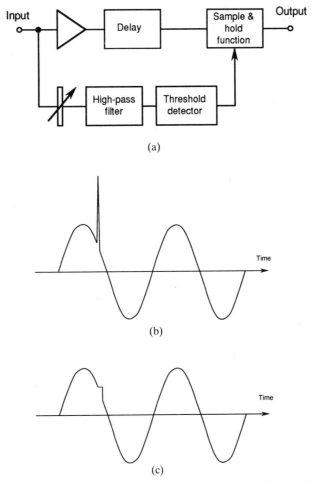

**Figure 18-15.** Analog tick and pop removal. (a) Basic circuit. (b) Waveform with tick. (c) Waveform after tick removal.

then the transfer should be made to one of the formats compatible with the program to be used. Manual de-ticking is a laborious process of actually cutting out the ticks themselves and splicing adjacent portions of tape back together. This was widely practiced many years ago, but it would not normally be done today except for a few very large noises that might not yield to subtler methods.

## 18.9.2 Analog Tick and Pop Removal

Analog tick and pop removal can be done with a device that operates as shown in Figure 18-15. The signal is fed through a delay line, so that it arrives at the output slightly behind the signal in the side chain. The side chain signal contains a high-frequency boost

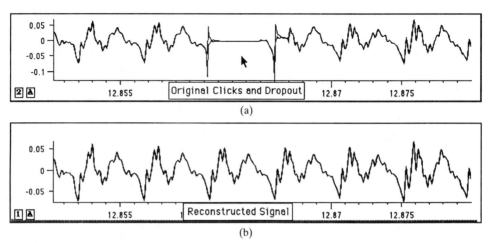

**Figure 18-16.** Sonic Solution's NoNoise process for restoring missing signals. (a) Signal waveform showing loss. (b) Reconstructed signal waveform. (*Courtesy Sonic Solutions*)

network, which then feeds to a threshold detector. Because of the impulsive nature of ticks and pops, their leading edge contains many high frequencies. This is what actuates the threshold, and that in turn is what actuates the sample-and-hold circuit at the output. Because of the slight signal delay in the main path, the command to sample-and-hold comes just before the program signal arrives at the output. The dwell time of the sample-and-hold action can be adjusted for minimum audibility for the kind of noises at hand. The input waveform is shown in (b), and typical action on the waveform is shown in (c).

During the 1970s, a number of consumer preamplifiers contained tick and pop removal circuits. Today, the function is carried out by digital means.

### 18.9.3 Digital Tick and Pop Removal

In many digital processing and editing programs, short segments of the program waveform can be viewed as amplitude versus time. Ticks and pops can usually be clearly seen, since their "spikey" appearance indicates high-frequency content that is outside the normal program bandwidth. Whereas the analog tick and pop removal method described in the previous section merely initiated a sample-and-hold at such a point, a "smart" digital system can examine adjacent portions of the waveform and determine a "best fit" trajectory of the waveform in the interval of the disturbance. Thus, the signal may be effectively reconstructed in the noise interval.

Figure 18-16 shows the use of Sonic Solutions' NoNoise signal processing program (14) in performing such signal restoration over a dropout interval of 5 msec. Information contained in the adjacent two cycles was used to reconstruct the signal.

### 18.9.4 Broadband Noise Removal

Here, the concern is the removal of broadband noise that has no cyclic components, such as tape hiss or granularity noise in disc transfer. The most common approach is to use a program-controlled low-pass filter with various thresholds. Basically, such a device works by rolling off high-frequency noise during low program levels, when the likelihood of high-frequency program content is low. Much of the time, this will work, but with complex musical programs, the approach may be plagued with effects of "pumping" and the removal of too much low-level high-frequency information. In general, this approach works well when the noise level is marginal; in those cases thresholds can be set so that residual noise is virtually eliminated. The key to successful operation is to ensure that the transition from wide to narrow bandwidth takes place when there is sufficient high-frequency program content to mask the change in hiss level itself. Not surprisingly, if the listener cannot hear the noise actually being rolled off, then the listener will not know that it has happened! The Burwen dynamic noise filter and the several consumer versions of Carver's Noise Correlators do remarkable jobs in this regard.

Harry Olson, of RCA fame, is credited with the description of an analog broadband noise-elimination scheme that broke the program spectrum into several bands, and within each band defined a minimum allowable signal floor. Any signal within a band that fell below this floor was considered to be noise and was squelched out. This was an elaborate system for its day and comprised about ten frequency bands. Lagadec described and demonstrated a digital realization of a similar scheme at an Audio Engineering Society Conference in 1984, this time making use of 256 bands for signal-to-noise analysis.

Sonic Solutions' NoNoise program extends the technique, using 2000 bands for analysis. Within each band, a threshold can be set so that any signal above the threshold will be treated as music and not be attenuated. Any signal below the threshold can be reduced in level by a predetermined amount. The author would like to draw attention to the many compact disc releases on the Philips label of historic recordings that have been processed using the NoNoise process. Most of these clearly demonstrate the capabilities of the program.

Obviously, good musical judgment must be used in setting up and using any of these systems. If it is desired to remove *all* the noise in an old 78-rpm recording, for example, various pumping and gating artifacts of the system will be all too audible.

## 18.10 SIGNAL RECONSTRUCTION

While we have only briefly touched on the subject, signal reconstruction can be carried to surprising lengths. Perhaps the most stunning example is the reconstruction of 1906 Caruso acoustical recordings by Thomas Stockham during the mid 1970s (11). Outside of noise and limited bandwidth, there is another problem with acoustical recordings, and that is the large number of peaks and dips in the response of the recording system. These peaks and dips are of the order of 10 to 20 dB deep and are essentially in the frequency range from about 200 Hz to about 3 kHz. The goal was to remove the artifacts of the recording system and present Caruso's voice as though it had been recorded over a modern, albeit bandlimited, system.

Stockham noted that there were two unknowns here—Caruso's vocal spectrum and the spectral characteristics of the recording apparatus, as it was set up for a given recording session. Using an elaborate digital technique, Stockham analyzed the Caruso recording on a frequency-by-frequency basis and arrived at a detailed frequency spectrum for the

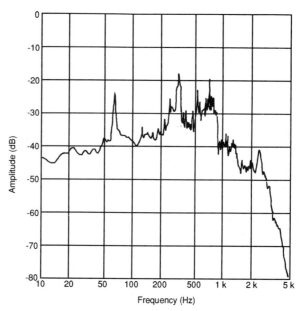

**Figure 18-17.** Stockham's removal of artifacts in acoustical recording; original Caruso recording spectrum. (*Courtesy T. Stockham*)

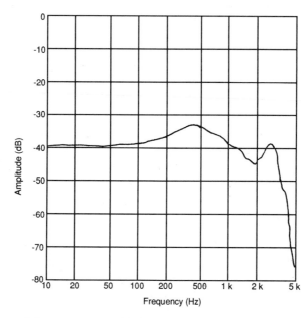

**Figure 18-18.** Spectrum of the program material shown in Figure 18-17 taken from an electrical recording. (*Courtesy T. Stockham*)

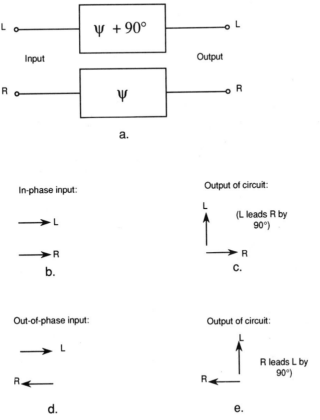

**Figure 18-19.** Use of all-pass networks for correcting polarity errors. (a) Network diagram. (b) Input signal in-phase relationships. (c) Output signal phase relationships shifted 90°. (d) Input signal out-of-phase relationships. (e) Output signal phase relationships shifted 90°.

recording. The result of this is shown Figure 18-17. The spectrum is the product of two unknowns, Caruso's spectrum and the spectrum of the recording system.

In order to separate the two, either Caruso's vocal spectrum, or that of the recording system, would have to be known. Stockham reasoned that the vocal spectrum of Caruso should not differ markedly from that of a vocalist of the same tradition singing the same piece of music. So a modern recording sung by Jussi Bjoerling was analyzed in the same manner. The result of that analysis is shown in Figure 18-18. The difference between the responses shown in the two figures represents that of the recording system. Stockham then synthesized a digital filter whose response was the inverse of the summed response, and then filtered the original Caruso recording through that digital filter. The result was Caruso's voice as it might sound with modern electrical recording, albeit noisy and bandlimited, as though it were coming through a small tabletop radio.

The entire analysis process would have to be done over again for each of the original recording sessions. Although Caruso' vocal spectrum could be considered constant over time, each recording setup was likely to have its own spectrum.

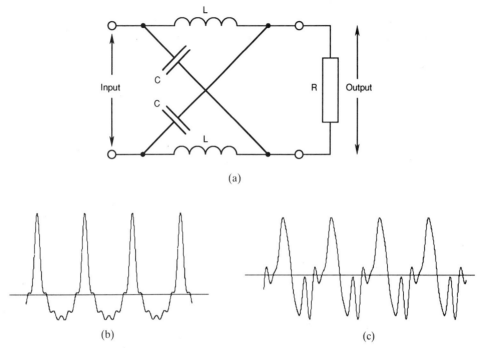

(a)

(b)                                                    (c)

**Figure 18-20.** All-pass phase shifting. The passive circuit shown in (a) has a flat amplitude characteristic over the frequency band but shifts the phase from 0° at low frequencies to 180° at high frequencies. An input waveform, as shown in (b), is phase-shifted through the circuit and emerges as shown at (c). The crest factor of the output signal is diminished through the circuit, but the rms and average values remain the same.

## 18.11 ALL-PASS PHASE SHIFT NETWORKS

Certain problems of faulty signal transmission can be alleviated with all-pass phase shift networks. For example, consider a stereo recording in which the bass line has been panned as a center image in opposite polarity, while all other center images have been panned in proper polarity! Although this is highly unlikely, its equivalent can happen using stereo pairs of microphones in which a single reversely-wired microphone cable has been accidentally used.

In our hypothetical case, if the bass line is corrected by changing polarity in one channel, then the vocal and other center images will now be in opposite polarity. The circuit shown in Figure 18-19 will alleviate the problem by shifting one channel 90° with respect to the other. When this is done, a broadband phase shift will make all of the in- and out-of-polarity signals effectively the same. In one case, the left channel will lead 90°, while in the other, the right channel will lead 90°. The listener will not hear this as such, but may note that the resulting phantom center images will have spread somewhat (see Section 9.7.1).

Another application for all-pass phase shifting is the reduction of high crest factor in certain complex audio signals. Details are shown in Figure 18-20. The passive lattice network (a) provides flat frequency response but shifts the phase of the signal from 0°

at low frequencies to 180° at high frequencies. As the result of this, a "spikey" waveform (b) will have its higher harmonics shifted so that it emerges as shown in (c).

This is often a matter of concern in broadcasting, where robust announcers with high crest factors tend to overmodulate the transmitter.

## BIBLIOGRAPHY

1. B. Bartlett, "A Scientific Explanation of Phasing," *J. Audio Engineering Society*, vol. 18, no. 6 (1970).
2. J. Blauert, *Spatial Hearing*, MIT Press, Cambridge, Mass. (1983).
3. D. Cooper and J. Bauck, "Prospects for Transaural Recording," *J. Audio Engineering Society*, vol. 37, no. 1/2 (1989).
4. M. Gerzon, Stabilizing Stereo Images," *Studio Sound*, vol. 16, no. 12 (1974).
5. D. Griesinger, "Equalization and Spatial Equalization of Dummy-Head Recordings for Loudspeaker Reproduction," *J. Audio Engineering Society*, vol. 37, no. 1/2 (1989).
6. D. Griesinger, "Theory and Design of a Digital Audio Signal Processor for Home Use," *J. Audio Engineering Society*, vol. 37, no. 1/2 (1989).
7. A. Oppenheim, *Digital Signal Processing*, Prentice-Hall, Englewood Cliffs, N.J. (1978).
8. M. Schroeder, "Progress in Architectural Acoustics and Artificial Reverberation," *J. Audio Engineering Society*, vol. 32, no. 4 (1984).
9. A. Springer, "A Pitch Regulator and Information Changer," *Gravesano Review*, vol. 11/12 (1958).
10. A. Springer, "Acoustic Speed and Pitch Regulator," *Gravesano Review*, vol. 13 (1959).
11. T. Stockham, et al., "Blind Deconvolution Through Digital Signal Processing," *Proceedings of the IEEE*, vol. 63 (April 1975).
12. J. Sunier, "Binaural Overview," *Audio Magazine* (December 1989).
13. T. Wells and E. Vogel, *The Techniques of Electronic Music*, University Stores, Inc., Austin, Tex. (1974).
14. M. Wright, "Putting the Byte on Noise." *Audio Magazine* (March 1989).

# 19

## ANALOG TAPE RECORDING

### 19.1 INTRODUCTION

Magnetic recording has shaped the evolution of contemporary recording in such a fundamental way that it is difficult to think of the creative process apart from the benefits of multitrack capability and ease of editing. The principle of magnetic recording has been known for over a century (14, 15), but the problems of noise and distortion kept it from being much more than a curiosity as far as studio recording was concerned. High-frequency bias was discovered in the 1920s (2), and with it the nagging problems of noise and distortion were on their way to being solved. But the physical medium itself remained a problem, Earlier experiments had used steel ribbon and wire, with their concomitant handling problems.

It was not until the late 1930s that all the right ingredients were to come together. The Germans developed the magnetophon, a tape recorder embodying high-frequency bias and excellent tape-handling characteristics. These early machines were brought back to the United States after World War II, and soon record and broadcasting companies had become convinced that the new medium had substantial advantages over the direct-to-disc recording process of the day. Developments came quickly, and tape manufacture made great strides. By 1950, magnetic tape had become established as the master recording medium for both record and broadcast industries.

Even as we enter the digital age, it is likely that recording engineers will be using, and aligning, analog tape recorders for many years to come. It is essential that they understand them intimately.

### 19.2 BASIC MAGNETIC CONSIDERATIONS

#### 19.2.1 Hysteresis

The process of magnetization is extremely nonlinear. By this, we mean that the application of an external magnetizing field does not result in a proportional amount of magnetization

270

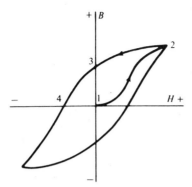

**Figure 19-1.** Typical hysteresis curve for a magnetic material.

of the test sample. Figure 19-1 shows what normally happens. $H$ represents the magnetomotive force applied to the sample and has the units of amperes per meter (A/m). The unmagnetized sample is indicated at point 1 in the graph. As magnetomotive force is applied to the sample, $B$, the magnetic flux density in the sample, increases in nonlinear fashion. $B$ has the units of teslas (T), or webers per square meter (Wb/m$^2$).

At point 2 in the graph, the flux density in the sample has reached its maximum value, or has *saturated*. If the magnetomotive force is removed, the flux density in the sample will not retrace its previous path, but will go to point 3 in the graph. This action is known as *hysteresis* (from the Greek meaning "to lag behind"). The sample is now said to be magnetized, and the remnant value of $B$, often indicated as $B_r$, is a measure of the flux density remaining in the sample. A magnetic material is said to be "hard" if the value of $B_r$ is large relative to the value of $B$ at saturation. It is said to be "soft" if the value of $B_r$ is low relative to $B$ at saturation.

Now, if a negative $H$ field is applied to the magnetized sample, the sample can be demagnetized. *Coercivity* is the measure of magnetomotive force required to do this, and $H_c$ is this value at point 4 in the graph. If the $H$ field is cycled between positive and negative saturation values for the sample, there will be a symmetrical loop, as indicated in the figure, known as a hysteresis loop.

For a magnetic recording medium, we require a hard magnetic material. We would also prefer that material to have high retentivity (so that the signal output will be high) and high coercivity (so that the signal cannot be easily erased).

### 19.2.2 Linearization Through High-Frequency Bias

Magnetic tape is basically a collection of minuscule hard magnetic samples coated onto a plastic ribbon. If we were to run this tape through a sinusoidally varying $B$ field, the hysteresis of the medium would not allow us to encode a replica of that varying field. What we would get would look more like that shown in Figure 19-2, or even worse. If HF bias is added to the audio signal, the problem is effectively corrected, and the transfer characteristic is made linear. Figure 19-3(a) shows the addition of HF bias to the audio signal. Figure 19-3(b) shows the the linearizing effect of various amounts of HF bias. The exact way HF bias accomplishes this linearity is not well understood.

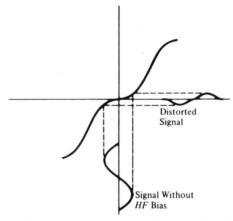

**Figure 19-2.** Distorted recorded transfer characteristic without bias.

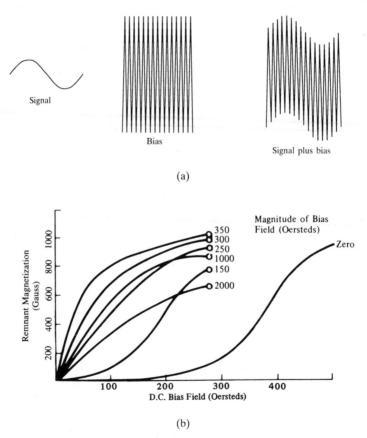

**Figure 19-3.** Effect of HF bias. (a) Bias and signal added. (b) Linearizing effect of varying amounts of HF bias.

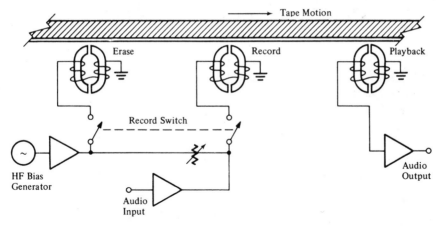

**Figure 19-4.** Basic principle of magnetic recording.

For low values of bias magnetomotive force, the transfer characteristic resembles the shape of the initial hysteresis curve itself, as shown in Figure 19-1. For progressively higher values of bias, the portion of the transfer characteristic near the origin becomes more linear, and for very high values of bias, the overall sensitivity of the transfer process is diminished. An operating point of 300 to 350 Oe/m would appear to be excellent. These curves, known as modified anhysteretic magnetization curves, clearly show the effect of HF bias on both linearity and sensitivity of the tape medium as a function of bias level.

## 19.3 THE RECORDING PROCESS

Once the tape medium has been linearized with HF bias, recording is a fairly straightforward procedure, as shown in Figure 19-4. As the tape moves from left to right, it first contacts the erase head. If the record switch is engaged, HF bias is fed to the erase head, and this effectively erases any remnant signal on the tape by subjecting it to many gradually decaying cycles of the bias frequency. (The frequency of the record bias generator is normally five to ten times higher than the highest audio frequency intended to be recorded; erase bias is often lower in frequency.) The tape then contacts the recording head, which is driven with a combination of HF bias and signal input. The playback head follows the record head, and at that point the recorded signal can be monitored directly from the tape.

## 19.4 THE PLAYBACK PROCESS

The relation between playback head and tape is shown in Figure 19-5. The hard magnetic iron oxide layer has been impressed with an audio signal by the record head, and this takes the form of time-varying positive and negative changes between "south" and "north" magnetic polarities, as shown in (a). For a high-frequency signal input, the wavelength is shown relative to the playback head's gap length. For low and mid frequencies, the

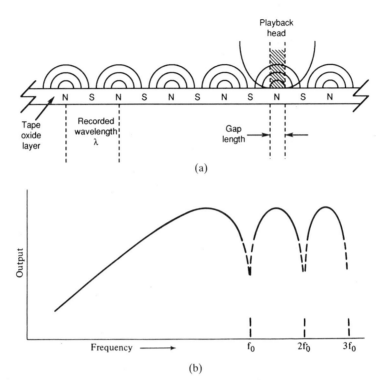

**Figure 19-5.** Relation between playback head gap length and HF response. (a) Recorded wavelength relative to gap length. (b) Nulls in response when wavelength and gap length are equal (or in multiples).

signal output from the playback head rises 6 dB per doubling of recorded frequency. However, when the wavelength of the recorded frequency approaches the gap length, the response begins to fall off, as shown in (b).

When the recorded wavelength is equal to the gap length, or integral multiples of it, there will be no output from the playback head. Therefore, the gap length of the playback head must be small enough to enable the recorder to cover the desired HF bandwidth. While these nulls in playback response were a problem in the early days of magnetic recording, the very narrow gaps used today have virtually eliminated the problem. For example, the first null frequency may be well out in the 70 kHz range at a recording speed of 38 cm/sec (15 inches/sec).

The basic post-equalization scheme for magnetic recording is shown in Figure 19-6. The output of the playback head is shown as curve (a), and the subsequent equalization at (b) produces the net output at (c).

## 19.5 MAGNETIC HEADS

Figure 19-7 shows a view of a typical playback head. Record and erase heads are quite similar in construction, differing primarily in gap length and the number of turns in the

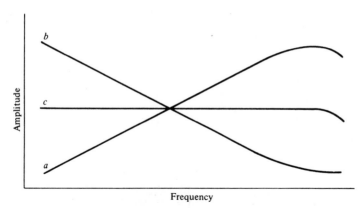

**Figure 19-6.** Basic playback equalization. The electrical output of the playback head rises with frequency for constant-flux recording, as shown at curve *a*. It must be equalized as shown at curve *b* for flat overall output, curve *c*.

windings. Both erase and record heads have relatively few turns of wire, while the playback head has many turns of fine wire.

Heads are normally constructed of thin laminations of magnetically soft metal. The purpose of the laminations is to minimize eddy current losses in the metal material. Gap length and uniformity are essential to proper performance of the heads. Table 19-1 gives typical gap dimensions for the various heads. It is essential that the playback head have a quite small gap, in order to "read" the short wavelengths on the tape. The record head does not require such a small gap in order to "write" the signal on the tape, inasmuch as the recording process takes placed at the trailing edge of the gap. It is important, however, that the gap edge be uniformly straight.

In the recording process, the mixture of bias and signal current flows through the windings, and a magnetic field is set up in the region of the gap. The field penetrates the tape oxide layer and the signal is permanently recorded.

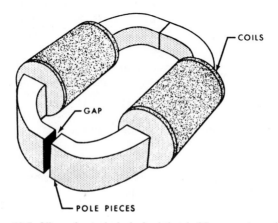

**Figure 19-7.** View of a typical playback head. (*Courtesy Ampex*)

**Table 19-1. Gap length for various heads**

| Heads | Gap length |
|-------|-----------|
| Erase heads | 125–25 μm |
| Audio recording heads | 12–2.5 μm |
| Audio playback heads | 6–1.5 μm |

The playback process is effectively the inverse of this. As the recorded tape moves over the gap of the playback head, the magnetic flux across the gap sets up a flux in the laminations, and the rate of change of this flux through the laminations induces a signal voltage across the windings.

## 19.6 MAGNETIC TAPE

The earliest tape used with the German magnetophon was a plastic material with iron oxide dispersed throughout it; one could record on one side or the other. Later, a tape with an oxide coating on a plastic base was developed, resulting in greater output due to the higher density of oxide adjacent to the head gaps. Early tapes used an acetate base, noted for brittleness, affinity for moisture, and general mechanical instability. Polyester bases are now universally used and have excellent mechanical properties.

The oxide used in manufacturing tape is *gamma ferric oxide* ($Fe_2O_3$). Gamma refers to the particular crystalline formation. The particle shape is needlelike, or acicular, and the desired particle length is about 0.5 to 0.7 μm. The oxide is mixed with a binder and other ingredients and is milled into a very smooth slurry. It is applied to a wide "web" of plastic, using a special coating head. Before the tape is passed through a drying oven, it is subjected to a strong dc magnetic field, which aligns the acicular particles in the direction of tape motion, a step which is essential in maintaining tape sensitivity. The tape is then dried, given a surface treatment, inspected, and finally slit into the desired widths. Oxide thickness is of the order of 12.5 μm, and the plastic base is usually about 40μm for normal play tape (1.5 mil tape). Every effort is made to ensure uniformity of the tape in order to minimize dropouts.

The dramatic improvement in tape over a period of three decades is seen in Figure 19-8. Taking Scotch type 111 as a reference, we can see how later formulations exhibited much greater HF sensitivity. This was reflected in the need for less signal preemphasis in recording with the later tapes, and accordingly lower distortion. Figure 19-9 shows the improvement in overall dynamic range capability of the same group of tape formulations.

As tape has improved in its dynamic range capabilities, the phenomenon of print-through has become more of a problem. Print-through is the transfer of signal from one oxide layer to another and is related to particle size distribution in the oxide layer. If the oxide–binder–plasticizer mixture has been improperly milled, there will be fine particles of oxide much smaller than desired dispersed throughout the mixture. These fine particles are very susceptible to the magnetic fields that are present in adjacent tape layers and tend to pick up those signals by direct contact. The effect is aggravated by

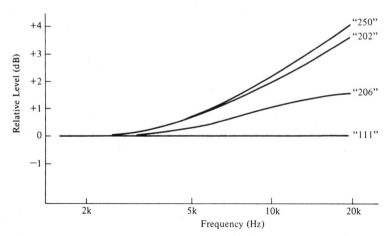

**Figure 19-8.** Relative HF sensitivity of several tapes normalized to Scotch type 111. In each case, long-wavelength bias was adjusted for maximum output. Playback head gap length was 2.5μm, and tape speed was 38 cm/sec. Scotch 202 tape was typical of the first generation of low-noise tape, and flat output required much less drive at high frequencies. Scotch 206 represented a trade-off of HF sensitivity for long-wavelength high-output capability. Scotch 250 combined high-output capability with increased HF sensitivity. (*Courtesy 3M*)

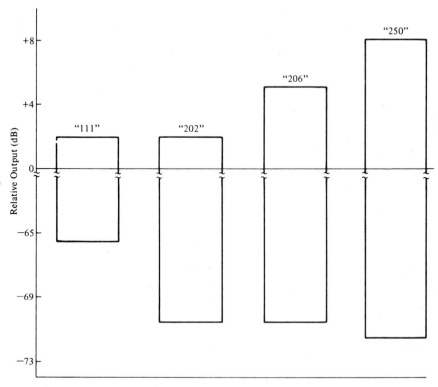

**Figure 19-9.** Dynamic range of various tapes. The tapes shown in Figure 19-8 are compared in overall dynamic range capability. The low noise of 202 is clearly seen, as is the added improvement of 206 in terms of overall output. Type 250 extends the performance further. (*Courtesy 3M*)

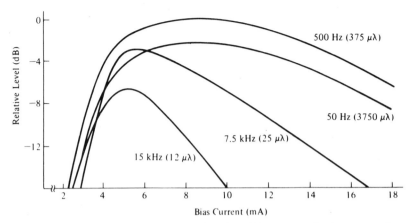

**Figure 19-10.** Tape output at several wavelengths as a function of bias current. Peak output at short wavelengths takes place at about 5 mA, while peak output at long wavelengths takes place at about 9 mA. Tape is normally biased for maximum output at long wavelengths, which is equivalent to "overbiasing" at short wavelengths.

long-term storage and by elevated temperature. Measurements indicate that adjacent layer print-through of full-level signals is generally in the range of −55 to −60 dB.

Mechanical requirements placed on tape call for long-term stability under a wide variety of storage conditions as well as smooth handling at high rewind speeds. In the last 25 years, professional tape has been manufactured with a 2.5 μm *matte* finish on the back side of the tape. During fast rewind and forwarding of the tape, the matte backing provides a high coefficient of friction with adjacent oxide layers, resulting in smooth winding.

### 19.6.1 Care and Storage of Tape

The following guidelines are presented for long-term care and storage of tape:

a. Tapes should be stored tail out, at proper winding tension.
b. Ensure that the work area is clean and free of small particles or debris.
c. Tape reels should be stored vertically at 5 to 32°C (40 to 90°F) and relative humidity of 20 to 60%.
d. All archival tapes should be stored on flanged reels, not hubs.
e. Archival tapes should be inspected periodically and rewound to alleviate any tendency for the tape to adhere to itself. Periodic inspection (every 2 years or so) may also identify any deterioration that would call for immediate retransfer of the material.

### 19.7 HF BIAS, DISTORTION, AND NOISE

Figure 19-10 shows the effect of bias settings on several recorded wavelengths. Note that at 500 Hz ($\lambda = 375 \mu$m) the output is greatest for a bias setting of 9 milliamperes, while at 15 kHz ($\lambda = 12 \mu$m) the output is greatest for a bias setting of about 5 milliamperes.

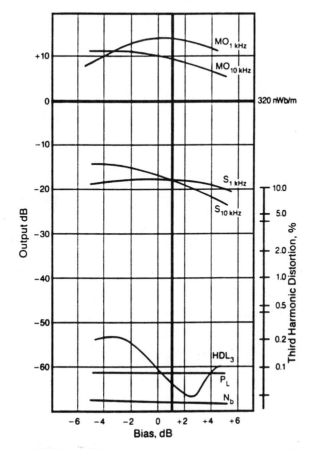

**Figure 19-11.** Performance of 3M type 996 mastering tape operating at 38 cm/sec (15 inches/sec) as a function of bias setting. Maximum output (MO) is shown of 1 kHz and 10 kHz. The tape is overbiased at 10 kHz by 3 dB, resulting in minimum third-harmonic distortion (HDL₃). Relative tape sensitivity (S) is shown for 1 kHz and 10 kHz. Print-through signal level ($P_L$) and weighted noise level ($N_D$) are shown. (*Courtesy 3M*)

Obviously, short and long wavelengths cannot both be optimized in output, and some compromise will have to be made. The general rule, however, is to set bias for minimum distortion and noise, ignoring the effect on sensitivity altogether.

Because the effects of bias can more clearly be seen at short wavelengths, the preferred way of setting bias is to adjust for maximum output at a suitably short wavelength, and then *increase* the bias by an amount that which will cause a 3-dB reduction of output. This is of course related to recording speed, and the following frequencies are normally chosen: 20 kHz at 76 cm/sec (30 inches/sec), 10 kHz at 38 cm/sec (15 inches/sec), and 5 kHz at 19 cm/sec (7.5 inches/sec). These frequencies all relate to the same recorded wavelength of about 38μm.

The effect of 3-dB overbiasing can clearly be seen in the manufacturer's data shown in Figure 19-11. Note that there are nulls in both distortion and noise that correspond to the −3-dB overbias at 10 kHz.

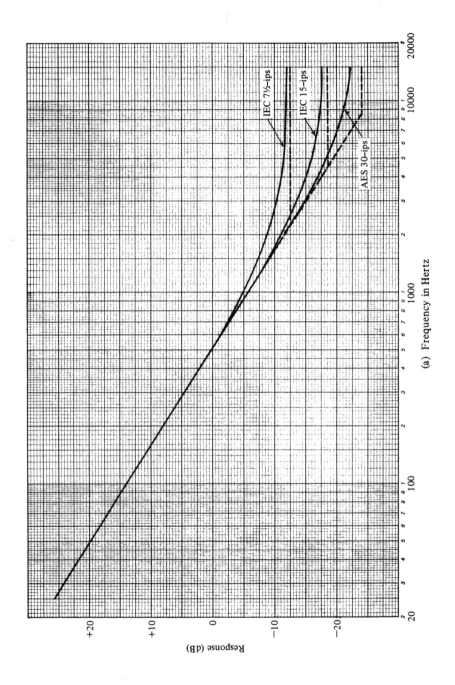

(a) Frequency in Hertz

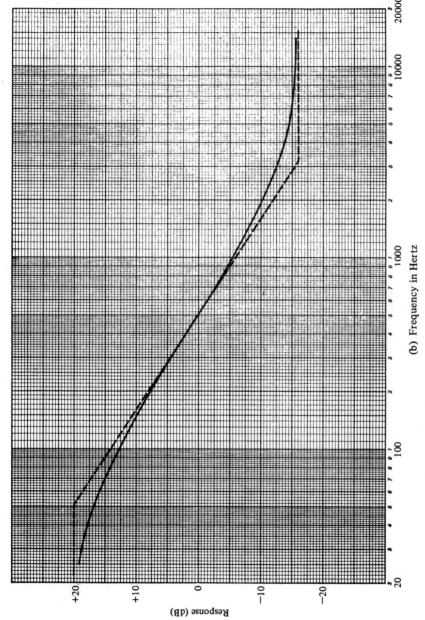

**Figure 19-12.** Standard playback curves. (a) IEC curves for 76, 38 and 19 cm/sec recording. (b) NAB playback curve for 38 and 19 cm/sec recording.

281

## 19.8 HF LOSSES AND PLAYBACK CURVES

In order for recordings to be compatible between machines and locations, playback response curves are rigorously defined, and standard test tapes are available as equalization references. If a tape is recorded with constant magnetic flux at all frequencies, then the output of the playback head will rise 6 dB per doubling of frequency, since the output voltage of the head is proportional to the rate of change of flux.

Thus, for constant-flux recording, the playback equalization curve must have a complementary 6 dB rolloff per doubling of frequency. This general tendency can be seen in the standard playback curves shown in Figure 19-12. In the IEC/AES data, note that there are separate playback curves for each recording speed. The HF break points in the curves are all spaced one octave apart, and they ensure that the amount of HF boost in the recording amplifier will be constant, for a given type of tape, whatever speed is used.

By comparison, the single NAB curve is used for both 38 cm/sec and 19 cm/sec playback. This indicates that at the slower speed more HF boost will be required in the recording amplifier, thus running some risk of overload at the slower speed.

Note that all of the playback equalization standards have break points at high frequencies at which the response levels off. This amounts to HF boost in playback that compensates for various effects that, taken as a group, tend to roll off the HF response of the recorder. These effects are:

a. *Playback head gap losses.* These are wavelength-dependent and will be more significant at lower tape speeds. The loss is given by:

$$\text{Loss (dB)} = 20 \log \left[ \frac{\sin (1.11\pi g/\lambda)}{1.11\pi g/\lambda} \right] \quad (19\text{-}1)$$

where $g$ is the gap length and $\lambda$ is the wavelength (both expressed in the same units).

b. *Oxide thickness losses.* For purposes of higher output at long wavelengths, it is desirable to make the tape oxide layer thicker. But the thicker coating is detrimental to HF response. This is again a wavelength-dependent loss, and at 38.1 cm/sec (15 inches/sec) the loss can amount to 12 or 15 dB at 20 kHz. The loss is given by

$$\text{Loss (dB)} = 20 \log \left[ \frac{1 - \exp (-2\pi d/\lambda)}{2\pi d/\lambda} \right] \quad (19\text{-}2)$$

where $d$ is the oxide thickness and $\lambda$ is the wavelength (both expressed in the same units).

c. *Spacing losses.* The effective distance of the oxide layer to the head is normally quite small, but some degree of separation will cause dropouts. The loss is given by

$$\text{Loss (dB)} = 20 \log \left[ \exp (-2\pi d/\lambda) \right] \quad (19\text{-}3)$$

where $d$ is the average distance from the tape to the head and $\lambda$ is the wavelength (both expressed in the same units).

**Table 19-2. Playback transition frequencies and corresponding time constants for professional tape recording**

| Standard | LF time constant (frequency) | HF time constant (frequency) |
|---|---|---|
| NAB | 3180μsec (50 Hz) | 50 μsec (3180 Hz) |
| IEC (19 cm/sec) | No transition | 70 μsec (2275 Hz) |
| IEC (38 cm/sec) | No transition | 35 μsec (4550 Hz) |
| IEC (76 cm/sec) | No transition | 17.5 μsec (9100 Hz) |

d. *Azimuth losses.* These losses result from misalignment of record and playback head gaps in the plane of tape motion. The loss is given by

$$\text{Loss (dB)} = 20 \log \left[ \frac{\sin ([W \tan \theta]/\lambda)}{[W \tan \theta]/\lambda} \right] \tag{19-4}$$

where $W$ is the track width, $\theta$ is the angle of misalignment between record and playback gaps, and $\lambda$ is the wavelength ($W$ and $\lambda$ expressed in the same units).

## 19.8.1 Alignment Tapes

Alignment tapes are produced under laboratory conditions and should be treated with care. They do not last forever, and old ones should be discarded if there is any question at all about their accuracy. The purpose of the tape is to adjust playback equalization, system gain, and head gap azimuth. These points will be discussed in greater detail in a later section.

Engineers often speak of *time constants* in their discussions of transition frequencies in system equalization. Time constants are related to frequency by the equation:

$$\text{Time constant} = \frac{1}{2\pi f} \tag{19-5}$$

In circuit design, time constants are a characteristic of resistor–capacitor combinations, and the engineer would rather work with time constants in determining transition frequencies. It is a shortcut in the laboratory, but a point of some confusion in the studio. Table 19-2 presents transition frequencies and time constants for standard playback curves, both professional and consumer.

There are no standard recording curves. Because of the wide range of tape and record head properties, various amount of boost will have to be used in order to get flat output in playback. Record equalization is thus a system variable, and, as seen in Figure 19-8, the requirements have changed markedly over the years.

## 19.10 REFERENCE FLUXIVITIES

When considering the magnetic flux level of a signal recorded on tape, we do not measure flux density. Rather, *surface fluxivity* is used; it has the dimensions of nanowebers per

## Table 19-3. Professional tape operating levels

| Fluxivity (nWb/m) | Description | Level dB | Measurement frequency (Hz) |
|---|---|---|---|
| 185 | Old Ampex reference level | 0 | 700 Hz |
| 200 | "Rationalized" reference level | +0.7 | 1 kHz |
| 250 | New U.S. elevated level | +2.6 | 1 kHz |
| 360 | Old European (DIN) level | +5.8 | 1 kHz |
| 510 | New European (DIN) level | +8.8 | 1 kHz |

meter (nWb/m). For many years, Ampex Standard Reference Level was the de facto standard in the industry. It was an empirical recorded level at 700 Hz that represented 1% total harmonic distortion in a given sample of tape.

Some years after its introduction, the surface fluxivity was measured to be 185 nWb/m using the short-circuit method. Still, there is some confusion regarding the measurement of surface fluxivity, because the same tone, measured using the open circuit method, gives 200 nWb/m. In the intervening years there have been many new standards, and the picture is not altogether clear. There are ample opportunities to make mistakes.

Table 19-3 presents a summary of the major tape operating levels in use today.

The U.S. 185 nWb/m standard was used in conjunction with the VU meter. During the same period, the DIN 360 nWb/m standard was used in Europe in conjunction with the various peak program meters. The nearly 6 dB level difference in reference tapes was just about equal to the average lead factor between the two kinds of metering, and the net result was that recordings made in the United States and Europe, on the same kind of tape, were at the same level.

The introduction of newer tapes during the 1970s prompted users on both sides of the Atlantic to go to elevated levels (+3 dB) in calibrating their recorders. Hence, another pair of reference fluxivities were needed which were 3 dB higher than their predecessors. For further discussion, see Section 12.5.


## 19.11 ELECTRICAL LINEARIZING TECHNIQUES

Disc cutting heads and amplifiers make use of inverse feedback to flatten their response curves and reduce distortion. In these systems the output signal is compared with the input signal, and any error detected is fed into the system in opposite polarity so that the error is corrected. By comparison, with tape recording there is no feedback from the remnant signal on the tape into the system input for error correction.

It is characteristic of systems with inverse feedback to exhibit good linearity and low distortion up to some point at which fundamental limits of the medium or device are reached; beyond that point there is rapid onset of clipping and gross distortion. The magnetic tape medium goes into distortion gradually; in the parlance of the art, it "overloads gently." In Figure 19-13 we see a typical transfer characteristic for the magnetic medium. If a "predistorter" is placed in series with the recording function and carefully

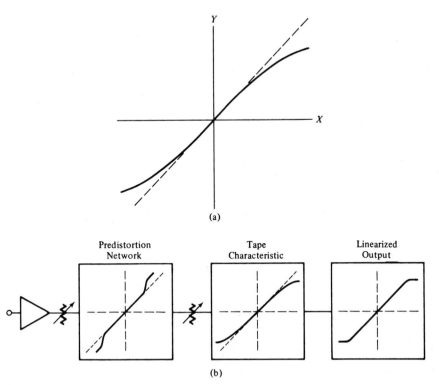

**Figure 19-13.** Predistortion in magnetic recording. The basic transfer characteristic of a tape recording system is linear over a wide range, as shown in (a). At the extremes, tape saturation results in significant nonlinearity. A predistortion network can correct some of this nonlinearity, as shown in (b), but cannot extend the fundamental limits of the system.

adjusted so that its input–output characteristics complement those of the tape itself, then the overall system transfer characteristic can be linearized. The process can be applied only to a limited degree, but the improvement can be significant at low frequencies.

Although the technique has been used in some professional recorders, it is not a part of the mainstream of current design practice. Chief difficulties are the delicate dependence of the process upon system gain and magnetic differences between batches of tape.

## 19.12 TAPE TRANSPORTS

### 19.12.1 Mechanical Considerations

Most tape transports in use today are of the so-called open loop type, as shown in Figure 19-14. Basically, the function of the tape transport is move tape at a constant linear velocity during the recording and playback processes and to provide quick and easy access to any part of the recording through fast-forward and rewind modes. These goals are not easily achieved, and design considerations have changed over the years as tape widths have progressed from 0.635, 1.27, 2.5, and 5 cm ($\frac{1}{4}$, $\frac{1}{2}$, 1, and 2 inch) widths.

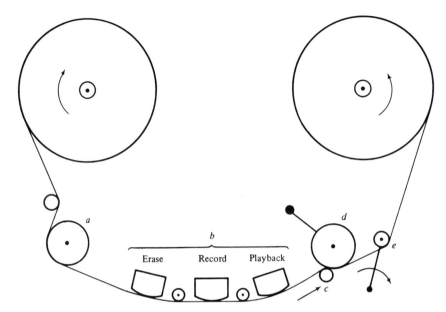

**Figure 19-14.** Typical mechanical layout for an open-loop transport.

First consider some of the problems inherent in the narrower tape widths operating at speeds of 19 and 38 cm/sec. Narrower tape, especially 0.635 cm, does not present significant guidance problems on the transport; it bends, or warps, easily enough to conform to the tape path. The greatest problem is *flutter*, a rapid instability in tape motion due to many causes. Mechanical irregularities in the transport are the chief cause, but "violin bow" action of the tape as it passes over the heads may contribute *scrape flutter*, which will produce a granularity or coarseness in the quality of the sound if it is excessive. To eliminate these problems there are numerous idlers, or rollers, in the tape path in intimate contact with the tape; their purpose is to smooth out the irregularities in the motion. Because of the low mass of 0.635 cm ($\frac{1}{4}$-inch) reels, the acceleration demands of the spooling motors in the fast-forward and rewind modes are minimal.

Examining Figure 19-14 in detail, we see the supply reel at the left side of the transport. It is supplied with reverse torque, or hold-back tension, during the record and playback processes. The tape passes around an idler at *a*, which serves to smooth out gross irregularities of the tape as it comes off the supply reel. As the tape passes the erase, record, and playback head stack at *b*, it is essential that tape motion be as smooth as possible. Often, small idlers are placed between the heads to filter what little scrape flutter may develop as the tape passes each head. Obviously, the nature of the finish of the oxide layer and finish of head surfaces play an important role in determining performance in this area.

As the tape passes the head stack, it goes through the *capstan/pressure* roller assembly at *c* and *d*. The capstan turns at constant angular velocity. Today, most capstans are an extension of the shaft of a servo-controlled dc motor, and great care is taken to ensure that the motion is uniform. The pressure roller holds the tape against the capstan so that

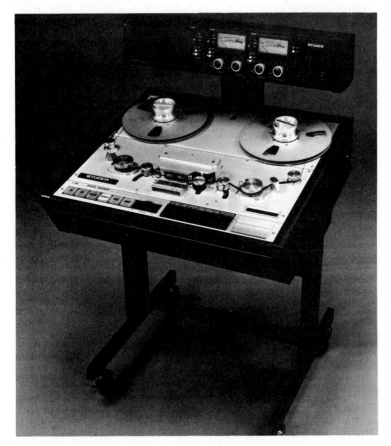

**Figure 19-15.** A modern 2-track recorder. (*Courtesy Studer Revox America, Inc.*)

capstan motion is transferred to the tape. The pressure roller is invariably made of synthetic rubber, smoothly surfaced on a precision bearing. The newer capstan motors, since they are electronically controlled, are capable of operating at several speeds, normally 76, 38, and 19 cm/sec (30, 15, and 7.5 inches/sec). On many machines, the speed can further be varied several percent around each of the nominal speeds.

As tape passes through the capstan drive, it loops over a spring-loaded guidance arm, shown at *e*, whose functions are to ensure even stacking of the tape as it winds onto the take-up reel and to detect tape breakage and avoid tape spill. Many of the details of Figure 19-14 can be seen in Figures 19-15 and 16, which are photographs of modern 2-track and 24-track recorders.

Many older tape recorders had occasional problems with "wow," a cyclic variation in tape speed that was caused by once-around irregularities in the spooling motors or other rotating parts of the mechanism. This is rarely encountered today.

Another problem of the past was timing accuracy. Due to uneven holdback tension from start to finish of the supply reel, there could be slight but perceptible changes in

**Figure 19-16.** A modern 24-track recorder. (*Courtesy Studer Revox America, Inc.*)

tape speed. This was a real problem in tape editing, when occasionally two segments of music had to be joined that were not quite of the same pitch.

Today's transports have progressed far beyond their predecessors in ease of operation. They are virtually foolproof; an operator may go directly from one mode to another without mishap. Sophisticated logic and motion sensing are part of any good professional tape transport and make it nearly impossible to spill or break tape, no matter what the operating mode. These functions have become all the more important with the increase in usage of 5-cm (2-inch) tape.

The mechanics of handling the wider tapes are quite different from those of narrower tape widths. An obvious difference is the greater mass of the tape reel and the consequent need for bigger spooling motors so that fast-forward and rewind functions can be handled efficiently. Tape guidance is a major problem. The wide tapes will not easily warp; so all tape guides must be precise and stable so that motion is at all times at right angles to the reference plane of the transport's top-plate.

Flutter is far less a problem with the wider tapes; the greater mass and higher recording speeds of 38 and 76 cm/sec result in significantly higher momentum, and this seems to filter many irregularities of tape motion. As a consequence, idlers tend to be smaller, and there are fewer of them on the wide tape transports.

### 19.12.2 Operational Controls

The four main operational controls on a tape transport are as follows.

*Play/Record.* This control engages normal forward motion of the tape and is used for playback and record activities. On many transports, the record function requires an additional control to be actuated at the same time as the play control. This often requires both hands of the operator, so inadvertent recording can be avoided. On many transports, there are safety switches on each channel to avert accidental recording.

*Stop.* This control disengages any other function involving tape motion, such as play, record, fast forward, or rewind.

*Rewind.* This control puts significant torque on the rewind spooling motor, with just enough back torque on the take-up motor to maintain a predetermined tension in the tape. The tape is rewound at high speed.

*Fast Forward.* This control does essentially the same thing as the previous one, except that the tape will be wound on the take-up reel. In both of these operations, the tape lifters will be raised so that tape will not contact the heads at high speeds. This is done for two reasons: to prevent unnecessary wear on the heads, and to prevent loud high-pitched noises, should the monitor volume control not be turned down.

In many newer machines, the spooling motors are differentially controlled so that in the fast-forward and rewind functions tape tension does not vary greatly.

For these functions, all controls are interlocked so that accidents cannot occur. For example, if a machine is in fast forward, the engineer can engage the record function simply by pressing the right controls. The machine will first go from fast forward to rewind. When it reaches zero velocity, it will then go into record. Older machines, some venerable ones, did not do this, and the engineer had to "program" all of the operations sequentially.

There are some optional features in the tape motion control area that are useful in editing:

*Shuttle.* This is a knob that lets the engineer shuttle the tape back and forth at a chosen speed so that a given program segment can be found quickly.

*Jog Mode.* This allows tape motion to follow exactly the position of the shuttle knob. The engineer can thus use it for identifying the exact place on the tape where a splice is to be made.

*Edit Play Function.* In many editing jobs it is desirable to remove lengthy segments of unwanted tape. The easiest way to do this is simply play the segments through the machine, allowing the tape to fall onto the floor, or into a waste can. In this mode, the take-up reel torque is disabled.

Other functions on the transport include:

*Reel Size Selector.* This function adjusts the torque on the spooling motors so that small hub reels can be used without concern for tape spill or stretching.

*Tape Speed Selector.* This control sets the speed of the capstan motor. It may or may not switch record and playback equalization at the same time.

## 19.13 TAPE SYNCHRONIZING AND INDEXING TECHNIQUES

As we have stated before, one of the great benefits of the magnetic medium is the ease with which tracks can be added to a recording at different times. This involves a variety of techniques, ranging from the simplest demands of "overdubbing" to automatic indexing and methods of synchronizing two or more machines.

### 19.13.1 Sel-Sync

Under the trade name Sel-Sync (Selective Synchronization), Ampex introduced a means of overdubbing, or recording new tracks in synchronism with previous tracks on the tape. Until this time, the overdubbing process usually involved re-recording of the previous material, while new material was added to it. As such, this process is almost as old as electrical recording itself, and there is a case where it was done on a Toscanini recording (13).

Ampex's method involved using the record heads for playback, so that the normal time gap between record and playback heads could be reduced to zero. The method is shown in Figure 19-17(a). Note that the input to each playback amplifier can be switched to either the playback or the recording head, or to the input for that track. In the synchronization mode, those tracks previously recorded (tracks 1, 2, and 3) would be played back over their respective record heads, while track 4 would be energized for recording in the normal way. The performer will monitor tracks 1, 2, and 3 over headphones.

In the early days of this technique, the frequency response of the record heads in their roles as playback heads left much to be desired; it was sufficient for monitoring purposes only. Later improvements resulted in playback in the synchronization mode virtually identical to the playback itself in terms of noise and frequency response. Thus, it became possible to combine and shift tracks on a multitrack master, as desired, to free up new tracks for subsequent recording. The technique is known as "bouncing."

### 19.13.2 Insert Recording

In many cases involving overdubbing, it is necessary for a recorder to go in and out of the record mode without producing annoying clicks or thumps on the tape. In order to do this, the bias at both the erase and record heads has to be turned on and off smoothly.

As a tape recorder normally goes into the record mode (punch-in), bias is switched to the record and erase heads simultaneously. Because of the spacing between the two heads, the segment of tape between them will not be properly erased. Furthermore, when

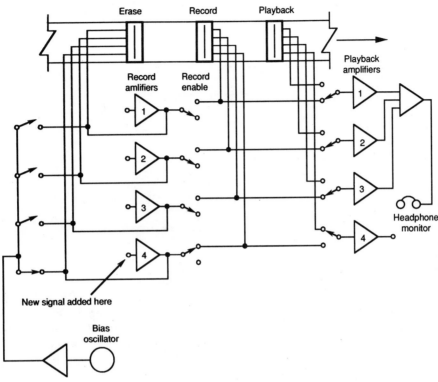

**Figure 19-17.** Basic flow diagram for Sel-Sync technique. A new signal is added on track 4 in synchronism with the previously recorded tracks.

the record function is turned off (punch-out), there will be a corresponding gap in the tape. At higher speeds these gaps are quite short, perhaps no more than 0.1 second, and they are often ignored.

The problem is solved by energizing the erase head before the record head by an amount equal to the time gap between them. Likewise, when going out of the insert recording mode, the erase head is deactivated before the record head by the same amount of time. Figure 19-18 shows details of the insert recording process.

### 19.13.3 Automatic Indexing and Rehearsal Mode

In the process of making an insert into a previously recorded track, it is necessary for the performer to "rehearse" with the tracks already recorded on the master tape. Shuttling the tape back and forth between starting and stopping positions is made easy by automatic indexing. In this procedure, the engineer enters beginning and ending timings. When the recorder reaches the end timing, it will recycle to the beginning, and stand by for the next pass. The timing cues on the tape can be slaved to a rudimentary counting mechanism, or, as in more recent machines, be controlled by an SMPTE time code track that has been recorded on the master tape. The general process is shown in Figure 19-19.

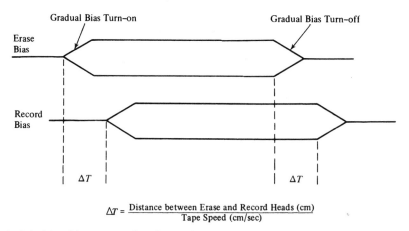

$$\Delta T = \frac{\text{Distance between Erase and Record Heads (cm)}}{\text{Tape Speed (cm/sec)}}$$

**Figure 19-18.** Principle of insert recording. Proper insert recording requires that there be a gradual HF bias turn-on and turn-off to ensure noise-free transitions in and out of the record mode.

In the rehearsal mode, the recorder will not go into record mode when the engineer punches-in; instead, the monitor selector on the track to be modified will switch to input, so that the artist will hear the new material to be added, without erasing previous material. When both producer and artist are reasonably confident that the maneuver has been rehearsed well enough to succeed, the engineer will go out of rehearse mode. When this is done, punching-in will then activate the record function until the engineer punches-out of that mode.

In these processes, the engineer will be working both at the console and at the remote control unit for the recorder. The remote control control unit provides a duplicate set of recorder mechanical, indexing, and monitor functions that can more conveniently be placed at the console.

### 19.13.4 SMPTE Time Code

Originally developed for synchronizing video equipment in post-production operations, SMPTE (Society of Motion Picture and Television Engineers) time code provides a reliable method for controlling audio recorders and console automation as well. The code gives information, updated 30 times per second, concerning video frame number, seconds,

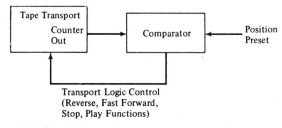

**Figure 19-19.** Block diagram for automatic indexing of a tape recorder.

minutes, and hours. The code format is binary coded decimal (BCD) recorded in biphase fashion. Figure 19-20 outlines the fundamentals of the system. Binary values of "0" and "1" are arranged in groups of four to represent the decimal numbers 0 through 9, as shown in (a). A typical 8-bit binary "word" is shown in (b), along with its waveform. Zero is represented by a shift in the waveform once per clock period, while two shifts per period represent the binary value of one. The code uses 80 bits to identify each video frame, and at 30 frames per second, the bit rate is 2400 per second. The complete code for one frame is shown in (c). Of interest is the fact that there are 32 spare bits that can be assigned by the user for other data, such as program identification, date, and so forth.

A code generator–reader is used to control two machines, as shown in Figure 19-21. At a cost of one track per machine, a pair of multichannel recorders can be operated effectively as a single machine, providing the engineer with considerable track capability. One machine is designated as the master machine and the other as slave. All logic functions on the slave machine will follow the master machine, and synchronism is assured under routine studio operating conditions.

## 19.14 TRACK WIDTH STANDARDS

Current track width standards for professional recording formats are shown in Figure 19-22. Dimensions are in inches.

## 19.15 TAPE RECORDER ALIGNMENT PROCEDURES

Tape recorders differ somewhat in their specific alignment requirements because of varying details of mechanical design. However, the following sequence of procedures is fundamental to all machines, and every recording engineer should know how and why they are performed. The following procedure assumes a typical two-channel stereo recorder.

### Mechanical alignment and check-out

1. Before subjecting an expensive alignment tape to an unknown transport, new or old, the engineer must first make sure that the transport is in proper mechanical order. Holdback tension of the supply and take-up reels should be within the range specified by the manufacturer. These should be measured in the normal play mode as well as in the fast-forward and rewind modes.
2. The capstan pressure roller thrust (in the play mode) should be within the range specified by the manufacturer. For these measurements, a simple 5-pound spring scale available at a hardware store will be useful.
3. Using a roll of expendable tape, the engineer should make sure that the machine operates properly in all of its transport modes and that the tape travels over the head stack with a minimum of up-an-down motion or skew. (Actually, any perceptible amount is a sign that something is not right, but a small amount may not be detrimental to overall performance.)

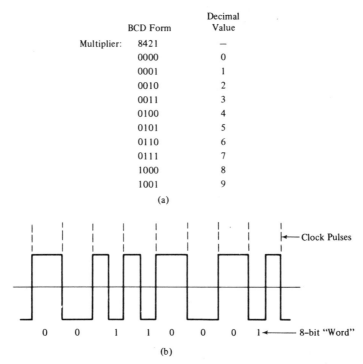

Figure 19-20. SMPTE address code. (a) Illustration of binary-coded decimal values and (b) structure of the biphase word. (c) Bit structure of a single video frame.

4. The transport should be thoroughly cleaned with an appropriate solvent recommended by the manufacturer. Most common here is isopropyl alcohol. Heads should be cleaned only with a cleaning solution approved by the manufacturer.

### Playback function check-out

1. All tape guides, idlers, and heads in the tape path must first be thoroughly demagnetized (degaussed), using a head demagnetizer. Remnant magnetism of heads or guides may increase the noise level and result in some degree of HF signal erasure from any tape played on the machine. Be sure that the machine is turned off before demagnetizing the heads.

   The proper use of a head demagnetizer is best learned from an experienced engineer. The typical demagnetizer has a fairly small gap, located between two metal probes. Ensure that the gap region has been covered with a small piece of electrical tape, so that there is no chance of scratching the laminations of the heads. Demagnetization of the heads requires that the gap of the demagnetizer be placed directly at the head surface, straddling the head gap. The demagnetizer is then moved up and down several times, and then pulled away from the head with a smooth motion.

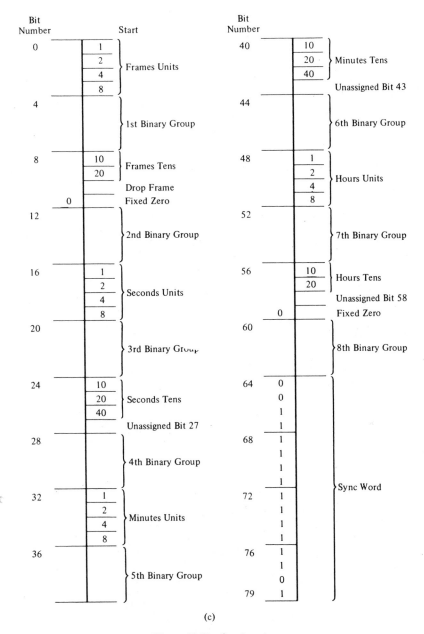

(c)

**Figure 19-20.** Continued.

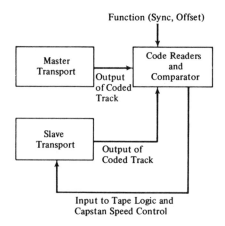

**Figure 19-21.** Synchronizing two tape transports with an address code. Two or more slave machines can be run in synchronism with a single master trasport. Various time offsets between transports are possible.

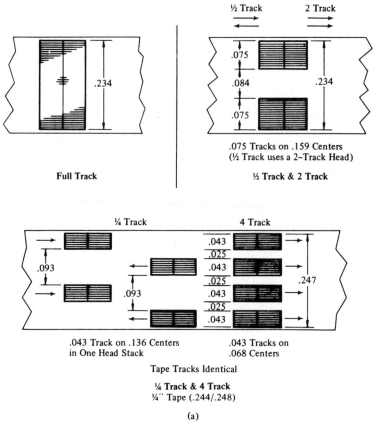

(a)

**Figure 19-22.** Various track width standards. All dimensions are in inches. (*Courtesy Ampex*)

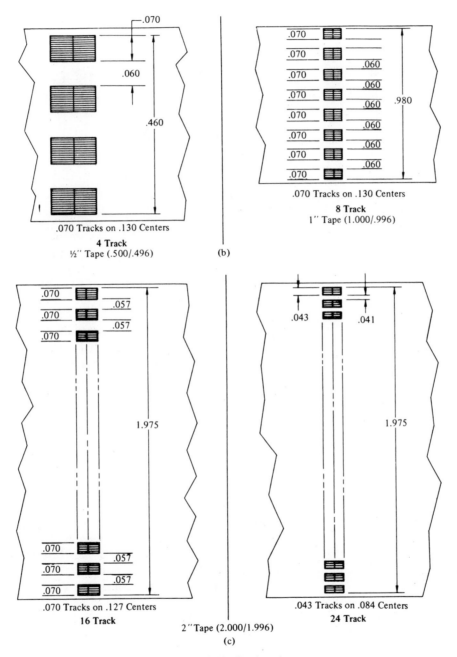

.070 Tracks on .130 Centers
**4 Track**
½″ Tape (.500/.496)

.070 Tracks on .130 Centers
**8 Track**
1″ Tape (1.000/.996)

(b)

.070 Tracks on .127 Centers
**16 Track**

.043 Tracks on .084 Centers
**24 Track**

2″ Tape (2.000/1.996)

(c)

**Figure 19-22.** Continued.

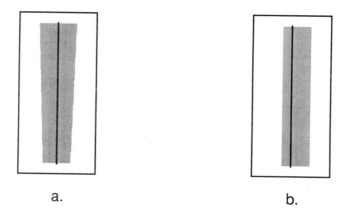

**Figure 19-23.** Head wear patterns. (a) Zenith misadjusted. (b: Head rotation misadjusted.

2. The terms *azimuth*, *zenith*, and *rotation* refer to the possible angular adjustments of a head. In addition, there are translational adjustments, such as head height and fore-aft positioning. In some older transports, all of these could be adjusted, or misadjusted, while in newer machines most of these dimensional aspects are locked in place. It is important that *all* of the heads be properly aligned, inasmuch as overall performance is the product of them all.

Head height controls side to side positioning and tracking of the signal on the tape. Misadjustment here could result in some degree of signal loss, if a properly aligned tape is played on a misaligned machine. Fore-aft positioning of the head determines the tape wrap around the head and gap. If there should be insufficient contact, then signal will become dropout-prone.

Long-term head wear depends very much on head rotation and zenith, as shown in Figure 19-23. *Zenith angle* refers to any tilt, from top to bottom, of the head in the plane perpendicular to the tape. For example, if the top of the head tilts toward the front of the transport, there will be more wear at the top of the head because the tape will bear harder on the head at the top. This case is shown in (a).

*Head rotation* describes the position of the head about the vertical axis. The correct position is for the head gap to contact the tape symmetrically. If this is not the case, then the pattern of head wear will be as shown in (b).

*Azimuth* refers to the head gap angle with respect to the direction of tape motion. Ideally, this angle should be 90°. If it is misadjusted, as shown in Figure 19-24, then there will be common mode signal cancellation if the stereo tracks are summed for mono. The frequency of cancellation will be that for which the azimuth angle $\alpha$ produces a half-wavelength ($\lambda/2$) displacement of the heads relative to the two tracks. Integral multiples of this frequency will also be cancelled. For a two-channel recording at a speed of 38 cm/sec, an azimuth error of 0.23° will cause cancellation at 15 kHz and its integral multiples. For the larger tape widths, the effects of azimuth misalignment will be proportionally greater.

Again, we stress that record and playback azimuth errors are additive; a correct recording played back on a misadjusted machine will be the same as a recording on

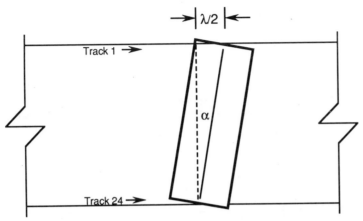

**Figure 19-24.** Azimuth adjustment. In addition to HF losses within a given track, azimuth errors will produce larger amounts of cancellation of common mode information if outer tracks are added together.

a misadjusted machine played back on a correctly adjusted machine, if the azimuth error angles are the same.

Azimuth is perhaps the most critical head adjustment in terms of audio performance, and correct adjustment for the playback head is now described. Connect the two outputs of the stereo machine to the vertical and horizontal inputs of an oscilloscope so that a Lissajous figure can be observed (see Section 12.7.2). Using that HF portion of the tape designated for azimuth adjustment, make small changes in the azimuth adjustment screw until the figure on the oscilloscope resembles a stable 45° (in-phase) line from lower left to upper right, and producing maximum output on the meters. If the head is considerably off azimuth, there may appear smaller false peaks in response, so the engineer should be certain that the maximum value has been attained. On a multitrack machine, the outside tracks should be used for this measurement.

3. Playback equalization is then adjusted with the sequence of tones provided on the tape for that purpose. Typically, the tones might be at the following frequencies: 31.5, 40, 63, 125, 250, 500, 1000, 2000, 4000, 6300, 8000, 10,000, 12,500, 14,000, 16,000, 18,000, and 20,000 Hz. These tones may vary between manufacturers, but what is obvious is that they are closely spaced at the frequency extremes, while being at octave intervals in the mid-band. Since the critical frequency adjustments on the playback of tape recorders are above 5 kHz and below 100 Hz, the extra "density" of frequencies is useful in fine-tuning the playback response. Using the various controls provided for the purpose, the engineer should adjust the playback equalization for flattest response.

If a full-track alignment tape is used for stereo equalization adjustment, there will be some LF errors, due to fringing of the long wavelengths around the heads. Most manufacturers of alignment tapes provide correction tables for this purpose, so that correct frequency response adjustment can be made.

4. The final playback adjustment is that of reference output level, and this is made

with that portion of the tape intended for operating level calibration. If a 185 nWb/m alignment tape is used, normal calibration (not elevated) requires that the gain be set so that this tone produces a meter reading of 0 dB. If the engineer wishes to calibrate to elevated level, this tone should be set for a meter reading of −3 dB. If an elevated level test tape is used, and the desired calibration is for elevated level, then the gain should be set for a meter reading of 0 dB.

It must be emphasized that a consistently applied standard is essential in any recording studio complex. No engineer should be allowed to make an arbitrary change in reference level.

### Record function check-out

1. Using the playback head as a secondary standard, the azimuth of the record head is adjusted by recording a HF tone (normally 15 kHz), and adjusting the azimuth of the record heads until there is a clear maximum in response in the output of the playback heads. An alternative method is to put the machine in sync mode and adjust the output of the record heads directly for maximum response, using the HF portion of the alignment tape intended for that purpose. This is the recommended procedure for late-model machines.
2. Setting record bias level is done by recording a HF signal (see Section 19.6) and adjusting record bias level to that the playback output is overbiased by 3 dB. This is normally done by first achieving peak output at the high frequency, and then further increasing bias until the output level drops 3 dB. The engineer should check the specification sheet for the particular tape stock in use for any particular instructions here. Also, the user's manual for the recorder may recommend alternate procedures.
3. Some machines have additional adjustments for bias waveform purity. These should be carefully adjusted, following manufacturer's instructions, inasmuch as this will affect the recorded noise level. If there is such an adjustment on the machine, it is wise to again demagnetize all heads after it has been adjusted.
4. Adjustment of record equalization is done by inserting frequencies with an oscillator at the input and adjusting the various record equalization controls until the flattest playback output is attained.
5. Record level calibration is set so that when making an A-B check of machine input versus output, the two levels will be the same. Thus, the tape recorder will be a unity-gain device under all operating conditions.

**Adjustment of bias erase current**    Manufacturer's instructions should be followed here. Older machines often exhibit interaction between record and erase bias requirement, resulting in fluctuations, depending on how many tracks were in record mode at a given time. This is not a problem in modern machines.

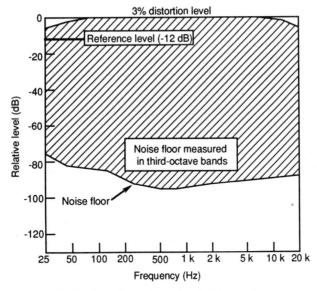

**Figure 19-25.** Overall tape recorder electrical performance.

### 19.15.1 Automatic Electronic Alignment

The procedures outlined above for machine checkout would be quite a chore if applied to a 24-track recorder. A number of modern machines provide for electronic adjustment of machine operating parameters so that the whole process can be simplified. These of course vary by manufacturer.

## 19.16 OVERALL DYNAMIC RANGE OF A RECORDER

In the normal process of recording, an engineer, monitoring levels with a VU meter will generally reach instantaneous program levels some 10 to 12 dB *higher* than the zero indication on the meter. Most of the time, the meter is simply showing normal excursions into the red, with only an occasional hard thump against the pin. Many high-output tape formulations today can handle levels up to 1000 nWb/m with no more than 3% harmonic distortion. This would seem to be a reasonable and safe upper limit to the analog tape recording process, and the use of 250 nWb/m as a reference for zero on the meter appears logical, inasmuch as the engineer knows that there is 12 dB headroom above that reference.

At the other extreme, the analog tape medium exhibits a reasonably smooth noise spectrum when viewed at constant percentage bandwidth. Figure 19-25 shows the "signal space" for a modern recorder using high-output tape, operating in stereo. Zero level here represents the 3% distortion point at middle frequencies, and the noise floor has been measured in one-third octave bands.

Noise specifications for tape recorders normally do not present data in this form. Usually, there is a broadband noise reading, and one or more weighted readings. For example, the recorder used in these measurements exhibits a broadband noise floor 68 dB below the 3% level, and an A-weighted noise noise floor 72 dB below the same reference.

Is this residual noise floor perceptible? Often it is, especially when it is considered that modern digital recorders are 20 dB better in dynamic range. This consideration leads naturally to the next chapter, which treats noise reduction techniques in recording.

## BIBLIOGRAPHY

1. K. Benson, *Audio Engineering Handbook*, McGraw-Hill, New York (1988).
2. M. Camras, *Magnetic Recording Handbook*, Van Nostrand Reinhold, New York (1988).
3. W. Carlson et al., U.S. Patent 1, 640,881 (1927).
4. D. Eilers, "Development of a New Magnetic Tape for Music Mastering," *J. Audio Engineering Society*, vol. 18, no. 5 (1970).
5. H. Ford, "Audio Tape Revisited," *Studio Sound*, vol. 21, no. 4 (1979).
6. D. Griesinger, "Reducing Distortion in Analog Tape Recorders," *J. Audio Engineering Society*, vol. 23, no. 2 (1975).
7. F. Jorgensen, *The Complete Book of Magnetic Recording*, TAB, Blue Ridge Summit, Pa. (1980).
8. S. Katz et al., "Alignment," *Recording Engineer/Producer*, vol. 6, no. 1 (1975).
9. J. Kempler, "Making Tape," *Audio Magazine*, (April 1975).
10. C. Lowman, Magnetic Recording, McGraw-Hill, New York (1972).
11. C. Mee and E. Daniel, *Magnetic Recording,* Volume III, McGraw-Hill, New York (1988).
12. D. Mills, "The New Generation of High Energy Recording Tape," *Recording Engineer/Producer*, vol. 5, no. 6 (1974).
13. C. O'Connell, *The Other Side of the Record*, Alfred A. Knopf, New York (1948).
14. V. Poulsen, "The Telegraphone: A Magnetic Speech Recorder," *Electrician*, vol. 46, pp. 208–210 (1900).
15. O. Smith, "Some Possible Forms of Phonograph," *Electrical World*, vol. 12, pp. 116–117 (1888).
16. P. Vogelgesang, "On the Intricacies of Tape Performance," *db Magazine*, vol. 13, no. 1 (1979).
17. J. Woram, *Handbook of Sound Recording*, H. Sams, Indianapolis (1989).

# 20

## ENCODE–DECODE NOISE REDUCTION (NR) SYSTEMS

### 20.1 INTRODUCTION

This chapter will discuss methods of compressing (encoding) a signal before it is recorded, and expanding (decoding) it when it is played back. In this manner, the compressed signal can be kept above the noise level of the recording medium. If the tracking of the playback expansion action is the inverse of the compression action, then the original dynamic relationships in the program will be kept intact. In the process, however, the recorder's noise floor will be modulated by the expansion action.

The principle has been known for many years, but difficulties associated with dynamic mistracking and audibility of noise modulation kept it from being widely applied to professional recording. These problems were substantially solved by Dolby type-A noise reduction, which was introduced in the mid-1960s. Later, the dbx, Burwen, and Telcom systems were introduced to professional recording, while Dolby type-B and type-C systems were introduced into consumer cassette recorders. The most recent development in the technology is the Dolby Spectral Recording (SR) process.

### 20.2 THE BASIC ENCODE–DECODE PROCESS

Figure 20-1 shows how a simple "companding" noise reduction system operates. Assume that we have a tape recorder with a dynamic range of 60 dB. The input signal to the recorder is compressed by 10 dB, and its output is expanded 10 dB, as shown in (a). The gain curves of the compressor and expander are shown in (b), and the overall action on the signal from input to output is shown in (c).

The action is easy to understand if we examine the process over a wide dynamic range. A very wide dynamic range can exist at the input of the compressor. Since the maximum amount of compression is 10 dB, the input dynamic range, whatever it is, will be 10 dB

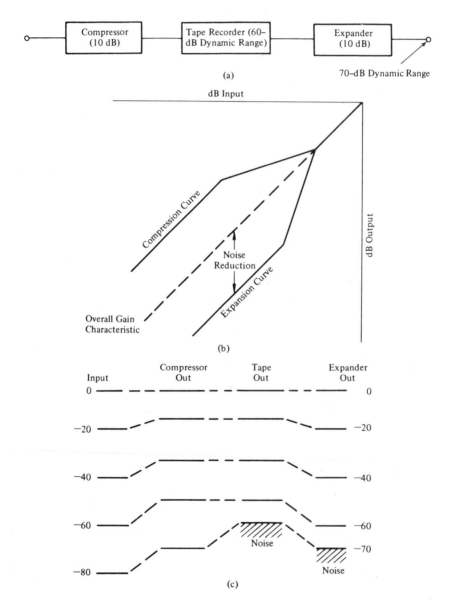

**Figure 20-1.** Fundamentals of a noise-reduction system. (a) Basic compressor–expander placement in the recording chain. (b) Gain curves for compression and expansion. (c) Level diagram through entire system, showing how noise generated in the tape recorder can be expanded downward and be less audible.

less at the output of the compressor. This compressed signal is then fed to the recorder, which has, in this example, a noise floor of −60 dB as seen at the output of the recorder. An expander is used to restore the original program dynamics by 10 dB, and the noise floor of the tape recorder will, on low level program, be heard at a level of −70 dB.

Note, however, that for high-level signals there is no net compression or expansion; in that case, the tape recorder exhibits its internal 60 dB dynamic range. Only when the input signal is at lower levels will there be any compression/expansion action through the system.

While the system described here can exhibit a dynamic range of 70 dB, it can never exhibit a signal-to-noise ratio greater than that of its weakest link, the tape recorder. In this case, the maximum signal-to-noise ratio can never be better than 60 dB.

## 20.3 THE DOLBY TYPE-A NOISE REDUCTION SYSTEM

Dolby minimized the audibility of noise floor shifting by splitting the bandwidth into four sections, as shown in Figure 20-2(a), and operating on each band separately (3).

The basic configuration of the compressor and expander are shown in (b). The circuit topology is unique to the various Dolby systems. In the compression mode, the side chain is connected as a positive feed-forward loop. At low input levels (−40 dB and lower), the side chain dominates because of amplification in that channel. At higher levels, the compressor in the side chain keeps the signal in that chain from exceeding −40 dB; thus, the direct path becomes dominant.

In the expander configuration, the side channel is reconfigured as shown. It has now become a negative feedback loop, reducing the gain in the direct path in the range of −40 dB and lower.

The four bands each have their own compressors, as shown in (c), and the action within the bands is completely independent. The response of a typical compressor is shown in (d).

Dolby modules can be switched between the encode or the decode functions, and when this is done, the circuit is switched to either the input of the recording section (for encoding) or to the output of the playback section (for decoding).

### 20.3.1 Principle of Least Action

The Dolby NR systems are unique in that high-level program follows a direct path through both encode compressor and decode expander. Only when the level in a given band is in the −40 dB range and lower will the side chains come into effect. Since the ear is relatively insensitive to small level variations when level is low, a small amount of system mistracking will be virtually inaudible.

### 20.3.2 Calibration Requirements

It should be clear that the Dolby NR systems require the record–playback function to operate as a unity gain, flat response system, since any deviations in level through the recorder would affect the low level thresholds in the playback decoding action.

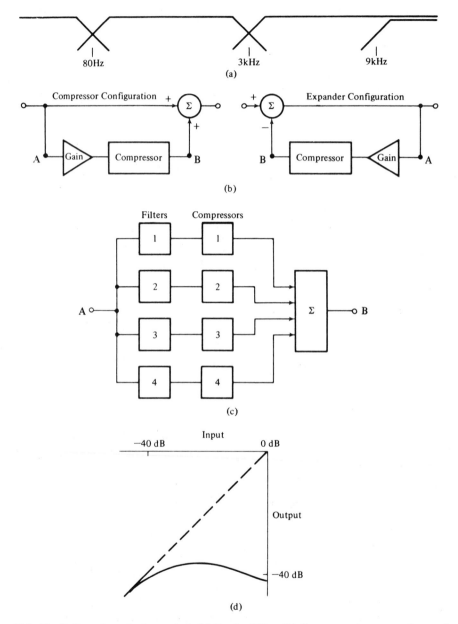

**Figure 20-2.** The Dolby noise reduction system. (a) Band splitting. (b) Compressor in compression configuration and in expansion configuration. (c) Block diagram of complete processor. (d) Gain curve for the compressor.

Further, the Dolby system makes use of an internal electrical reference level. This reference level, known as Dolby level, can be set via a small meter on the front of the unit. There is an internal generator that produces the distinctive Dolby tone. This is an 850 Hz tone, with periodic interruptions at 0.75 second intervals that give it a chirping sound.

Normal practice is as follows. When recording a Dolby-encoded tape, the tone generator is set to a calibration point on the meter, and the tone recorded at the chosen operating level on the recorder. When that tape is subsequently played back, the tone, which is at the head of the tape, is adjusted to the *same* calibration point on the Dolby unit's meter. When this is done, the incoming signal will be at the correct level internal to the Dolby unit, and the decoding action will track the previous encoding action.

Thus, there is no such thing as Dolby tape level per se; the Dolby tone can be recorded at any reasonable level, and as long as that tone is correctly calibrated to the Dolby unit on playback, the NR system will work properly. Generally, standard practice is to relate the prevailing tape calibration level to Dolby level. However, if a tape arrives at the studio minus the Dolby tone, a little experimenting will have to be done to determine the correct calibration. If the tape was made in the United States, one can assume that either 185 or 250 nWb/m is equivalent to the missing tone, and the Dolby unit can be calibrated with one of the test tapes. If the tape has come from Europe, the assumption can be made that either 360 or 510 corresponds to the missing tone. Let the ears be the judge.

Figure 20-3 shows a photograph of a set of Dolby A encode–decode units rack mounted for multitrack use.

**Figure 20-3.** A 24-channel noise reduction system. (*Courtesy Dolby Laboratories*)

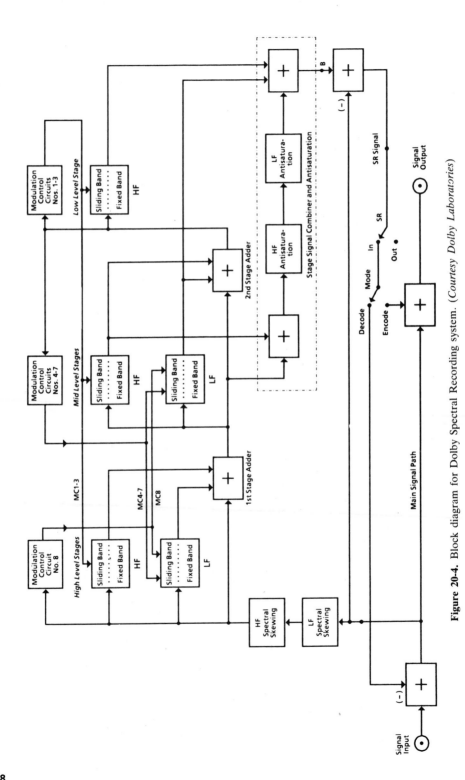

**Figure 20-4.** Block diagram for Dolby Spectral Recording system. *(Courtesy Dolby Laboratories)*

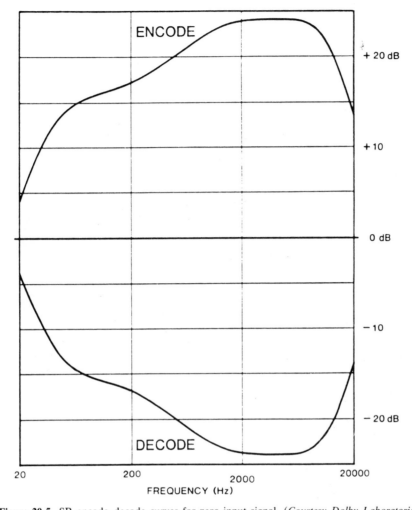

**Figure 20-5.** SR encode–decode curves for zero input signal. (*Courtesy Dolby Laboratories*)

## 20.4 THE DOLBY SPECTRAL RECORDING (SR) PROCESS

Spectral Recording represents a significant advance over A-type NR. It has much in common with A (fixed frequency bands) and with the B and C-types (sliding bands). As can be seen in Figure 20-4, the system is quite complex. Note, however, that it has the same encode–decode switching topology as the earlier Dolby systems. In the encode mode, the side chain is in a positive feed-forward configuration; in the decode mode it is in a negative feedback configuration (4).

The effectiveness of the system for low-level signal inputs can be seen in the encoding and decoding curves shown in Figure 20-5. The total amount of effective equalization is about 24 dB in the mid-band, indicating a net 24-dB noise reduction in the range where hearing is most sensitive. Thus, the tape recorder whose noise spectrum was described

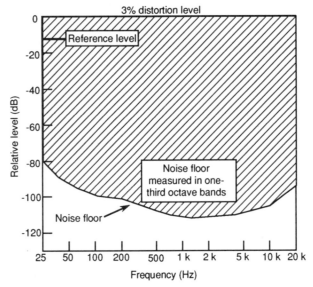

**Figure 20-6.** Signal space for an analog recorder operating with Dolby SR. Noise measurements made on third-octave center frequencies.

in Figure 19-26, would, if it were using SR, have an equivalent noise spectrum as shown in Figure 20-6. In some portions of the spectrum, the effective dynamic range exceeds that of 16-bit digital recorders (see Chapter 21).

SR is unique in the way it can adapt to very narrowband input signals. Figure 20-7 shows a family of encoding curves for a 200-Hz tone that has been input to the system at levels of +20, 0, −20, and −40 dB. These curves indicate that between 0 and +20 dB there is little action on the input signal itself (principle of least action), while at lower and higher frequencies the input is boosted up to 20 dB, providing for that much noise reduction in playback.

As the input is reduced to −20 dB, the record gain at 200 Hz increases about 14 dB. As the input is reduced to −40 dB, the record gain increases an additional 10 dB, indicating that, at an input level of −40 dB, there is about 24 dB boost of the signal, allowing it to ride well over the noise floor. For signal input well below −40 dB, the record gain reaches a maximum of about 23 dB.

The ability of SR to adapt its gain contour to almost any signal spectrum comes as a result of its three internal threshold levels and the progressive action of both fixed and sliding bands in shaping the overall contour. Another feature of SR is its use of both HF and LF rolloff (anti-saturation) circuits in the encoding function to ensure that the tape recorder will never see an input signal that could cause either HF or LF overload. Remember that the playback curves are the inverse of the record curves, so that flat overall response is always assured.

Dolby SR recordings are identified by a pink-noise signal with a 20 msec interruption at 2-second intervals. For playback calibration, the reproduced noise signal is compared at 4-second intervals with the internal generator so that level and spectral balance judgments can be made.

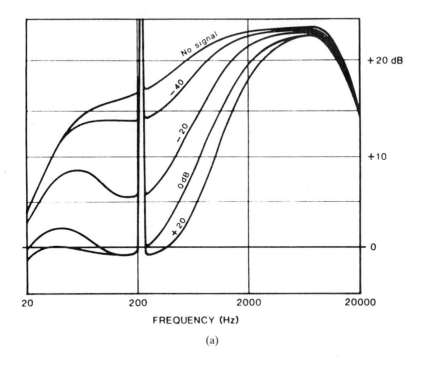

(a)

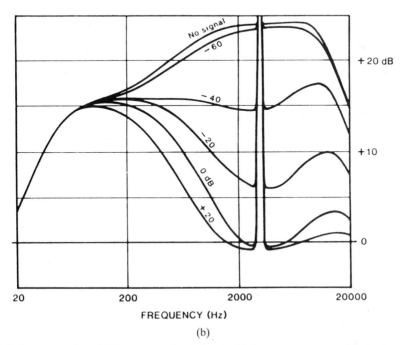

(b)

**Figure 20-7.** Unique operation of SR on narrow-band signals. (a) Encode curves for a 200-Hz input signal. (b) Encode curves for a 3-kHz input signal. (*Courtesy Dolby Laboratories*)

## 20.5 THE dbx NOISE REDUCTION SYSTEM

Figure 20-8 presents details of the dbx NR system. Essentially, the input signal is pre-emphasized (as shown in (c)) and is fed to a voltage-controlled amplifier (VCA), whose gain is controlled by a level-sensing circuit that provides a 2-to-1 compression ratio. The signal that is recorded is both boosted in HF response and compressed (1).

In the decode mode, the level sensing circuit derives a voltage that produces a 2-to-1 expansion ratio. At the output, the signal is de-emphasized, and flat response is restored. Because the compression and expansion curves are complementary over such a wide dynamic range, the dbx system can sustain wide level mismatches with no adverse effects. This is not to say, however, that manufacturer's calibration instructions are to be ignored.

There are two versions of dbx NR. Type 1 is used in professional recording activities, while type 2 is used in consumer media. The differences are in detection thresholds as well as in the shape of pre- and de-emphasis curves.

## 20.6 THE BURWEN NOISE REDUCTION SYSTEM

This system is not normally encountered today. Like the dbx system, it was a single band system, but with a 3-to-1 ratio of compression and expansion. The input signal was pre-emphasized, and the output de-emphasized (2).

## 20.7 THE TELCOM c4 NOISE REDUCTION SYSTEM

This system uses four bands (similar to Dolby A) and a wide-range compression-expansion ratio of 1.5-to-1. As such, it has many of the advantages of both Dolby A and dbx systems. Although far from obsolete, it is not normally encountered in recording operations.

## 20.8 THE EMT NOISEX NR SYSTEM

The Noisex system predated the Dolby systems and was first available to the professional industry during the 1960s (6). It is similar to the Telcom system, but is rarely seen today.

## 20.9 INTERFACING NR SYSTEMS IN THE STUDIO

A 24-track recorder will usually have associated with it a rack containing 24 switchable NR modules, and for effective operation the modules should switch from encode to decode as the individual channels are switched between record and sync/playback modes. The only way around the switching problem is to provide 24 encoding modules and 24 decoding modules, and this is normally out of the question.

Some recorders provide for NR cards to be directly mounted in the machine. In this case, the switching operation takes place as each channel on the recorder is switched between its record, sync, or playback modes.

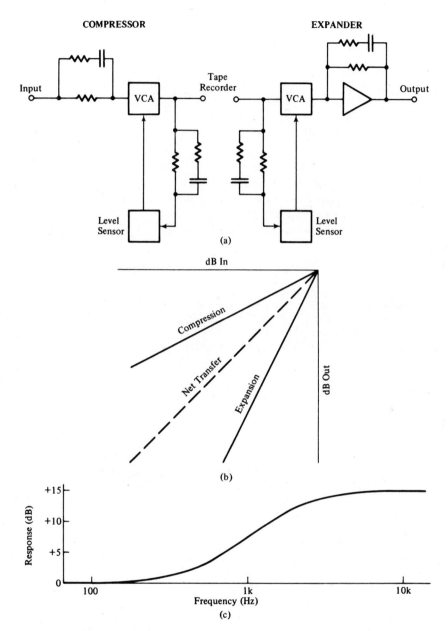

**Figure 20-8.** The dbx noise reduction system. (a) Compressor and expander modules. (b) 2-to-1 encode–decode gain curves. (c) Encode pre-emphasis response curve (the inverse curve is used at the output to restore flat response).

## 20.10 AUDIBILITY OF NR SYSTEMS

On the surface of it, NR systems seem to offer something for nothing. There is certainly a psychoacoustical factor working in their favor, and that is the ear's relative insensitivity to shifts in the noise floor if the noise is already at a sufficiently low level below the signal. All of the successful systems have mastered the problems of gain tracking, so that dynamic errors are not great. In addition the ear is surprisingly tolerant of them when they do occur. It is the occasional bit of noise modulation that can be problematic.

With Dolby A, it is possible for isolated soft sounds in the 100 to 200 Hz range to alter the gain in the second band (80 to 3 kHz), resulting in subtle noise modulation when there is nothing in the upper frequency ranges to mask the shift in noise level. Light isolated timpani strokes can cause this, if the monitor level is somewhat raised.

With dbx, large amounts of LF program content—an organ recording, for example— can cause the operating point to shift over a wide range, occasionally resulting in audibility of noise modulation from the recorder.

Thus far in the author's experience, SR seems to be immune to such problems (5).

## BIBLIOGRAPHY

1. D. Blackmer, "A Wide Dynamic Range Noise Reduction System," *db Magazine*, vol. 6, no. 8 (1972).
2. R. Burwen, "Design of a Noise Elimination System," *J. Audio Engineering Society*, vol. 19, no. 11 (1971).
3. R. Dolby, "An Audio Noise Reduction System," *J. Audio Engineering Society*, vol. 15, no. 4 (1967).
4. R. Dolby, "The Spectral Recording Process," *J. Audio Engineering Society*, vol. 35, no. 3 (1987).
5. J. Eargle, "Hands on: The Dolby Cat. 280 Spectral Recording module," *Recording Engineer/Producer*, vol. 18, no. 2 (1987).
6. J. Wermuth, "Compander Increases Dynamic Range," *db Magazine*, (June 1976).
7. J. Woram, *Sound Recording Handbook*, H. Sams, Indianapolis (1989).

# 21

## DIGITAL RECORDING AND SIGNAL PROCESSING

### 21.1 INTRODUCTION

Commercial digital recording of music dates from 1972, when the Nippon Columbia Company introduced an eight-channel digital converter for use with a quad format video recorder. By the end of the 1970s, a number of formats had been developed, and during the decade of the 1980s digital recording established itself as a virtual standard for two-channel mixdown activities. While there are two contending standards for digital multichannel recording, that area is still dominated by analog technology, largely due to the high costs of digital.

In all performance areas except frequency response, digital recording exceeds the best of the analog art. In terms of frequency response, analog recording can easily cover the range from 20 Hz to 30 kHz; digital recording has the capability of recording dc signals, but HF response limits have been set in the range of 20 kHz. This, at least in principle, disturbs many audiophiles.

The best analog machines today exhibit a dynamic range of 70 to 72 dB (A-weighted, 76 cm/sec, standard track width). With professional digital standards, the dynamic range is slightly in excess of 90 dB. In analog recording of wide dynamic range classical music without noise reduction, the listener is almost always aware of tape noise under critical listening conditions. With digital recorders, one rarely, if ever, is aware of noise due to the digital process; usually, noise due to microphones will intrude first.

At higher tape speeds, time-base instability (wow and flutter) in analog recorders may be as low as 0.04%; in the digital format, time base instabilities are virtually unmeasurable.

While the best analog recording process exhibits layer-to-layer print-through on the order of −55 to −60 dB, print-through is nonexistent in digital recording.

In analog recording, modulation noise, an increase in background noise apparent only when signal is present, is on the order of 55 to 60 dB below the input signal. It does not exist in the digital domain.

Even a single tape copy in the analog domain will result in some degradation in noise, distortion, and time base stability. By contrast, any number of successive transfers (clones) may be made in the digital domain with no deterioration.

Analog tape recordings have been known to deteriorate with time, and such deterioration is irreversible. While digital recordings are fragile and demand careful handling, long-term stability is inherent in the process. For example, a digital tape that shows any signs of deterioration can normally be cloned to newer tape stock before the deterioration has gone too far.

Program editing in the analog domain is quick and simple. In the digital domain, extra equipment is required, and the process is often more time consuming. However, digital editing is capable of far greater precision, and there are certain kinds of edits the digital technique affords that analog technique simply cannot match.

On a per-channel basis, digital technology is more expensive than analog, in both tape and equipment costs. The increasing use of R-DAT (Rotary Digital Audio Tape) for two-channel recording in many professional activities has already pointed the way for significant cost reductions.

With the sole exception of frequency response, the performance characteristics of digital recording appear to exceed those of analog recording by significant margins. While the principles of digital recording will receive most attention in this chapter, aspects of format conversion, the all-digital studio, and signal processing in the digital domain will be discussed.

## 21.2 SAMPLING THE INPUT SIGNAL

In analog recording, the audio signal is impressed on a medium and becomes part of it. The groove walls of a stereo LP are analogs, so to speak, of the left and right electrical signals, and any flaw or imperfection in the groove wall is inherent in the signal as well.

In digital (or numerical) recording, the signal is not recorded directly; rather, it is sampled at close time intervals and is quantized, or given a numerical value. It is the numbers that are are recorded, and as long as the numbers can be recovered accurately during the playback process, the signal can be reconstructed in its entirety. The sampling rate determines the upper frequency response limit of the recording system, while the degree of quantization, or resolution, determines the dynamic range of the system.

A sine wave must be sampled at least twice during the period of the waveform in order to be reconstructed. The sampling rate, $f_s$, is known as the Nyquist rate, and $f_s/2$ is known as the Nyquist frequency. Thus, if we want to maintain recorded bandwith to 20 kHz, we will need a Nyquist rate of at least 40 kHz. In practice, the rate is chosen to be somewhat higher, in order to simplify input filtering requirements. The choice is of a 44.1 kHz sampling frequency in the Compact Disc and most digital recorders have been designed with a 20-kHz system bandwidth in mind.

It is essential to avoid any input signals that are higher than the Nyquist frequency. If they enter the system and are sampled, they will be "aliased" downward in frequency. Figure 21-1 shows how this occurs. The small dots on the input signal represent the sampled points. Note that the dots define a much lower frequency, as indicated by the dashed line.

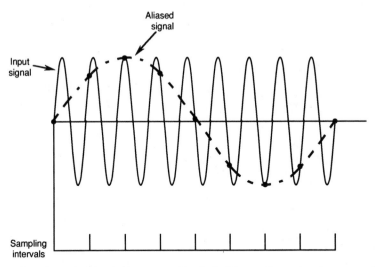

**Figure 21-1.** Sampling above the Nyquist frequency. The dashed line outlines a low-frequency alias component.

Another view is shown in Figure 21-2. This shows an input spectrum, which is within $f_n$, the Nyquist frequency. After sampling, the spectrum is arrayed about successive multiples of the Nyquist rate, $f_s$. Two frequencies, $f_1$ and $f_2$, which are higher than $f_n$, are added to the signal, and they alias downward into the passband of the system at frequencies of $f_s - f_1$ and $f_s - f_2$.

It is essential to use an anti-aliasing low pass filter at the input to prevent out-of-band signals from entering. Such a filter is shown in Figure 21-3(a). Because of the nonflat group delay through the filter, a square wave is passed through the filter with a "ringing" characteristic as shown in (b). Many filters are further modified with an all-pass phase shift network (c) that effectively flattens the group delay. When this has been done, the filter's response to a square wave is as shown in (d), with a smaller amount of ringing at both leading and trailing edges.

## 21.3 QUANTIZING THE INPUT SIGNAL

Any numerical system can be used in the quantizing process, but the *binary* system is preferred, because of its use in computing and the vast array of off-the-shelf hardware that can be used in designing the recorders. In binary counting, there are only two numbers, 0 and 1, and these are called *bits*. Table 21-1 shows a comparison of binary and decimal counting.

Binary numbers can be manipulated mathematically and of course form the basis of all digital computer activities. Just as decimal counting proceeds by powers of 10, binary counting proceeds by powers of 2. This is clear from the "binary tree" shown in Figure

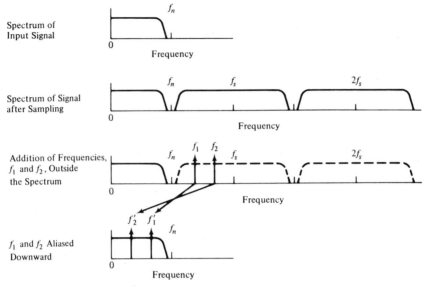

**Figure 21-2.** Another view of frequency aliasing. The input signals to a digital recording system are arrayed about successive multiples of the Nyquist sampling rate, $f_s$, $2f_s$, etc. The Nyquist frequency, $f_n$, is one-half the sampling frequency and is the normal upper limit to program input. If frequencies $f_1$ and $f_2$ (outside the range of $f_n$) are introduced into the system, they will be transferred, or "aliased" downward into the audible range.

**Table 21-1. Binary and decimal counting**

| Binary | Decimal |
|--------|---------|
| 0000 | 0 |
| 0001 | 1 |
| 0010 | 2 |
| 0011 | 3 |
| 0100 | 4 |
| 0101 | 5 |
| 0110 | 6 |
| 0111 | 7 |
| 1000 | 8 |
| 1001 | 9 |
| 1010 | 10 |
| 1011 | 11 |
| 1100 | 12 |
| 1101 | 12 |
| 1110 | 14 |
| 1111 | 15 |

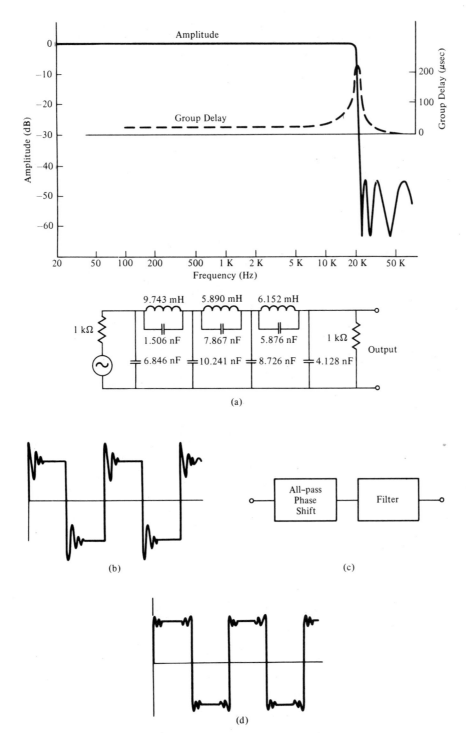

**Figure 21-3.** Characteristics of a high-quality seventh-order Chebyshev filter for anti-aliasing at the input of a digital recording system. (a) Response and schematic. (b) Square wave response. (c) Adding time correction. (d) "Corrected" signal minimizes overshoot. (*Filter data courtesy Victor Companies of Japan*)

**319**

21-4. The tree shown goes through the fifth power of 2, defining 32 states. The $2^1$ level is often referred to as the most significant bit (MSB), and the $2^5$ level is referred as the least significant bit (LSB). State "*a*" can be defined by the binary number 10110, state "*b*" by 01011, and state "*c*" by 00010.

This is called a 5-bit system, and we can use it, as shown in Figure 21-5, to "record and play back" a segment of an input waveform. Because there are only 32 possible states, the shape of the recovered waveform will be quite noisy, as shown. The recording of this input waveform would consist of a string of 5-bit messages, or *words*, as they are known. Each word would have been derived the same way we arrived at 5-bit descriptions of states "*a*," "*b*," and "*c*" in the previous figure.

In a 16-bit system, there are $2^{16}$, or 65,536 possible states for quantizing the input waveform. Each additional power of two halves the spacing between adjacent branches in the binary tree, producing an increase of 6 dB in dynamic range. Thus, for a 16-bit system, the maximum dynamic range capability is 16 times 6, or 96 dB. In practice, this value may be reduced somewhat for other beneficial trade-offs.

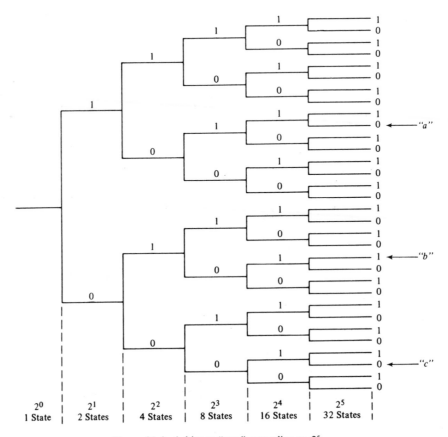

**Figure 21-4.** A binary "tree" extending to $2^5$.

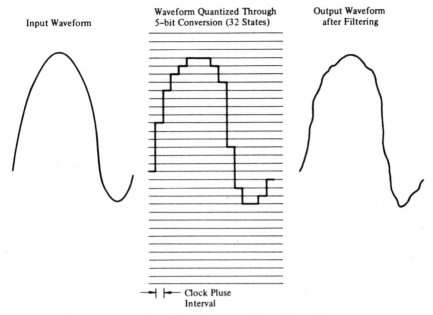

**Figure 21-5.** Input waveform quantized to $2^5$, or 32, states.

## 21.4 RECORDING SYSTEM BLOCK DIAGRAM

### 21.4.1 Dither and Anti-aliasing Filter

Figure 21-6 shows a basic flow diagram for a digital recorder. Dither noise is added at the program input; it is a very low-level signal that has a value of $\pm\frac{1}{2}$LSB, and its beneficial effect is shown in Figure 21-7. If no dither is present, input signals less than the LSB "fall in the cracks" and produce large amounts of distortion. If dither is added, the input signal will never be less than one LSB, and the dither will duty-cycle modulate the LSB transitions. After filtering, the input signal, even though it is less than one LSB, can be recovered, along with the dither noise itself.

It has long been observed that the ear can detect midband sinewave signals "buried" in wideband noise that may be up to 12 dB greater. This represents a negative signal-to-noise ratio, but it is important to state that the decay of a sound should be heard to fade away into system noise with no trace of discontinuity at all. The addition of dither at the input ensures that a digital recording system will do justice to such low level signals.

### 21.4.2 Analog-to-Digital (A/D) Conversion

The accuracy of A/D conversion is at the heart of the digital recording process. For a 16-bit, 44.1-kHz sampling rate system, over 700,000 bits of program data are generated per second per channel! A block diagram of an A/D converter is shown in Figure 21-8. The incoming signal is fed to a sample-and-hold circuit, which is updated every 22.7 microseconds by a signal from the clock generator. During this very short interval, the

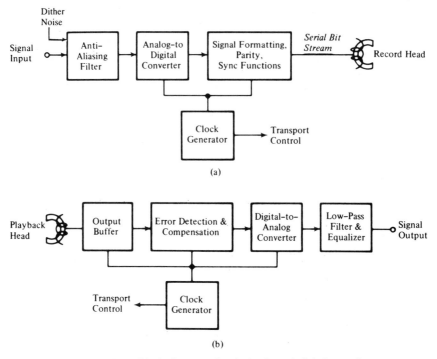

**Figure 21-6.** Block diagram of a single-channel digital recorder.

converter processes the input signal, quantizing it into 16 bits generated in parallel. The conversion from analog to digital takes place sequentially in the successive approximation register, beginning with the MSB. The output of the register is fed to a D/A (digital-to-analog) and then to a comparator, where the signal is compared with the input in order to approximate the next bit.

The time it takes for the converter to do this is known as settling time, or conversion time. The best 16-bit converters available today exhibit settling time in the range of 10 microseconds or less. A/D converters used for digital recording make use of *linear* scaling; that is, the analog range is even divided into $2^n$ equally spaced intervals, where $n$ is the number of conversion bits.

## 21.5 ENCODING THE SIGNAL ON TAPE

After quantizing, the signal is processed into the desired recording format. Synchronization signals are added, as is error-correction data. Error-correction data is used to detect and correct errors in the overall record-playback process. It is essentially a scheme for providing signal redundancy to reconstruct the signal, should it be momentarily lost due to dropouts. The signal density on the tape is much greater in digital than in analog, making the system more prone to dropouts. In an analog system, small dropouts may go by unnoticed, but in a digital system, even a minor dropout will affect a number of bits

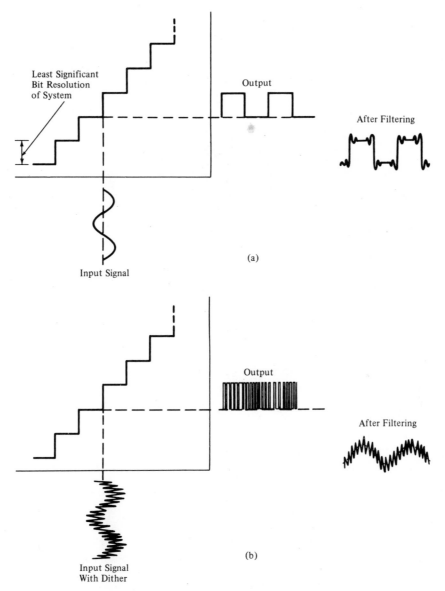

**Figure 21-7.** Effect of dithering. (a) Inputs less than the LSB will be reproduced as clipped signals. (b) Addition of dither about equal to $\frac{1}{3}$ the LSB results in duty cycle modulation of the input signal.

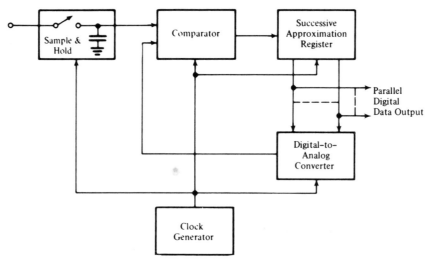

**Figure 21-8.** Details of an analog-to-digital converter. By successive approximations and feeback via digital-to-analog conversion, the signal is quantized into parallel digital outputs.

of data. Without some degree of error correction or compensation, severe noises can be the result.

### 21.5.1 Error Detection and Correction

In order to "correct" a digital word, we must be certain that an error has occurred. The most straightforward way to do this is by adding a *parity bit* for each word and storing that bit at some other position on the tape. Table 21-2 presents a group of 8-bit words, and a parity bit for each word. When the number of ones in each word is even, or zero, the parity bit is assigned a value of 0; when the number of ones in each word is odd, the parity bit is assigned a value of 1.

This provides with a statistical way of determining when a word has been transmitted with an error. If the parity bit and corresponding word agree, the chances are good that

### Table 21-2. Examples of parity bits

| 4-Bit binary numbers | Parity bit |
|---|---|
| 0000 | 1 |
| 0001 | 0 |
| 0010 | 0 |
| 0011 | 1 |
| 0100 | 0 |
| 0101 | 1 |
| 0110 | 1 |
| 0111 | 0 |

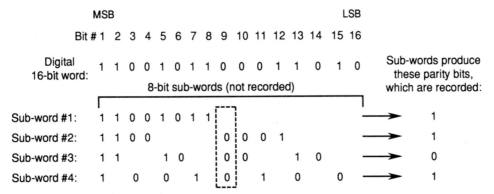

**Figure 21-9.** Illustration of correcting bit error with parity bits.

the word has been transmitted accurately. However, there is always the chance that two bits in the word have been transmitted in error. If this has happened, the word and its parity bit will still agree, and we will have no way of knowing that the word is actually wrong. There is the further chance that the parity bit itself was transmitted in error; in that case, the word will be deemed wrong when it is not. Statistically, however, a single parity bit is quite accurate, but not foolproof.

In an earlier digital recording format, the signal was recorded twice on tracks physically separated on the tape. Each recorded word had its own parity bit, and when an error was detected, the playback logic instantly switched over to the other track, on the good assumption that there was not a fault at that exact signal point on the tape. There it stayed until the next error cropped up; then the playback logic switched back to the other track. This was a very reliable method of recording, but it was inefficient in that the process required 100% signal redundancy.

While single parity bits can identify an error, they cannot correct it. More sophisticated error-correction methods are now used for both purposes. Athough the technology is quite complex, we can examine a simple example of how such a scheme works. Figure 21-9 shows a typical 16-bit word. From that 16-bit word, four subwords are generated, as shown. Subword 1 consists of the first 8 bits of the main word; subword 2 consists of bits 1 through 4 and 9 through 12, and so forth. Each one of these subwords then generates a parity bit, as shown at the right edge of the figure. There are four of these parity bits, and they are stored on the tape at a different location from that of the main 16-bit word.

Assume, on playback, that bit #9 has been erroneously detected as 1 instead of 0. A single parity bit, as discussed earlier, could only tell us that the word had a high probability of being in error. With the four parity bits we have generated, we can find the error, and thus correct it. If bit #9 has been detected as 1, then the parity bits for subwords 2 and 3 will indicate errors in those two sub-words. Since bit #9 is the only one that makes use *only* of those two subwords, it is clear that bit #9 is the one that is in error.

As another example, assume that bit number 15 had been detected as 1 instead of 0. Then, the parity bit for subword 4 would indicate an error. Since #15 is the only bit that makes use only of subword 4, it is clear that #15 is in error.

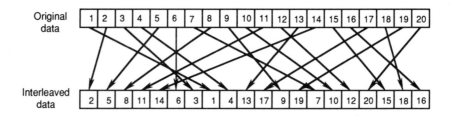

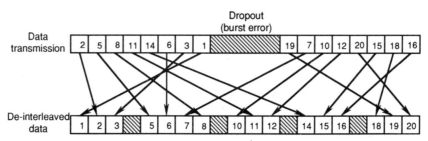

**Figure 21-10.** Through data interleaving, burst errors can be distributed so that they appear more like random errors.

For further correction, groups of parity bits can produce other parity bits for cross-checking, and the process can extend as far as the design engineer wishes to go.

### 21.5.2 Interleaving of Recorded Data

The error-correction methods we have described are at their best when dealing with random errors during playback. However, many problems in playback are due to *burst errors*. These are large errors that wipe out a great deal of data in one place on the tape, and may be caused by dropouts, damaged tape, or by debris between head and tape. Interleaving of data on the tape is a method of making burst errors appear as random errors, as shown in Figure 21-10. Interleaving spreads the errors over a larger range, thus enabling the error correction program to function more smoothly.

### 21.5.3 Error Concealment

While the techniques just discussed enable the vast majority of errors in digital playback to be detected and corrected, there will from time to time be errors that cannot be corrected. Under these conditions the error will have to be concealed or otherwise made inaudible as such. Figure 21-11 shows two common techniques: linear interpolation and repeat of previous good data. More complex methods of interpolation have been used in which the trajectory of the waveform has been calculated and used to generate missing data.

When too much data has been lost, the playback function has no recourse but to go into a mute mode, signifying catastrophic failure of the system.

## 21.6 BINARY CODES FOR TAPE RECORDING

When expressed in familiar terms of bandwidth, digital recording has demands that are well into the 2.5 to 3 MHz range. A professional helical-scan video cassette recorder (VCR) has sufficient bandwidth to accommodate a pair of 16-bit channels sampled at 44.1 kHz, and a number of digital processors have been designed for this purpose. With changes in the modulation scheme, these video recorders can handle up to 4 channels. For multichannel recording, open-reel fixed-head machines are necessary, since they facilitate the essential jobs of overdubbing and punching in.

The tape used in digital recording has a much thinner oxide coating than that used for analog so that bit resolution is greater. On the other hand, because saturation recording ("on" and "off") is used, the noise performance of the tape is relatively unimportant. The surface finish must be very fine, and dropouts virtually nonexistent.

A common modulation method used in digital recording is NRZ (non-return to zero) and is shown in Figure 21-12. The signal as taken from the tape and equalized may show rounded edges, and even appear sinusoidal. With subsequent conditioning the signal can normally be restored. Of course there will be borderline decisions made during the conditioning operation, and these may be in error, thus invoking the error-correction program in the reproducer.

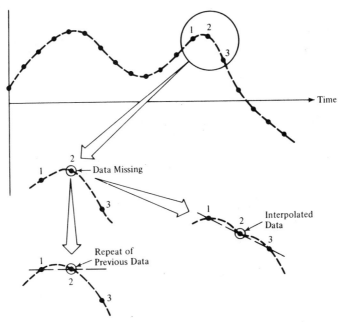

**Figure 21-11.** Error concealment. When data is lost, a digital word can be compensated either by simply repeating the previous word or by linear interpolation between adjacent reliable words.

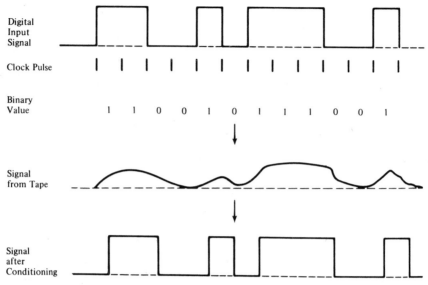

**Figure 21-12.** Recovery of digital signals from tape. Digital data is recovered with considerable loss of detail. Provided there are no dropouts, the data can be reconstructed with accuracy.

## 21.7 PLAYBACK SIGNAL PROCESSING

After the digital signal has been reconstructed, it is fed to a buffer stage where it is stored and "clocked out" under precise control of a crystal oscillator. The storage range of the buffer is sufficient to accommodate normal variations in the incoming data rate due to minor tape speed fluctuations and flutter. The output of the buffer is then fed to a stage that extracts synchronization and error-correction data. Error-correction and concealment are performed, and the digital signal is then fed to the D/A converter.

The output filter in a digital recorder is called a *signal reconstruction filter*. Basically, it is a low-pass filter, but for accurate reconstruction of the waveform it should be time-corrected so that each output sample from the D/A converter yields a $(\sin x)/x$ function. This requirement is shown in Figure 21-13(a). Sequential $(\sin x)/x$ pulses will then sum to give accurate reconstructions of LF signals (b) and HF signals (c).

Figure 21-14 shows details of a D/A converter.

## 21.8 INDUSTRY STANDARDS

As we move into the decade of the 1990s, digital multichannel recording remains dominated by the Sony (DASH) and Mitsubishi (PD) systems. Both of these systems support two-channel open-reel equipment as well. For the multichannel machines, prices remain quite high, and this is keeping the recording industry's investment in multitrack analog recorders very current. The addition of Dolby SR to multitrack analog recorders will probably maintain that currency until such time as digital consoles are commonplace in leading studios.

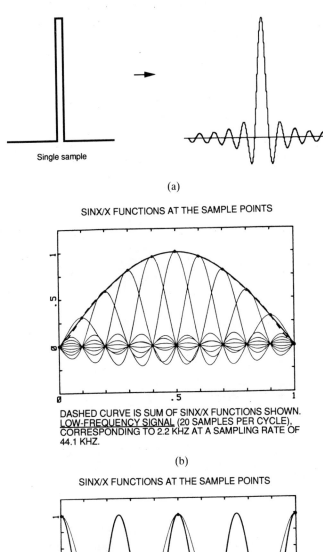

Single sample

(a)

SINX/X FUNCTIONS AT THE SAMPLE POINTS

DASHED CURVE IS SUM OF SINX/X FUNCTIONS SHOWN. LOW-FREQUENCY SIGNAL (20 SAMPLES PER CYCLE), CORRESPONDING TO 2.2 KHZ AT A SAMPLING RATE OF 44.1 KHZ.

(b)

SINX/X FUNCTIONS AT THE SAMPLE POINTS

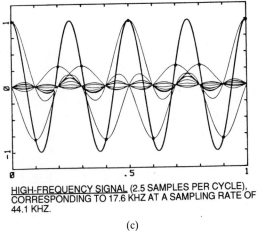

HIGH-FREQUENCY SIGNAL (2.5 SAMPLES PER CYCLE), CORRESPONDING TO 17.6 KHZ AT A SAMPLING RATE OF 44.1 KHZ.

(c)

**Figure 21-13.** (Sin $x$)/$x$ recovery of signal. (a) The reconstruction filter at the output of the D/A converter generates a (sin $x$)/$x$ response for each signal sample. (b) Typical LF signal recovery. (c) Typical HF signal recovery. *((b) and (c) Courtesy S. Lipschitz and J. Vanderkooy, from AES Digital Audio Tutorials)*

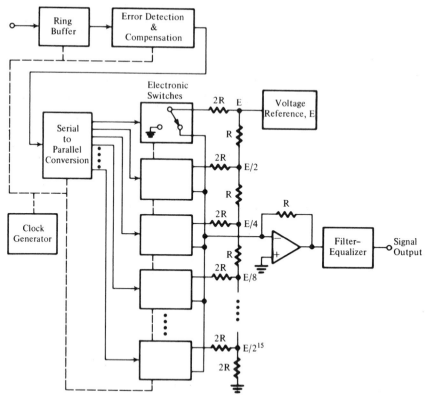

**Figure 21-14.** Details of the D/A converter. The analog output signal is generated by electronic switches, one for each bit, that scale the reference voltage according to powers of 2.

The industry is virtually agreed that 16-bit quantization is sufficient for the majority of recording demands. Sampling rates vary from 44.1 kHz (for the CD), to 44.056 kHz (for television work), to 48 kHz for highest-quality audio applications. However, if the final product is to be the CD, then it makes sense to record directly at 44.1 kHz rather than to use a format converter later in post-production. Mitsubishi has proposed an archival digital recording system that uses 20-bit quantization and a 96 kHz-sampling rate. Such a system would have a dynamic range of about 120 dB (about the equal of the ear!) and audio bandwidth extending to 40 kHz.

As with the computer industry, the various formats can "speak" to one another via several interface standards. Presently, the *AES-EBU* interface is widely used at the two-channel level. The interface uses a standard XLR three-conductor cable to transmit serial data between recorders and other digital processing devices. It can accommodate up to 24-bit resolution at a number of sampling rates.

The *SDIF-2* (Sony Digital Interface) is used between pieces of Sony digital equipment. It requires parallel connections for each channel and an additional word sync connection between devices.

The *ProDigital* (PD) *A/B/C-Dub* is used with Mitsubishi and Otari and can be used for data transfer between machines based on the PD format as well as with certain DASH configuration machines.

*Multichannel Audio Digital Interface* (MADI) is a proposed method for interfacing multichannel digital devices. It can accommodate up to 56 channels at sampling rates 32 kHz to 48 kHz with resolution of up to 24 bits per channel. It is serial, requiring only a single connection at each end of the bus.

The *Sony 1630* (earlier models were the 1600 and 1610) VCR-based format for two-channel recording established itself in the early days of the CD as the medium of exchange for recordings between record companies and CD processing plants. It normally uses the U-matic VCR format for data storage. It is a 16-bit system and can operate at sampling rates of 44.056 kHz or 44.1 kHz. It interfaces directly with the Sony two-channel model DAE-3000 editor, which is almost universally used in the industry for CD mastering. Thus, its currency is ensured for years to come. It has capability for AES-EBU and SDIF-2 interface.

The *JVC model 900*-series of digital recording and editing equipment for use with VCRs was widely embraced in the early 1980s for its sonic qualities and operational flexibility. In recent years, it has not been aggressively supported by the manufacturer, but remains a viable system.

The *EIAJ* (Electrical Industries Association of Japan) two-channel video formats were intended for consumer use with standard Beta and VHS video recorders. It was a surprise to all when the Sony PCM-F1 attained the status with professional users that it did in the early 1980s. Countless CDs were mastered on these low-cost systems. Interface gear for using them with Sony editors is made by Harmonia-Mundi Acustica.

The big contender at the low cost, two-channel level of operation is the *R-DAT* (rotary digital audio tape) recording system, which uses a small tape cassette. Again, it was intended as a consumer medium, but its chances of succeeding there are slim. Instead, it has been widely embraced by the professional community for two-channel recording, largely because of small size and low cost. Like the video-based systems, it makes use of a helical scanning system, but it does not make use of the standard video frame structure. R-DAT is not always free of trouble, but its convenience counts for a great deal. Most of the professional machines can record directly at 44.1 kHz (the sampling rate of the CD) and have AES-EBU and SDIF-2 outputs for direct interface with two-channel digital editors.

Figure 21-15 shows photographs of a two-channel digital recorder (a), and a multichannel recorder (b). In virtually all operational aspects, these machines are the same as their analog counterparts.

## 21.9 DIGITAL AUDIO DATA COMPRESSION

The purpose of audio data compression is to optimize limited digital channel capacity so that audio signals can be transmitted with adequate frequency response and dynamic range. Applications include broadcasting, transmission of digital audio over very limited

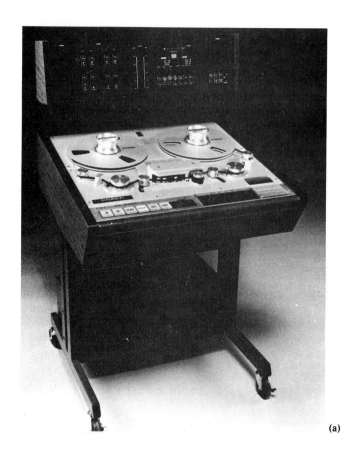

(a)

(b)

**Figure 21-15.** (a) A 2-track digital recorder. (*Courtesy Studer*). (b) A 32-track digital recorder. (*Courtesy Mitsubishi*)

channel capacity, and future consumer digital formats. Some of the techniques which can be used here are:

a. *Adaptive differential modulation.* The differences between successive samples can be encoded rather than their absolute value, and the differential interval can be scaled for the program level at hand.
b. *Band-splitting.* The accuracy of quantization can be adjusted to each band depending on signal level and the sensitivity of the ear to artifacts in each band.
c. *Linear prediction.* Speech and music signals are highly resonant and contain much spectral redundancy. Such signals can be encoded efficiently using reduced bit rates.

The overall reduction in channel capacity is remarkable; some systems are capable of operating on only four bits, representing a 4-to-1 data rate improvement over traditional digital technology (21). As with analog noise reduction, there may be specific signal conditions that "fool" the system and are audible, at least to some listeners. There is also much opportunity for future improvement.

## 21.10 THE ALL-DIGITAL STUDIO

While digital recording represents state-of-the-art performance of digital hardware, it remains in many regards a relatively simple task in the overall picture of digital signal processing. While in the digital domain, signals can be combined, limited, equalized, reverberated, or processed in just about any way imaginable. In short, all the recording tasks that are currently done in the analog domain are possible in the digital domain. Only loudspeakers and microphones must, of necessity, remain analog devices, since they are the physical boundaries between the acoustical and digital worlds. There is no fundamental reason, however, why microphones and loudspeakers could not be conceived as A/D and D/A converters, given the necessary development in their respective fields.

From the viewpoint of the operator, an all-digital studio probably would not appear too different from today's advanced automated studios. One could certainly conceive of less complex consoles in terms of the number of faders, switches, and knobs within arm's reach. The architecture of a digital console could be speedily adapted to the specific tasks at hand, and fewer controls would be needed if they could be easily reassigned and relabeled. Some of this flexibility exists today in the more sophisticated automated console systems.

The benefit to the end user is that an acoustical signal in the studio might remain entirely in the digital domain from the time of the initial A/D until the time of D/A conversion in the home. This prevails today in many direct-to-stereo recordings, but is rarely the case in multichannel recording.

Figure 21-16 shows a flow diagram for a digital audio control system, as manufactured by Rupert Neve of England. In this system, signals from the studio are converted as early in the chain as possible, and they remain in the digital domain through the final recorded product. Only for studio monitoring, or for playback in the home, does the signal finally reach the D/A converter.

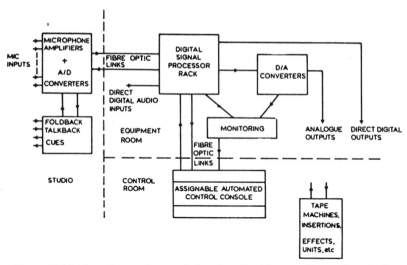

**Figure 21-16.** Flow diagram for an all-digital studio. (*Courtesy Rupert Neve Inc.*)

# BIBLIOGRAPHY

1. B. Blesser, "Digitization of Audio," *J. Audio Engineering Society*, vol. 26, no. 10 (1978).
2. J. Bloom, "Into the Digital Studio Domain," *Studio Sound*, vol. 21, no. 4/5 (1979).
3. J. Borwick, *Sound Recording Practice*, Oxford University Press, New York (1987).
4. M. Camras, *Magnetic Recording Handbook*, Van Nostrand Reinhold, New York (1988).
5. E. Engberg, "A Proposed Digital Audio Format," *db Magazine*, vol. 12, no. 11 (1978).
6. R. Ingebretsen, "A Strategy for Automated Editing of Digital Recordings," presented at the 58th AES Convention, New York, 4–7 November, 1977.
7. M. Lambert, "Digital Audio Interface," *J. Audio Engineering Society*, vol. 38, no. 9 (1990).
8. H. Nakajima et al., *Digital Audio*, TAB Books, Blue Ridge Summit, Pa. (1983).
9. H. Nyquist, "Certain Topics in Telegraph Transmission Theory," *Transactions of the AIEE* (April 1928).
10. A. Oppenheim, *Applications of Digital Signal Processing*, Prentice-Hall, Englewood Cliffs, N.J. (1978).
11. K. Pohlmann, *Principles of Digital Audio*, H. Sams, Indianapolis (1985).
12. H. Rodgers and L. Solomon, "A Close Look at Digital Audio," *Popular Electronics* (September 1979).
13. C. Shannon, "A Mathematical Theory of Communication," *Bell System Technical Journal* (October 1968).
14. K. Tanaka, et al., "A 2-Channel PCM Rate Recorder for Professional Use," presented at the 61st AES Convention, New York, 3–6 November, 1978.
15. Y. Tsuchiya et al., "A 24-Channel Stationary Head Digital Audio Recorder," presented at the 61st AES Convention, New York, 3–6 November, 1978.
16. J. Vanderkooy and S. Lipschitz, "Resolution Below the Least Significant Bit in Digital Systems with Dither," *J. Audio Engineering Society*, vol. 32, no. 3 (1984).
17. R. Warnock, "Longitudinal Digital Recording of Audio," presented at the 55th AES Convention, New York, 24 October–2 November, 1976.
18. J. Woram, *Sound Recording Handbook*, H. Sams, Indianapolis (1989).
19. J. Woram and A. Kefauver, *The New Recording Studio Handbook*, Elar, Commack, N.Y. (1989).
20. *Digital Audio*, Collected papers from the AES Conference, Rye, N.Y. 3–6 June, 1982.
21. *High Quality Four Bit Digital Audio*, product bulletin produced by Audio Processing Technology Ltd., Oxford, UK.

# 22

## CLASSICAL RECORDING AND PRODUCTION

## 22.1 INTRODUCTION

This chapter will discuss the musical and technical factors involved in producing classical recordings for commercial release. It will be concerned with selecting the recording venue, planning the sessions, placing the microphones in order to produce a desired recording perspective, and planning logistical details of equipment and staffing.

## 22.2 THE COMMERCIAL RECORDING ENVIRONMENT

### 22.2.1 Economic Factors

Long before a record company schedules the recording of an album, certain economic questions will have been addressed. Among these are:

1. Is there a clear market for the product? Does the album have a unique concept, or will it simply do battle with many other versions currently in the catalog? Does the artist or ensemble have a strong name or reputation in the marketplace?
2. Will the cost of the sessions and subsequent post-production be recouped over a reasonable time period? With orchestral recording fees ranging in the tens of thousands of dollars, this question may entail financial projections far into the future.

If the answers to these questions are favorable, the next step is to assign a producer to the project.

### 22.2.2 The Role of the Producer

The producer is responsible for the following:

1. Preparing a budget for the sessions and ensuring adherence to that budget.
2. Working with the artist or conductor in planning how the sessions will proceed. For example, does the artist or conductor feel comfortable only with long, complete takes, as in actual performance? Or is the artist willing to work with numerous shorter takes?
3. Determining the sonic aspects of the recording. In practice, this is a joint responsibility of both producer and engineer, and many producers rely heavily on the advice and expertise of engineers they have successfully worked with. Included here are such important points as details of stereo placement of instruments and the balance of direct and reverberant sound pickup. It is essential that the producer and engineer have virtually identical conceptions of how a given recording should sound if the sessions are to be productive.
4. Musical supervision of the sessions. This involves studying the score with the artist and/or conductor well ahead of the sessions so that both will have the same expectations. The producer further slates, or announces, all the takes and keeps timings, and otherwise ensures that all sections of the score have been covered adequately during the allotted time of the sessions.

   Musical logistics demand a careful analysis of personnel. For example, will all players be required for all sessions? If not, then there can be significant savings through careful scheduling of the program.
5. Supervising all musical aspects of editing and post-production. The producer represents the company in all matters involving the company and the musicians' union, and the producer may find himself in the roles of diplomat as well as taskmaster as he performs his work. In all these roles. he must remain cool and collected—and very much in control of things. A stern hand is often needed, since few sessions can run on collegial consensus alone.

### 22.2.3 The Role of the Engineer

The engineer has the following responsibilities:

1. Checking out and certifying remote recording venues. Such points as ambient noise level, acoustical suitability, and creature comforts are covered here.
2. Taking responsibility for the performance of all recording equipment and directing the technical crew. Quick solutions of all technical problems arising during a session are essential.
3. Translating the producer's sonic wishes into reality, through choice of microphone type, quantity, and placement. In this regard, many producers are content to leave the matter entirely in the hands of the engineer.
4. Performing all balancing functions at the console during the sessions.
5. Working with the producer, as required, in details of post-production. (In many

large companies, editing may be carried out by specialists working from scores previously marked by the producer.)

Like the producer, the engineer must remain collected and very much in charge of all technical matters when problems arise. He should know his equipment well and vouch for its reliability. He should keep detailed setup notes so that a given microphone array and level settings can be accurately duplicated in the same venue months, or even years, later.

### 22.2.4 Staffing

In smaller recording companies, there are qualified persons who can function as both engineer and producer, but invariably there will be assistants on hand to operate equipment and to help with setup. Often, as in the case of solo recordings, it is easy for a single producer-engineer to run the session. The clock is often ignored at times like this, and the pace is less harried.

At the other end of the spectrum is the recording of a large orchestral work or an opera. In such cases the producer will require several assistants to help in blocking out stage movements, and the engineer may require several assistants to ensure continuous overlap of tape recorders and to make rapid equipment changes.

## 22.3 THE STUDIO VERSUS THE REMOTE RECORDING VENUE

For most classical recording, a good degree of ambience or reverberation is desirable. The recording space must be large to provide this, and most recording companies, at least in the United States, cannot afford to maintain a large studio for classical recording requirements. There are a handful of exceptions here, but even these often call for the use of some artificial reverberation.

Thus, most classical recordings are made in remote recording venues. Orchestras of course would prefer to record in their normal performance halls, but these are often unsatisfactory for the recording of large-cale works. Specifically, the reverberation times in many halls are not long enough for orchestral recording. Reverberation times in the 2- to 2.5-second range are ideal.

In the case of concert halls with a proscenium and a deep orchestra shell, there are additional problems. The purpose of the shell is to project sound toward the audience during concerts. This may be a problem in recording, inasmuch as the back of the orchestra exists in one acoustical environment, while the front of the orchestra is in another. For recording purposes, the entire ensemble should clearly be in the same acoustical space, and stage extensions are often used to project all players well into the house.

Among the spaces used for remote classical recording are churches, ballrooms, and a surprisingly large number of Masonic meeting halls throughout the United States. Most of the good rooms are fairly old, built in a day when lots of concrete and plaster were used for interior surfaces. On the debit side, these older locations are apt to be noisy, cold in winter, and hot in summer. While newer buildings are more apt to be comfortable, they are likely to be acoustically inferior to their older counterparts, because of excessive acoustical absorption.

It is clearly the engineer's responsibility to check out and certify remote venues, and the following are some of the points that should be looked at:

1. Is the space acoustically appropriate? If it is too live, can it be partially draped to reduce reverberation time? Not much can be done for a space that has too short a reverberation time, but in some instances large expanses of plywood have been used to cover absorptive seating areas to good effect. Some engineers have covered seating areas with plastic sheeting, with some improvement in sound reflectance at high frequencies.
2. If there is a stage, does it project well into the house, or will a stage extension be required?
3. Is air handling quiet, or must it be turned off during actual recording?
4. What about various comfort factors and facilities for the musicians?
5. Can a control room be adequately set up close by so that the conductor or artist does not have far to walk? Do not forget to arrange for extensive damping materials to make the control room sufficiently absorptive.
6. What about external noise? Traffic around the building should be observed for at least a week, and any unusual patterns should be noted. Careful note should be made of any other activities that may be scheduled in adjacent spaces in the same building. In rare cases, overflights of private aircraft can be curtailed, if the problem is addressed far enough ahead of time. Often, civic authorities may cooperate in rerouting automotive traffic.
7. What about electrical service? Is it adequate and free of troublesome transient disturbances?

During a recording made in a remote location, it is essential that the engineer keep a good ear open to extraneous noises of any kind. It is his responsibility to track down and solve such difficulties.

A video monitoring link between the control room and the performance area is quite useful, but not absolutely necessary. The video monitor provides many useful cues for both engineer and producer. In an orchestral recording, it can heighten verbal communication with the conductor. With a small group, it can provide secondary cues regarding performers' attitudes and needs.

A private phone link between the producer and the conductor is essential in recording large-scale orchestral works and operas, inasmuch as it allows discussion of subtle and often touchy musical details involving soloists, such as intonation, diction, and the like.

A properly designed studio will have few or none of the noise and comfort problems inherent in most remote locations. This leaves us only with the acoustical disadvantages of most studios, but in many cases, it is possible to work around these through the use of high-quality artificial reverberation. It is strongly recommended that studios be given this consideration for smaller musical forms, such as solo instruments and small chamber groups.

## 22.4  STEREO VERSUS MULTICHANNEL RECORDING

A great deal of classical music can, and should, be mixed directly to two-channel stereo at the recording session itself. Only when there is a clear musical need for post-production balancing flexibility should consideration be given to multichannel recording. Today, many producers and engineers are routinely recording large orchestral and choral works directly to two-channel stereo. It is imperative of course that such sessions be well planned and that balances be established early in the session. Using as few microphones as are really needed will make this job easier.

By comparison, some producers prefer the post-production flexibility of balancing at a later date. This flexibility is not cheap, and it can serve as a nagging point of disagreement between producer and conductor or artist. We should always ask whether it is actually worth it.

Obviously, recording an opera calls for multichannel flexibility. Time is always at a premium, and balances are often problematic during the sessions themselves. There are, in fact, many things here that can legitimately be "fixed in the mix."

## 22.5  SOME ACOUSTICAL PROPERTIES OF MUSICAL INSTRUMENTS AND ENSEMBLES

In general, the recording engineer needs only to remember that most instruments and ensembles radiate forward and upward in the direction faced by the player. We cannot divorce the immediate surroundings from the radiation pattern, and reflections off the floor are important. It is important that microphone placement take advantage of these reflections. Musicians should never be seated on carpeted surfaces, and sections of plywood may have to be used if carpeting cannot be removed.

At low and mid frequencies, most instruments radiate essentially omnidirectionally, while at high frequencies there is usually a preference for radiation along specific axes. Brass instruments will radiate higher harmonics preferentially along the axis of the bell. Stringed instruments radiate high frequencies in a rather complex way. Often, the sheen of massed strings is better picked up above and in front of the group, rather than directly overhead. The overhead pickup may emphasize stridency at mid-high frequencies. Review Section 1.8.1 for a detailed discussion of musical instrument radiation patterns.

Projection of low frequencies from bass viols is usually helped by placing them against a wall, or by placing large, rigid reflective baffles directly behind them.

The role played by the raised cover of a piano or harpsichord is obvious, and microphones should be placed so that they can "look into" the instrument.

It usually comes as a surprise to recording engineers that the dynamic ranges of most instruments are as small as they are. The data of Figure 22-1 gives a clear indication of this. A string quartet, for example, may normally play over a dynamic range which does not exceed 30 dB, and there should be little problem in recording such an ensemble with a recorder capable of handling a 90-dB signal-to-noise range. The piano has been observed to to produce initial keystroke dynamic ranges not exceeding about 35 or 40 dB.

Of course, when an orchestra plays loudly, all players are involved, and brass and percussion predominate. When the orchestra plays very softly, there may be only a few

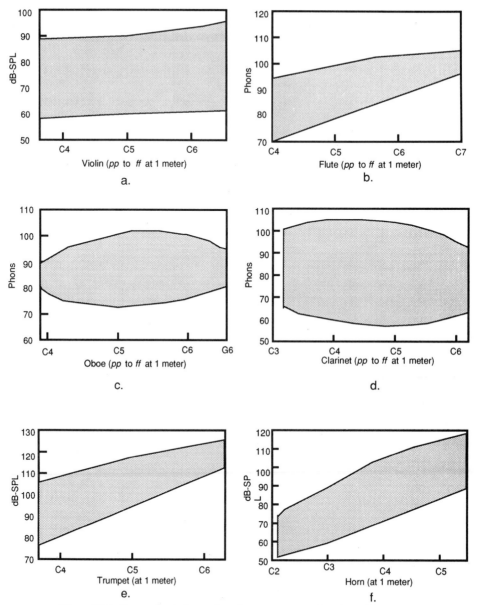

**Figure 22-1.** Output levels for various instruments as a function of frequency.

stringed instruments. The acoustical power may range from, say 30 watts for the full ensemble to less than a microwatt for the softest passages. The resulting dynamic range may be 70 to 75 dB, and if the acoustical surroundings are quiet enough this will pose problems for analog recorders operating without noise reduction. Digital systems, with their 90 dB-plus dynamic range can handle these ranges without compromise.

**Table 22-1. Maximum power outputs and levels of various musical sources**

| Source | Maximum power output (W) | $L_p$ at 3.3 m (10 ft)[9] (dB) |
|---|---|---|
| Male speech | 0.004 | 73 |
| Female speech | 0.002 | 70 |
| Violin | 0.01 | 79 |
| Bass viol | 0.07 | 88 |
| Flute | 0.3 | 94 |
| Clarinet | 1.0 | 99 |
| Trumpet | 2.5 | 106 |
| Trombone | 5.0 | 109 |
| Orchestra | 15.0 | 97[2] |

Notes: 1. Calculations made assuming $DI = 1$.
2. Calculated from a distance of 10 m.

The remaining problem is one of playback. Not many home environments have low enough residual acoustical noise to allow full appreciation of of low-level program without having high-level program be inordinately loud.

Table 22-1 shows some of the published data regarding power output from various instruments and ensembles.

The question of manual gain manipulation in serious classical recording comes up many times. We would all prefer to think that it is not necessary, and of course never done. That is not the case at all, and hardly a classical orchestral recording is made without some degree of gain manipulation, if only a slight adjustment (3 dB or so) of level between softer movements and louder ones. Every FM station has a program compressor in the line; the more carefully the levels in the recording have been structured, the less there is for the compressor to do.

Another problem is the occasional recording that begins so softly in level that the customer is prompted to increase system gain at the outset—only to have to lower it when the music gets louder. As difficult as it is to believe, many customers will return such recordings as defective!

Engineer and producer must see eye to eye in these matters and do what they think best. It goes without saying that informed manual changes of gain will always sound better than anything done with a compressor.

## 22.6 RECORDING SOLO INSTRUMENTS

This section discusses the recording of solo instruments, and for the most part, presents many options that have been observed to work. These are not the only approaches, and there are successful engineers and producers who have worked out their own techniques different from those discussed here.

### 22.6.1 Setting the Atmosphere

Solo instrumental sessions are rarely done by the clock. Adequate recording time should be scheduled, but the performer should not be pushed to cover a certain amount of material in a certain amount of time. It is assumed that the soloist is adequately prepared for the sessions.

Soloist and producer should plan before the sessions just how things will run. Some performers prefer to make complete takes of entire pieces or movements. While this approach will provide the producer with enough material for editing, it may result in needless rerecording of passages already covered.

Most soloists feel comfortable with one or two complete takes of a movement, followed by recording insert takes, long or short, as determined by both producer and performer, after listening to tape playback. In this collaboration, the performer may act to some degree as co-producer of the recording.

On rare occasions, the performer will wish to record in relatively short takes, starting at the beginning, and overlapping until an entire movement is completed. As difficult as it seems, there are performers and conductors who can maintain consistent tempos and formal conceptions of a piece of music while recording in this way.

Every effort should be made to ensure the physical comfort of the player, even to the extent of some indulgence.

### 22.6.2 Condition of the Instrument

If a soloist's own instrument is used, then it can reasonably be assumed that it will be of excellent quality and in excellent shape. It is customary, however, to rent larger keyboard instruments, such as grand pianos and harpsichords, and they may not always be good enough for solo recording.

In concert performance, we can tolerate a piano of moderate quality, but in a recording environment that instrument may be unacceptable. Details of regulation are very important, as is precise tuning. Many times, a pianist is not the person to decide which instrument to use. A pianist may favor an instrument that projects well into a concert hall, but such an instrument may be entirely too bright and aggressive for normal recording perspectives.

A freshly tuned instrument may produce a beautiful sound. As the session proceeds, the instrument will lose this fine edge, and long before it sound "out of tune," its sound may take on a certain harshness or roughness. This is the point at which the tuner should be called in. While a stand-by tuner may be expensive, it is a luxury that may be worth the cost. Many recording engineers carry a tuning hammer and mutes for tuning of unison strings, and we recommend that all engineers learn the rudiments of this from a qualified piano technician.

### 22.6.3 Recorded Perspectives: The Stereo Stage

A fundamental decision to be made by the producer and engineer is the nature of the stereo pickup. Some questions to be answered are:

1. How wide should the solo instrument appear on the reproduced stereo stage? A guitar, or any other similarly small instrument, should not appear to stretch from loudspeaker to loudspeaker. A piano, on the other hand, can easily occupy a significant part of the stereo stage.
2. What should be the balance between direct sound and room ambience, and how long should the reverberation time be? Things to be considered here are the historical context of the music, as well as the normal expectations of the listener. One expects a guitar work to be heard in an intimate setting, while a piano work of Liszt may call for an obvious concert hall setting.

While simple microphone techniques are the easiest way to record solo instruments, multiple microphone techniques, if carefully planned and skillfully handled, can produce excellent recordings. The measure is not the number of microphones, but rather how they are used.

### 22.6.4 Playing Style and Approach to the Instrument

The question is often raised: should the player alter playing style for a recording? The answer is mixed. No attempt should be made to alter dynamics for the sake of a recording, as useful as that would seem to be. To do so would probably upset the delicate kinesthetic relationship between player and instrument. What can easily be accomplished are changes such as the following:

1. A pianist can use the una corda (soft) pedal in different ways to alter timber and dynamics of the instrument.
2. Players of instruments with registration stops, such as the organ or harpsichord, can easily alter registration, as may be required by a recording.
3. Percussion players are generally quite willing to use softer or harder mallets or hammers, as required.

The musical decisions here almost always have to do with the need for projection into a large concert hall, as contrasted with the acoustical relationships of closely placed microphones. For these reasons, it is important that both producer and engineer have a good knowledge of instruments, their acoustical principles, and the characteristics of specific makes and models.

### 22.6.5 Recording the Piano

The solo piano is a difficult instrument to record in a classical musical setting. A quick survey of current recordings will clearly demonstrate the wide range of sounds and perspectives that have been obtained. Many of them are unsatisfactory, and the biggest problem seems to lie in the choice of instrument. There is no substitute for a well-regulated concert grand that has not been voiced to be overly bright.

The stereo stage should ideally be as shown in Figure 22-2. The instrument should not seem to stretch from loudspeaker to loudspeaker, but rather occupy the center one-third

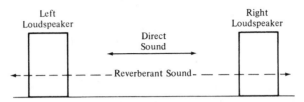

**Figure 22-2.** Ideal stereo stage perspective for the piano.

to one-half of the stage, with reverberant information coming subtly from the entire field between the loudspeakers. In general, high-frequency detail should come from the left of center and low-frequency detail from right of center. Normal microphone placement will provide this.

Various coincident and near-coincident microphone arrays give consistently good results with the piano. Figure 22-3 shows the range of distances and heights for microphone arrays that have given excellent piano pickup. Figure 22-4 shows how coincident arrays can be altered to vary the respective image widths of the instrument itself and the reverberant field.

Front-to-back ratios in the microphone pattern choice will largely determine the ratio of direct-to-reverberant sound in the recording. The piano-to-microphone distance will influence this significantly as well. The family of supercardioid patterns between the normal cardioid and bidirectional patterns will afford flexibility here.

The essential factors in achieving the correct perspectives are the splay angle between microphones, the microphone patterns, and the microphone-to-piano distance. Variations

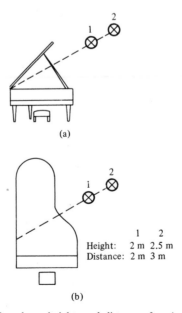

**Figure 22-3.** Microphone heights and distances for piano recording.

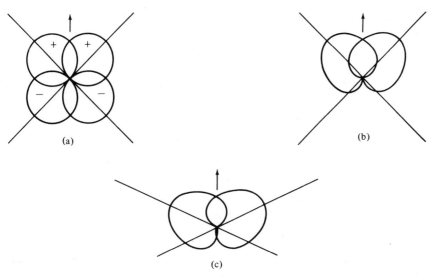

**Figure 22-4.** Coincident patterns and splay angles for controlling width and direct-to-reverberant ratios. (a) Bidirectional microphones at 90°; normal image width, with considerable reverberation. (b) Cardioids at 90°; narrow image, with minimum reverberation. (c) Cardioids at 131°; normal image width, with minimum reverberation.

should be experimented with, preferably well ahead of the session. On some occasions the engineer and producer will prefer the sound of a particular microphone array at a certain distance but observe that there is not enough reverberation. In this case, rather than move the microphones back, it may be more advantageous to place a secondary pair of microphones in the reverberant field, and add what is needed that way.

Spaced left–center–right microphone arrays can be used in piano recording, but they are apt to produce a very large piano image. Increasing the level of the center microphone will narrow the piano image and the reverberant spread. Reducing the level of the center microphone will widen the presentation. A closely spaced pair of microphones—say, no more than 1 meter (3 feet)—will produce a very pleasant sound that may lack image specificity. For impressionistic music, this may work well.

Some engineers prefer to record the piano with the cover removed. When the piano is placed on a stage with a highly reflective canopy, this method may work well. The microphones are placed 2 to 3 meters (6 to 10 feet) above the sound board and pointed downward. The sound is apt to be quite rich and a little "spacey."

An accurate monitor setup is essential in establishing the parameters of a piano recording, since many of the musical decisions have to do with apparent stage width of the instrument and the reverberant field. Remember that the perception of the reverberant field is a subtle thing, and careful listening is essential before all details can be pinned down. The dynamic range of the piano is large, and overload in the recording medium is quite obvious when it occurs. Digital recording makes the job much easier, because of its extremely wide dynamic range. For analog recording, noise reduction is recommended, and maximum levels on the medium should be carefully gauged.

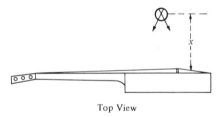

Top View

**Figure 22-5.** Recording the solo guitar or lute. Distance *x* should be about 1 to 1.5 meters (40 to 60 inches).

### 22.6.6 Recording the Harpsichord

Many of the principles that apply to piano recording are applicable here. There are several important differences, however. While the modern piano is a mechanically quiet and smoothly regulated instrument, the harpsichord, whatever its vintage, is apt to be noisy. There are many "clunks" and "thunks" in the action, and if the instrument is recorded too closely, these will be very apparent. Proximity effect of directional microphones may aggravate the problem, and a remedy for this may be the use of 50- or 80-Hz sharp high-pass filters.

Musical considerations may dictate recording the instrument in rather reverberant environments, typical of the eighteenth century. Because of its relatively rich HF content and precise attack, the harpsichord may be presented against a denser reverberant background than is appropriate for the piano.

### 22.6.7 Recording the Guitar and Lute

These instruments are small, and they are normally recorded close in. Apparent stereo width of the instrument should be about one-third the stereo stage, and coincident or near-coincident microphone arrays will do this handily. Reverberation should convey a feeling of intimacy; that is, it should be relatively short (1 to 1.5 seconds), and there should be enough of it to support the relatively thin texture of the instrument. Remember that the lowest string on the guitar, E, is 82 Hz.

Figure 22-5 shows some of the options in stereo pickup of these instruments. Proximity effect may add an unnatural LF rise if directional microphones are used, and the engineer should be prepared to remove some of this with a shelving-type equalizer.

The guitar or lute may easily be recorded in a relatively dry studio, since artificial reverberation, if of high enough quality, will work well with these instruments. The high-frequency response of the reverberant signal should be rolled off above about 5 or 6 kHz.

A certain amount of finger noise is inherent in playing these instruments, although some players are noisier than others. There is not much a player can do about this, and it is best not to confront the player with the problem. A more distant perspective will alleviate the problem somewhat, but this must be weighed against other musical values.

Normally, these instruments cover a moderate dynamic range, so there are few problems of noise or overload.

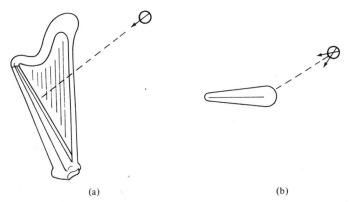

(a)                                    (b)

**Figure 22-6.** Recording the solo harp. (a) The microphone pair is placed slightly to one side. Distance *x* should range from 1 to 2 meters (40 to 80 inches). (b) Top view.

## 22.6.8 Recording the Harp

It is almost impossible for a good player to make an ugly sound on a well tuned harp. There are many microphone approaches that work well, and the engineer needs only to keep in mind that the instrument is not very loud and that noise can intrude with too great distances. Figure 22-6 shows one approach to placing microphones. Image size should be appropriate, but the voluptuousness of the sound invites some producers to array it across the entire stage width. Even in a dry acoustical setting, little artificial reverberation will be needed, because of the sustained nature of the instrument.

## 22.6.9 Recording the Pipe Organ

The pipe organ can vary from a relatively small self-contained, portable instrument up to an extremely large multidivision instrument arrayed around a large room. Most organs are located in houses of worship, and in those settings they often benefit from long reverberation times. The ideal reverberation time for an organ is in the 2.5- to 4-second range. Large cathedrals and European churches may have reverberation times well in excess of 6 seconds. While this degree of reverberation can enhance certain religious functions, it makes for difficult recording.

Modern organs have borrowed heavily from traditions of eighteenth-century North German organ design, and two basic layouts are shown in Figure 22-7. The design shown in (a) is typical of installations in the rear gallery of a church. An important aspect of the design is the rück-positiv division, located on the gallery railing apart from the rest of the instrument. Since there is good stereophonic interest from side to side, a coincident microphone pair will usually provide excellent pickup. The positiv division should appear centered in the stereo array, and it should appear rather forward in terms of fore–aft perspectives. The precise location of the stereo microphone pair should be determined with this relationship in mind, and typical distances range from 3 to 6 meters (10 to 20 feet) from the gallery rail. Some engineers have made good use of line microphones (see

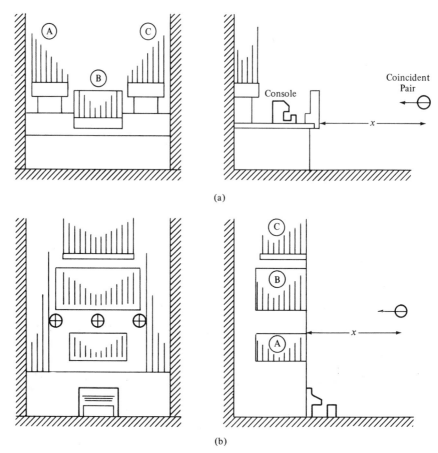

**Figure 22-7.** Recording the organ. (a) A rear gallery installation, divisions arrayed from left to right. (b) An organ with divisions arrayed vertically.

Section 5.5) to gain added "reach" at high frequencies in picking up distant sections of organs. This may be useful in isolated cases.

If the environment is fairly reverberant, then the single microphone pair will pick up enough ambience. In less reverberant spaces, a secondary stereo pair, well back in the room, will provide necessary ambience. Microphone height should preferably be at the average height of the instrument.

The design shown in Figure 22-7(b) is usually located at the front of a church, and the various divisions are arrayed vertically. The problem here is little or no left-right stereo interest between divisions. However, within a given division, there will be some stereophonic effect, due to the alternating layout of pipework from side to side. This is apt to be subtle, and a spaced microphone array will enhance it. Left–center–right microphone arrays spanning a distance of 6 meters (20 feet) often work well. The level of the center microphone should be carefully set so that it does not dominate, producing a large monophonic component in the stereo mix. Choice of patterns depends on the

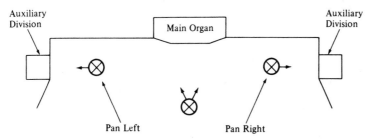

**Figure 22-8.** Recording a very large organ.

pickup of reverberant information. A very live room may call for directional microphones.

Vertical microphone arrays are tricky to deal with, but they could be used to pick up the various divisions in a conventional stereo perspective. The approach is not generally recommended, however.

For extremely large instruments arrayed horizontally, a single coincident microphone pair cannot be placed closely enough to the instrument, and individual microphones, panned as required, will have to be used. This is shown in Figure 22-8.

Special attention should be paid to accurate pickup of extremely low frequencies, and, for these purposes, wide-range monitor loudspeakers are essential. Large organs easily extend down to the 25- to 30-Hz range, and the engineer should ensure that his microphone locations are doing proper justice to those frequencies.

## 22.7 RECORDING CHAMBER ENSEMBLES

### 22.7.1 Definition

As discussed here, chamber ensembles generally range from two to about twelve players. Instrumental sonatas or vocals with piano accompaniment are at one end of this spectrum, while octets and larger groups, with one player per part, are at the other end.

### 22.7.2 Influence of Musical Styles

The producer and engineer should be aware of the musical requirements of various periods. Works of the baroque and classical periods can be heard against a more reverberant backdrop than can most modern works. Works of the nineteenth century will call for richness in texture, which may translate into fullness at mid and low frequencies. While playing styles will cover a good bit of this, the choice of recording venue and microphone pickup approach can complement these requirements. Music written for religious functions will usually require more reverberation than secular works.

### 22.7.3 Arraying the Musicians

For public performance, solo musicians normally face the audience. In a recording environment, we can alter positions as required. The need is for good eye contact between

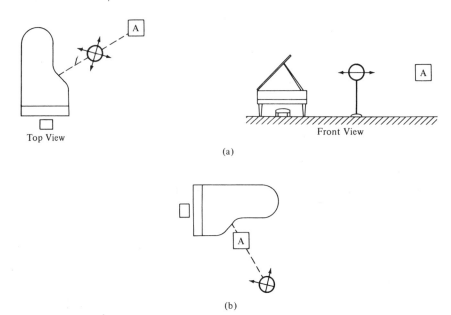

**Figure 22-9.** Piano with solo instrument. Soloist at A. (a) Using both in-polarity quandrants of crossed bidirectional microphones. (b) Using a coincident pair of cardioids or hypercardioids.

players, as well as proper balance. While players may at first be reluctant to depart from their traditional positions, they can usually adapt to new ones. The engineer should work out several possibilities for pickup for a given session well before the recording and discuss them with the producer. Between them, they can usually block out workable positions that the musicians can adapt to.

### 22.7.4 Piano with Solo Instrument or Voice

Figure 22-9(a) shows how a soloist can maintain good eye contact with the pianist, while the engineer can get the desired balance. The piano can be played with the cover full up, and instrumental balance is simply a matter of scaling distances from the microphone.

Crossed bidirectional microphones must be used here, and this immediately raises the question of absolute polarity. Which instrument should be on the "+" side and which on the "−" side of the microphones? The engineer might experiment here, but in all likelihood, there will be little if any audible difference on most program material.

A more conventional arrangement is shown in Figure 22-9(b). A woodwind soloist may feel more comfortable close to the piano. A sideways pickup position will allow good eye contact, while not affecting pickup, due to the fact that the instrument radiates over a quite wide angle. The fore–aft position of the soloist will alter balances as required.

In recording solo instruments with piano accompaniment, it is important to keep them both in proper scale. It would be a mistake for the piano to sound as if it were in one acoustical environment, while the soloist seemed in another. It would likewise be a mistake for either player to dominate the other through faulty balance.

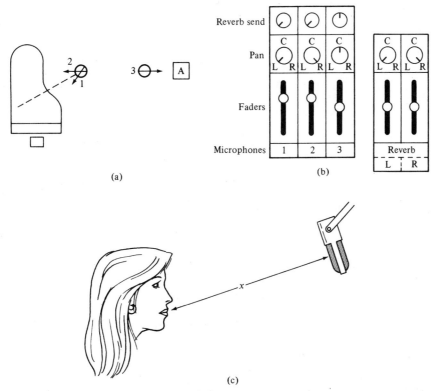

**Figure 22-10.** Piano with solo instrument or vocalists in the studio. (a) Studio setup. (b) Console setup: piano microphones panned left and right; no reverb send. Solo microphone panned center; moderate reverb send. (c) Proper relation of vocalist to microphone: distance $x$ can vary from 0.5 to 1.5 meters (20 to 60 inches).

In a studio setting, the pickup technique shown in Figure 22-10(a) may be useful. While reverberation will almost never be called for with the piano, it is a certainty that it will be needed for the soloist. The effect should be subtle, and too little is better than too much. The solo microphone will allow separate reverberation feed, as shown in Figure 22-10(b). Above all, both piano and soloists should sound as if they are in the same acoustical environment.

Soloists should never feel constrained, but they need to appreciate the requirements of proper recording balance. A vocalist should never use a hand-held microphone, since this will ensure that levels will range far and wide. A square, perhaps 0.6 meter (2 feet) on a side, can be marked off the floor and the soloist instructed to remain within the square. The microphone position should be slightly above the soloist, pointing downward toward the mouth or the solo instrument, as shown in Figure 22-10(c).

Many singers can cover an extremely wide dynamic range. While manual gain control, or compression, of the dynamic range is applied sparingly in most classical recording, some vocalists will require a significant amount. The good judgment of the producer is indispensable here.

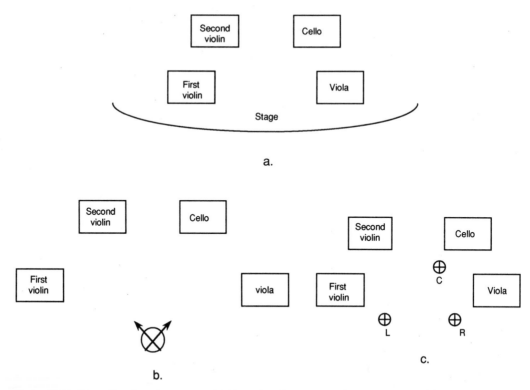

**Figure 22-11.** Recording the string quartet. (a) Normal performance seating arrangement. (b) Suggested seating for recording with coincident pair. (c) Alternative microphone arrangement using three omnidirectional microphones.

## 22.7.5 Recording Chamber Groups

Chamber groups pose many problems in recording. The players in a string quartet normally array themselves as shown in Figure 22-11(a). Here, the separation between players is no greater than it has to be, since visual contact is so important to good ensemble playing. When so closely spaced, it is difficult to get a pickup with good stereo localization without moving in quite close to the ensemble. If at all possible, the group should be persuaded to space themselves in a wider arrangement, as shown in Figure 22-11(b). In this way, a coincident or quasi-coincident pair can provide good stereo pickup at a distance above the floor of, say, 2.5 to 3 meters (7 to 10 feet), while maintaining good blend and cohesion. The back lobes of the microphone patterns may be adjusted for the final balance of direct to reverberant sound. Intimacy is important, and images should pretty well fill the stereo stage. In a studio setting, some artificial reverberation, no more than about 1.5 seconds, in the midband, should be added. These same comments apply generally to string quartets that have been augmented by one or two string parts.

Many engineers prefer to record small chamber groups with spaced omnidirectional microphones. While this approach presents some problems in stereo imaging, it often has the virtue of allowing the group to remain seated in their normal close-in manner. Figure

22-11(c) illustrates a typical application. Here, a string quartet is grouped around three omni microphones, which are panned left, center, and right. The left and right microphones accent the first violin and viola, respectively. The center microphone locks the cello firmly in the center, while pulling the second violin and viola slightly inward. The center microphone further allows the bass line to be precisely adjusted, relative to the other instruments.

It is not necessary to have the players on hand to make an initial balance check with a given microphone placement. Having a person occupy the players' chairs sequentially and talking will give the engineer a good idea of stereo imaging at each position. This should of course be refined with the players in position.

### 22.7.6 Small Instrumental Groups with Piano

Some of the groups included in this category are the piano trio (piano, violin, and cello), the piano quintet (piano and string quartet), and the piano wind quintet (piano, oboe, clarinet, bassoon, and horn). As a rule, the piano is placed in the center with the other instruments disposed left and right. A general preference places the treble instruments to the left and the lower pitched ones to the right. Coincident or quasi-coincident microphone pairs are probably easiest to work with, and whenever possible, the piano cover should be fully open. Fore–aft positioning of the various instruments relative to the microphones will achieve proper balance. Several pickup possibilities are shown in Figures 22-12(a) and (b) for the groups arranged as in normal concert seating.

In a studio setting, the players can be rearranged as shown in Figures 22-12(c) and (d). Here, the players have been arranged in a circle for good eye contact. More microphones are used, offering greater balance flexibility,

A variant here is the harpsichord in a baroque musical context. The combination of harpsichord with a bass instrument, such as cello or bassoon, doubling the bass line, forms the continuo musical function. In performance, a harpsichordist will often use louder stops in order to be heard at a distance. In a recording session, the instrument will be heard well enough, and the player should be asked to use a softer unison stop for this function. Otherwise, the instrument will be too aggressive. Recall that the harpsichord, like the organ, relies entirely on the choice of stops for performing at various volume levels.

### 22.7.7 The Unaccompanied Chorus

The unaccompanied chorus normally numbers 18 to 40 singers, and they are usually arrayed as shown in Figure 22-13. A coincident or near-coincident microphone array is a good starting point, and the addition of two flanking microphones often gives a great deal more flexibility in balance, while creating a more spacious stereo perspective. The occasional solo line sung my a member of the chorus will need no special pickup; however a vocal soloist with choral accompaniment should always be treated differently. A separate microphone may be used, but a simpler technique is to place the soloist on a riser in the center front of the chorus so that the main microphone array will pick up the soloist with the correct balance.

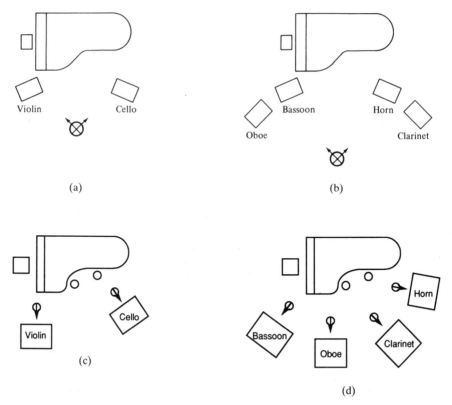

**Figure 22-12.** Chamber groups with piano. (a) The piano trio; microphones about 2 m high and about 2 m from the piano. (b) Wind quintet; microphones about 2 m high and 2.5 m from the piano. (c) Reseating the trio in the studio. (d) Reseating the quintet in the studio.

Reverberation is important in the texture of a good choral recording. A recording made in a large church will of course benefit from the natural acoustics of that space. A recording made in a studio will require judicious use of added reverberation, and reverberation times in the 2- to 2.5-second range are appropriate. The quality of the artificial reverberation should be carefully chosen to resemble that of a natural performance environment, and it is better that the reverberation be too short than too long.

## 22.8 The Chamber Symphony Orchestra

The typical chamber orchestra numbers about 40 players, and the usual instrumentation is given in Table 22-2.

This is the orchestra of the last half of the eighteenth century and first third of the nineteenth. Small ensembles of similar instrumentation are popular today, and the literature has continued to grow over the last 150 years. In later works for chamber orchestra, the size has increased slightly to accommodate additional instruments as needed. All of the concertos of the classical period were written with the natural balances of the

**Table  22-2. Normal  instrumentation  of  the
chamber orchestra**

| 1st Violins | 7 | Flutes | 2 | Horns | 2 |
|---|---|---|---|---|---|
| 2nd Violins | 7 | Clarinets | 2 | Trumpets | 2 |
| Violas | 5 | Oboes | 2 | Percussion | 2 |
| Cellos | 4 | Bassoons | 2 | | |
| Bass Viols | 2 | | | | |

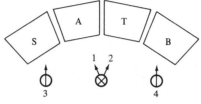

**Figure 22-13.** A moderate-size chorus. Soprano, alto, tenor, and bass sections (left to right). Chorus on risers.

chamber orchestra in mind, and in classical concerto performance, the larger symphony orchestra is normally scaled down appropriately.

### 22.8.1 Natural Balance of the Chamber Orchestra

The chamber orchestra is relative easy to record because it is inherently a well-balanced ensemble. There is usually no brass ensemble as such, and performance practice of the eighteenth and early nineteenth centuries calls for a rather soft-edged, lightly blown brass sound. Early instruments did not have the flexibility of their modern counterparts, and playing in general was softer than is common today. The early-instrument movement emphasizes these concerns all the more.

The seating arrangement prevalent in early days was as shown in Figure 22-14(a), and some modern chamber orchestras use this arrangement. A more modern seating arrangement is shown in (b). If the work being performed includes timpani and trumpets, then the horns are properly placed apart from the woodwinds in order to give more spatial delineation on the stereo stage. In some smaller works, there will be no trumpets or timpani, and the horns will properly function as part of the woodwind ensemble. In this case, they should be placed within that section, as shown in (c).

Seating details such as these should be carefully planned with both conductor and producer well ahead of the recording session. Try not to make seating changes during the sessions themselves.

### 22.8.2 Selecting a Recording Venue

An ensemble the size of a chamber orchestra stretches the limits of all but the largest studios. Remote venues, such as churches, performance halls, and large ballrooms have

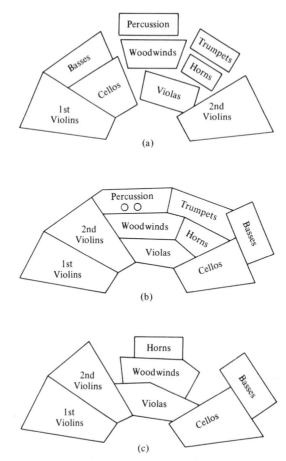

**Figure 22-14.** Seating arrangements for the chamber orchestra. (a) Older seating arrangement. (b) Modern seating arrangement. (c) Alternate seating arrangement for reduced orchestra.

been used, and it is important that the reverberation times be in the 1.8- to 2.5-second range at mid-frequencies. Ideally, the reverberation time below 250 Hz should be somewhat shorter so that the texture does not become muddy. A secondary reverberant pair of microphones will be useful in some rooms. Use these microphones carefully. Too little is better than too much.

### 22.8.3 Microphone Techniques

Figure 22-15(a) shows an excellent approach for recording a chamber orchestra. While a spaced left–center–right array can be used, the approach shown yields more flexibility. Some engineers favor only the central coincident or near-coincident array, while others will add some degree of pickup from the flanking left and right microphones for more side-to-side delineation and ambience. Microphones 1 and 4 are often omnidirectional,

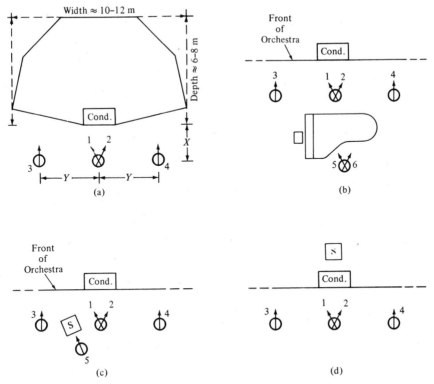

**Figure 22-15.** Microphone placement for the chamber orchestra. (a) Basic pickup, where $X$ = 1 to 1.5 meters, and $Y$ = one-third the width of the orchestra. Microphones 1 & 3 panned left; 2 & 4 panned right; 3 & 4 about −6 dB relative to 1 & 2. Microphones about 2.5 to 3 m high. (b) Orchestra with piano; orchestra microphones as in (a); piano pickup as desired. (c) Soloist with orchestra; use cardioid on soloist and position via panpot for center presentation. (d) Soloist at S, with natural balance as picked up by main microphones.

but in live rooms it may be advisable to use cardioids. Microphones 2 and 3 are normally of cardioid or figure-8 pattern. In particular, the ORTF array is favored by many engineers for this application.

The frontal microphone array will give some preference to the strings; this is good, inasmuch as these instruments form the musical backbone of the ensemble, and are often a bit lacking in weight. It is important that there be a seamless array of string sound across the entire stereo stage, whatever the seating arrangement. No effort should be spared here, and it may be advantageous to physically spread the entire orchestra somewhat in order to create a larger overall sound source. Do not hesitate to move wind players back or closer in, as required, in order to achieve the correct balances.

In recording a piano concerto, it is most convenient if the solo instrument is placed behind the main microphone pair and picked up with a separate stereo pair, as shown in (b). This approach allows maximum flexibility in balancing solo and orchestra. If the piano is placed in front of the conductor, the soloist may have to play softer than normal in order to produce an acceptable balance.

### Table 22-3. Instrumentation of the modern symphony orchestra

| | | | | | |
|---|---|---|---|---|---|
| 1st Violins | 16 | Flutes | 3 | Trumpets | 4 |
| 2nd Violins | 16 | Piccolo | 1 | Horns | 6 |
| Violas | 12 | Oboes | 3 | Trombones | 3 |
| Cellos | 10 | English Horn | 1 | Bass Trombone | 1 |
| Bass Viols | 10 | Clarinets | 3 | Tuba | 1 |
| Harps | 2 | Bass Clarinet | 1 | Percussion | 4 |
| | | Bassoons | 3 | Timpani | 1 |
| | | Contra Bassoon | 1 | | |

A solo string instrument or vocalist normally stands to the left of the conductor, as shown in (c). This convenient position allows good eye contact between conductor and soloist, but it has the disadvantage of positioning the soloist a little left of center on the stereo stage. A center position is more desirable, or at least traditional, and an accent microphone for the soloist enables the engineer to steer the soloist back to the center. Also, this microphone will provide a bit more presence on the soloist. No more should be used in the mix than is necessary to produce the desired effect.

An alternate approach places the soloist directly in front of the conductor, as shown in (d). A soloist microphone may or may not be required to get the right balance.

### 22.9 Recording the Large Orchestra

The orchestra of the late nineteenth and twentieth centuries usually numbers 90 to 105 players at full strength. Typical instrumentation is shown in Table 22-3, and a typical seating plan is shown in Figure 22-16.

In spite of their large number, the strings are no match for the full impact of the brass and percussion sections. As a result, *tutti* (full) sections in large romantic and modern works often find the strings overshadowed by those louder sections. This situation exists all too often in the concert hall, and, unfortunately, modern orchestras have been getting

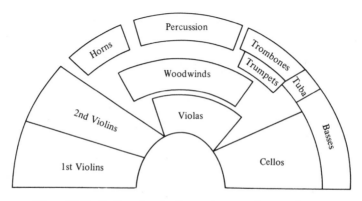

**Figure 22-16.** Seating plan for the modern symphony orchestra.

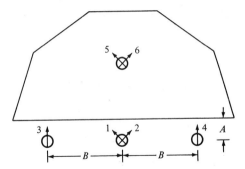

**Figure 22-17.** Recording the symphony orchestra. Microphones all about 2.5 to 3.5 m high, depending on perspectives desired and acoustical conditions. $A = 1.5$ to 2 m; B is about one-third the width of the ensemble.

worse in this regard. Recording engineers and producers can correct some of this, inasmuch as inverse square relationships at the microphones across the front of the orchestra will favor the strings. This is also a justification for placing an additional stereo pair in the middle of the orchestra, so that there is some control over fore–aft balances in the orchestra.

### 22.9.1 Microphone Techniques

Figure 22-17 shows a common approach to recording a large orchestra. If possible, the sections should be spread out a bit more than normal, but certainly not to the extent that the players will be isolated from their neighbors. The wider spacing will allow more stereo separation with the microphones at comfortable working distances.

For added stereo interest, the various percussion instruments should be arrayed across the back of the orchestra in a wider arc than usual. Even if this requires an extra player, the results may be worth it.

If there is a bass drum, it is advantageous to turn it sideways so that the head faces toward the front. This simple expedient will avoid having the main microphone array in the null zone of the bass drum's primary resonance, and the result will be a much better sound from the instrument.

Microphones 1 and 2 can be either a coincident or a near-coincident pair. Their height is normally 2.5 to 3 meters (8.5 to 10 feet) above the floor, and the distance $A$ is normally about 2 meters (6.5 feet) from the front edge of the orchestra. Microphones 3 and 4 may be of the same pattern as 1 and 2; however, many engineers prefer omnis, even when 1 and 2 are directional. The distance $B$ is roughly one-third the frontal width of the orchestra. Microphones 1 through 4 have their principal axes pointed downward at about 30°.

Microphones 5 and 6 are normally the same in pattern as 1 and 2 and are placed in front of the woodwind section at about the same height. They are pointed downward about 45°.

Balancing proceeds as follows. First, the main stereo pair is brought up on a pair of faders. The sound should be well balanced, with the strings not too prominent. Listen for proper direct-to-reverberant balances, and correct any problems by moving the main pair fore or aft, as required. Make relatively small adjustments. With only the primary pair, the stereo stage may seem just a little narrow. This may be corrected by bringing up the flanking pair (microphones 3 and 4). Normally they are operated at a level no higher than about −6 dB, relative to the main pair. Listen for subtle highlighting of the first violins and cellos, as well as a slight enhancement of ambience and a sense of spaciousness. Use only as much of the flanking pair as is necessary to strike a balance between precise localization on the one hand, and richness and opulence of sound on the other.

The approach described here presents the "best of both worlds." The coincident or near-coincident pair gives precision in localization, while the spaced microphones increase the density of lateral reflections so necessary for creating a sense of space. Both elements are essential in commercial recording. Finally, the back stereo pair can be raised just enough to limn out brass and woodwind details.

In some halls, a house pair of microphones can be used to increase the amount of reverberant pickup. This secondary stereo pair should be no farther from the main pair than 10 meters (33 feet). The pickup method is critical. In most applications, a coincident or near-coincident pair will not produce an impression of space that will complement the direct sound pickup of the orchestra. Often, with these pickup methods, the reverberation seems to recede into the center of the stereo stage. Spacing the microphones will correct this, and spacings of 2 to 4 meters work quite well.

In halls that have prominent reflections from the back wall, the house microphones may be used for masking purposes. For example, a back wall reflection that is delayed 100 msec from the direct pickup will be minimized by having house microphones placed at a distance of about 10 meters. The house microphones will intercept sound from the stage and back wall at time intervals of about 30 msec and 60 msec, and thus provide temporal masking for the reflection as it returns to the primary microphones.

### 22.9.2 Use of Accent Microphones

Accent microphones are placed within a meter or so of certain instruments in order to accent, or highlight, them. These should not be thought of "soloists' microphones." but rather as a means of correcting fundamental balance problems. Instruments such as harp and celesta are fairly soft; any attempt to play them loudly may create a rather ugly sound. Often, an accent microphone provides just what is needed. The first stand of bass viols is another candidate for an accent microphone. Here, the intent is to strengthen the bass line, should that be necessary, by providing a slight LF rise through proximity effect.

Another use for accent microphones is to increase the direct-to-reverberant ratio for a particular instrument. Many times, instruments in the percussion department (a xylophone, for example) generate considerable reverberant power and tend to sound loud, but too far away. A discreetly used accent microphone can make the instrument sound closer, but of course no softer. It is essential that accent microphones be panned into the stereo array at exactly the same position the targeted instruments occupy when heard only with the main stereo pair.

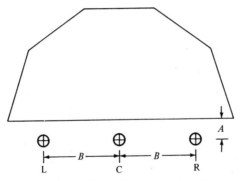

**Figure 22-18.** Orchestral recording with spaced omnidirectional microphones. *A* and *B* as in Figure 22-17.

The reader is referred to Section 9.5.2 for details of implementation of accent microphones.

### 22.9.3 Orchestral Recording with Spaced Microphones

Many recording engineers and producers favor a simple left–center–right microphone array across the front of the orchestra, as shown in Figure 22-18. Usually, these are omni microphones, but directional microphones (often the subcardioid) are used if the environment is too reverberant.

The critical element in balancing the the array is setting the level of the center microphone. Since most recordings made with three spaced microphones are mixed directly to stereo, the balance has to be carefully determined at the outset. If there is too much center fill, the stereo stage takes on a mono aspect. If there is too little, there will be a sense of a depression, or hole, in the middle of the stage. When the balance is just right, there will be a smooth continuum of sound across the stereo stage. As in all recording, much depends on good taste, but most engineers usually end up with the center microphone about −6 dB relative to the flanking microphones.

Working distances tend to be about the same as, or slightly greater than, those given in Figure 22-17.

### 22.9.4 Recording the Orchestra with Soloist

The comments made earlier with regard to soloist and chamber orchestra apply here as well. The main difference is one of scale, with greater distances between the soloist and the orchestra. Only in rare occasions will it *not* be necessary to use microphones with the soloists, and care should be taken that the balances are just. Too many commercial recordings place the soloist far in front of all else. While this may be gauged to sell records, and possibly salve the soloist's ego, it does the music a disservice.

A stereo microphone array is recommended, even when the solo instrument is small, such as a violin. The location of the microphones may be fairly close, 1 meter (3 feet) or so from the player. Remember that these are essentially accent microphones, and that there will be considerable sound from the soloist entering the main microphones.

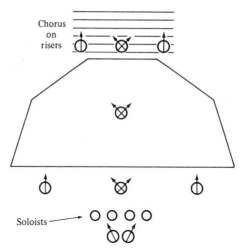

**Figure 22-19.** Recording the orchestra augmented with chorus and soloists.

On some occasions, the soloist will, for whatever reason, be rather weak with respect to the orchestra. In these cases, more signal from the soloist's microphones will be required in the mix, and the direct-to-reverberant balance in the solo line will be higher than with the orchestra. In these cases it is desirable to use a slight amount of artificial reverberation, just enough to correct the direct-to-reverberant imbalance. It will almost never be recognized as such and will be a great help in restoring a natural perspective.

### 22.9.5 Recording Very Large Ensembles

Operas and large symphonic works that are augmented by chorus and soloists often require heroic measures on the part of the recording engineer. Here there is justification for multitrack recording, since mixing directly to stereo may be impossible. The usual problems are those of inadequate rehearsal time and the fact that the cast may have never performed the work in public. There may be many takes of the same section, and performer's vocal quality may vary from day to day. Then there are special off-stage effects which must be accommodated.

While we take multitrack advantages for granted, it is sobering to read how John Culshaw and the English Decca engineers recorded Wagner's *Ring* cycle at the very beginning of the modern stereo era in the late 1950s and early 1960s (8).

The basic microphone techniques for these large works parallel most of what has been discussed in this chapter. The important difference is the management of these resources on multitrack tape required for post-production flexibility.

A work calling for large orchestra augmented with chorus and soloists might be arrayed as shown in Figure 22-19. The chorus is on risers behind the orchestra, while soloists are in front of the orchestra.

In operatic recording, the chorus is usually smaller than that with a large orchestra, and it might best be placed in front of the orchestra, assuming that the recording space

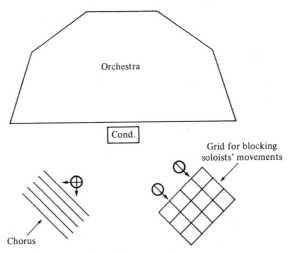

**Figure 22-20.** Recording operatic resources.

allows this. A certain amount of simulated stage movement is necessary for the soloists, and this required a fair amount of space. Again, this activity takes place in front of the orchestra. A possible setup is shown in Figure 22-20.

## BIBLIOGRAPHY

1. J. Backus, *The Acoustical Foundations of Music*, Norton, New York (1969).
2. A. Benade, *Fundamentals of Musical Acoustics*, Oxford University Press, New York (1976).
3. A. Benade, "From Instrument to Ear in a Room: Direct or Via Recording," *J. Audio Engineering Society*, vol. 33, no. 4 (1985).
4. L. Beranek, *Music, Acoustics & Architecture*, Wiley, New York (1962).
5. J. Borwick, *Sound Recording Practice*, Oxford University Press, New York (1987).
6. R. Caplain, *Techniques de Prise de Son*, Editions Techniques et Scientifiques Francaises, Paris (1980) (in French).
7. C. Ceoen, "Comparative Stereophonic Listening Tests," *J. Audio Engineering Society*, vol. 20, no. 1 (1970).
8. J. Culshaw, *Ring Resounding*, Viking Press, New York (1957).
9. J. Culshaw, *Putting the Record Straight*, Viking Press, New York (1981).
10. N. Del Mar, *Anatomy of the Orchestra*, University of California Press, Los Angeles (1983).
11. M. Dickreiter, *Tonmeister Technology*, Temmer Enterprises, New York (1989).
12. J. Eargle, *The Microphone Handbook*, Elar, Commack, N.Y. (1982).
13. J. Eargle, *Music, Sound, & Technology*, Van Nostrand Reinhold, New York (1990).
14. F. Gaisberg, *The Music Goes Round*, Macmillan, New York (1942).
15. R. Gelatt, *The Fabulous Phonograph*, Lippincott, New York (1955).
16. J. Jecklin, "A Different Way to Record Classical Music," *J. Audio Engineering Society*, vol. 29, no. 5 (1981).
17. S. Lipschitz, "Stereo Microphone Techniques: Are the Purists Wrong?" *J. Audio Engineering Society*, vol. 34, no. 9 (1986).
18. J. Meyer, *Acoustics and the Performance of Music*, Verlag Das Musikinstrument, Frankfurt (1978). Translated by Bowsher and Westphal.
19. C. O'Connell, *The Other Side of the Record*, Knopf, New York (1941).
20. H. Olson, *Musical Engineering*, McGraw-Hill, New York (1952).

21. J. Pierce, *The Science of Musical Sound*, Scientific American Books, New York (1983).

22. A. Previn, *André Previn's Guide to the Orchestra*, Macmillan, London (1983)

23. O. Read and W. Welch, *From Tinfoil to Stereo*, H. Sams, Indianapolis (1959).

24. E. Schwarzkopf, *On and Off the Record: A Memoire of Walter Legge*, Scribners, New York (1982).

25. D. Woolford, "Sound Pressure Levels in Symphony Orchestras and Hearing," presented a the 1984 Australian Regional Convention, Audio Engineering Society, 25–27 September 1984, preprint number 2104.

26. *The Phonograph and Sound Recording After One Hundred Years* (Audio Engineering Society, New York) *J. Audio Engineering Society*, vol. 25, no. 10/11 (1977).

27. *Stereophonic Techniques*, an anthology published by the Audio Engineering Society (1986).

# 23

# POPULAR RECORDING AND PRODUCTION

## 23.1 SCOPE OF STUDY

Popular music embraces a wide variety of styles, and recording approaches can range from the simplest stereo pickups to complex multi-microphone arrays in recording large studio orchestras and rock groups. The one factor in common to most pop recording is the general reliance on the engineer's and producer's taste in creating a sonic texture quite apart from that which may exist naturally. That is to say, the creation of a stereo stage, at the hands of the recording engineer, is more important than the simple recreation of an acoustical stereo stage. But there are certain values which grow out of the acoustical experience per se, and it is important that the recording engineer whose main interest may be popular music understand the techniques discussed in Chapter 22.

Many of the points concerning balance are of course reserved for the mixdown session, and it is assumed that the engineer and producer are working with a 16- or 24-track recorder. Only the smallest pop or jazz sessions lend themselves to direct two-channel, without multitrack backup.

## 23.2 THE STUDIO ENVIRONMENT

Studios for popular recording range in size from those intended for overdubbing vocal or instrumental solos up to those large enough to accommodate a 30- or 40-piece studio orchestra. A room large enough to accommodate a sizeable group may typically be 4200 cubic meters (150,000 cubic feet) in volume.

It is important that the studio be well isolated from outside noise sources, and this often leads to expensive architectural decoupling of the space from its surroundings. Air handling must be quiet, and ductwork must not provide a leakage path between adjacent studios.

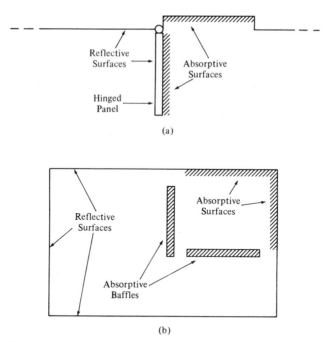

**Figure 23-1.** Absorptive and reflective conditions in the studio. (a) Adjustable wall panels. (b) Division of the studio into reflective and absorptive areas.

### 23.2.1 Acoustical Requirements

Popular music studios generally tend to be fairly absorptive in their internal acoustical treatment. The reason for this is to facilitate the pickup of individual instruments, or small instrumental sections, with minimum leakage between microphones. Keeping the reverberant level low is one way to control this.

However, an early reflection pattern is desirable in order to generate natural stereo perspectives, and some studios have acoustics that are variable over a greater or lesser degree. Some of the techniques which have been used for this are shown in Figure 23-1.

### 23.2.2 Isolation Requirements

Requirements for isolation of louder instruments have led to the use of acoustical baffles (often called "goboes") to provide isolation of direct sound. The effectiveness is related to size. Figure 23-2 shows how effective such devices may be. Such baffles may be constructed from wood, lined with absorptive surfaces, and equipped with casters for easy moving. Large rectangular blocks of urethane foam of similar shape can be used just as easily.

Very loud (or soft) sound sources may be placed in an isolation booth in order to minimize leakage. The most common applications here are for the drum set (whose sound

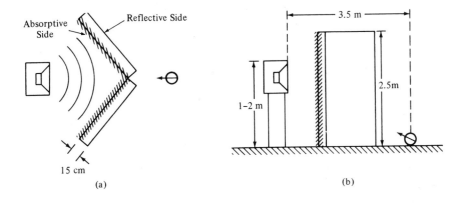

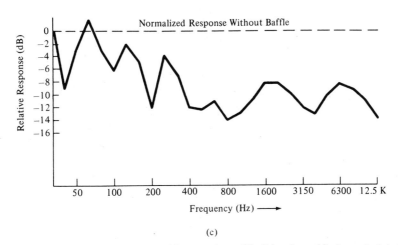

**Figure 23-2.** Effect of an absorptive baffle. (a) Top view. (b) Side view. (c) Acoustical isolation versus frequency.

tends to leak into other open microphones), and vocalists (whose microphone tends to pick up sound from the louder instruments in the studio). It is important that isolation booths have good sight lines into the control room and into the studio. Acoustically, they should exhibit smooth low-frequency absorption.

## 23.3 THE STEREO SOUND STAGE

In popular recording, the recording engineer creates an artificial continuum of sound across the stereo stage. His basic tools are the individual microphone outputs, panpots to position them, and time delay and reverberation to lend ambience. He need not be limited here, and it is possible and desirable in many kinds of pop recording to combine natural stereo perspectives with artificial ones.

### 23.3.1 Panned versus Stereo Pickup

Because of the diverse acoustical output levels of most instruments used in popular recording, a natural balance, per se, is often difficult to attain. As a way around this problem, the engineer can pick up each one separately and pan the signal to a specific point on the stereo stage. He will of course adjust all balance relationships during the process. On some occasions, a pair of like instruments can be picked up with a single microphone.

Certain large sources of sound, such as a drum set, piano, or a vocal group, can be picked up in natural stereo perspective and positioned on the stereo stage as desired.

It is possible to record, say, a big band jazz ensemble by means of a single coincident pair, since this kind of ensemble is inherently self-balancing. As a matter of practicality, accent microphones would need to be used on piano, guitar, and acoustic bass, since these are relatively soft instruments and have traditionally been amplified in performance settings.

There is no question that this is more "natural" than the the multi-microphone approach, and the recording may be appreciated by the audiophile segment of the recording buying public. However, such a recording does not conform to the expectations of most record listeners and musicians, and it is apt to be rejected as a commercially viable option for the producer.

The best overall approach is to combine both close microphone techniques and natural stereo techniques. Above all, the recording should convey a sense of ambience as well as one of precise localization and presence.

### 23.3.2 Dealing with Diverse Levels

Players do not always perform at consistent levels, and the recording engineer, working with the producer, will have to make adjustments during the course of a recording. (The terms balance engineer and mixer are often used to describe the recording engineer as as he performs this function.)

In particular, the balance between instrumental solos and accompaniment must be carefully delineated, and the recording engineer must know, either through reading a score or chart, or be being verbally cued by the producer, just when a solo passage is to begin and end.

In popular music and jazz, the recording engineer is continuously making adjustments in relative levels of many signal components. Most of these adjustments are minor ones on the order of plus or minus 3 dB or less, but vocal soloists may require up to 10 or 12 dB of gain control, depending upon actual microphone technique.

## 23.4 RECOMMENDED MICROPHONE CHOICE AND PLACEMENT

This section will discuss microphone choice and placement for recording particular instruments or groups of instruments, taking into account various physical, acoustical, and musical relationships. In general, cardioid microphones will be most useful in these applications, because of relative insensitivity to leakage from adjacent sound sources. In

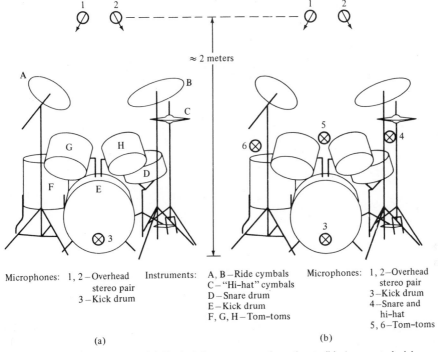

**Figure 23-3.** The drum set. (a) Typical drum set seen from front. (b) Augmented pickup.

addition, the proximity effect of the cardioid has been identified with the expected sound texture of many instruments.

### 23.4.1 Percussion Instruments

This is a broad category, and the discussion will begin with the drum set, or drum kit, as it is often called. The modern drum set consists of the following elements, played by one person:

1. Kick drum (actuated by the right foot)
2. Snare drum (played with either sticks or wire brushes)
3. "High-hat" cymbal set (played with sticks or brushes)
4. Two "ride" cymbals (played with sticks or brushes)
5. Two or more tom-toms (played with sticks)

The arrangement and actual number of individual elements in the set may vary from player to player.

In a jazz setting, a relatively simple three-microphone approach will be sufficient, as shown in Figure 23-3(a). Here, there is an overhead spaced stereo pair and a single microphone for the kick drum. As a general rule, a rather hardy cardioid dynamic

1, 2–Stereo pair

**Figure 23-4.** The marimba, vibraphone, and xylophone.

microphone can be used for the kick drum, while extended-range cardioid capacitor microphone are used overhead. The kick drum microphone is usually panned to the center, while the stereo overhead pair can be positioned as desired. Generally, that stereo pair will not be spread across the entire stage. Rather, it will be panned inward for somewhat narrower presentation, or it will be panned so that it appears between center and right, or center and left.

If the drum set is featured in the recording, more microphones may be used, as shown in Figure 23-3(b). Care must be taken so that players do not create air movements close to the microphones. If this cannot be controlled, wind screens must be used. The additional microphones are placed rather close to the drum heads, and they must be capable of handling quite high acoustical levels. They are panned to their respective positions on the sound stage. In rock recording, it is customary to spread the drum set over the entire width of the stereo stage.

When picked up at short distances, there are often spurious resonances in drum sets. These should be carefully damped. Drummers are usually well aware of these problems, and they will usually solve them after a little listening in the control room.

In rock recording the drum set is often placed in a large isolation booth to minimize leakage into other open microphones.

Among the tuned percussion instruments normally encountered are the xylophone, marimba, and vibraphone. Figure 23-4 shows a suggested pickup for these instruments.

Most of the non-tuned percussion instruments used in popular recording are fairly small; thus, they radiate fairly evenly in all directions. Cardioid microphones placed 0.6 to 1 meter (2 to 3 feet) overhead will usually give excellent results. Quite often, a single player will be asked to perform on a number of these instruments, and he should be made aware of just what the particular pickup requirements are. Many Latin percussion instruments are best picked up at fairly close quarters when they are played at not too high levels.

Overall, no reverberation needs to be added to percussion instruments, unless for special effect.

In general, percussion players can easily adapt playing styles and techniques to accommodate the needs of recording, and experimentation is encouraged.

### 23.4.2 Brass Instruments

Because radiation takes place from the bell of the instrument, the radiation pattern of brass instruments can be deduced from the data shown in Figure 1-22. In general, the fundamental frequencies of all brass instruments have wavelengths that are fairly long with respect to the bell diameter, and we can assume that the fundamentals will be radiated omnidirectionally.

When played loudly, all brass instruments will produce considerable harmonic development, and the higher harmonics can become quite directional along the axis of the bell. A microphone placed 1 meter (3 feet) in front of a trumpet will pick up an unnaturally bright sound. Some high-frequency roll-off is justified, and many recording engineers choose to do this by selecting a microphone whose HF response is rolled off. Older-model ribbon microphones are quite popular in this application. The players themselves often prefer these older microphones, inasmuch as the recorded sound is more like that which they hear while playing. Do not hesitate to experiment with various models and types of microphones.

By simple scaling of wavelengths and bell diameters, the directional properties of the other brass instruments can be determined. In the case of the tuba and French horn, the musical context is usually that of the large studio orchestra, and only accent microphone pickup is normally required.

In actual performance, players move about slightly, with the axes of their instruments pointing on- and off-microphone. This is perfectly natural, and nothing should be done to discourage it.

Figure 23-5 shows pickup approaches for various brass instruments. Note that in larger groups a single microphone can be used to pick up a pair or instruments. For players who move around a good bit, it is sometimes necessary to mount a small microphone directly to the bell of the instrument. There are a number of very small electret microphones intended for this purpose.

Reverberation is normally used with brass instruments.

### 23.4.3 Woodwind Instruments

Typical microphone usage is shown in Figure 23-6. Only the saxophone has its bell positioned to radiate in the frontal direction, and in both live performance and in recording its sound is quite bright when it is played at loud levels. As with brass instruments, it is often necessary to use a small microphone mounted directly on the instrument. This is not quite as easy to do for the woodwinds, inasmuch as the bulk of sound radiation from these instruments is via the open tone holes. Only for the lowest note on the instrument is radiation entirely from the bell. The best position for mounting the microphone is outside the bell, reaching up slightly and back so that it is positioned

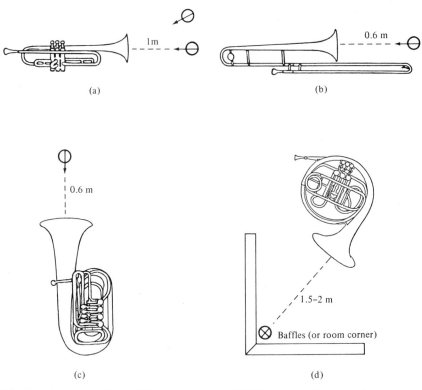

**Figure 23-5.** Brass instruments (solo pickup). (a) Trumpet. (b) Trombone. (c) Tuba. (d) French horn (as seen from above).

about 15 cm (6 inches) over the lower tone holes. In this position, there will be a good balance of sound.

Reverberation is normally used with woodwind instruments.

### 23.4.4 String Ensembles

Because they are relatively soft instruments, strings are almost always used in multiples, and a natural stereo pickup is traditional. In popular recording, they are used only in large studio orchestras, and their presentation on the stereo stage normally encompasses the entire width. The string complement usually numbers:

| | |
|---|---|
| 1st Violins | 6–8 players |
| 2nd Violins | 6–8 players |
| Violas | 4–6 players |
| Cellos | 4 players |

There is usually one bass viol, and it is picked up separately from the rest of the ensemble. Figure 23-7 shows details of picking up the string ensemble.

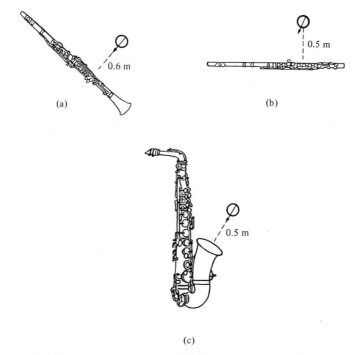

**Figure 23-6.** Woodwind instruments (solo pickup). (a) Clarinet and oboe. (b) Flute. (c) Saxophone.

In arraying the players, allow a space about 1.5 meters on a side for each stand (pair) of violins and violas. Allow a space about 2 meters on a side for each stand of cellos.

The height of the microphones over the instruments is rather critical. If too close, the sound will be edgy. At greater distances, these problems go away, but we then face the problems of excessive leakage into the string microphones from the louder instruments in the studio. This is an age-old problem, and it has gone unsolved in many recordings. The problem often begins with the musical arrangement itself, where massed strings may be pitted against loud brass and percussion. An obvious solution is to record the louder instruments at one time, and then add the strings later, through multitrack overdubbing. If this this capability is not available, then the mixing skills of the engineer must be called upon to reduce the levels of the string faders during silent section—while getting the level back to normal when the instruments come back in. This can more easily be done in multitrack mixdown.

Some large studios have the luxury of a separate adjacent room large enough to isolate the strings from louder instruments, while allowing eye contact through large windows between the two rooms (see Section 23.7.3). Headphone monitoring is essential in this case.

### 23.4.5 Keyboard Instruments

The piano is the chief instrument here. As a rule, a pair of microphones will be used, whether or not the pickup is intended for stereo presentation. Many people are shocked

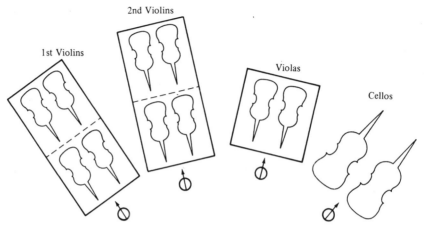

Notes:    1. Use one microphone per four to six players in each section.
2. Pan as follows: 1st violins—left; 2nd violins—left center; violas—right center; cellos—right.

(a)

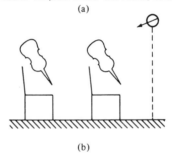

(b)

**Figure 23-7.** String ensemble pickup. (a) Plan view. (b) Side view (typical).

when they see microphones placed 30 cm (12 inches) or so above the strings—but such techniques work well! Figure 23-8 shows some of the variations here. It always helps if the instrument is smoothly regulated, even to the extent of being "toned down."

If the piano is featured, then a somewhat traditional stereo pickup may be appropriate, with the stereo pair placed just outside the case, but generally no farther away than 1.5 meters (5 feet).

The harpsichord and celesta are often used for special musical effects. These instruments produce low-frequency action noises, and an 80- or 100-Hz high-pass filter will remove them.

### 23.4.6 The Guitar

The acoustic, hollow-bodied guitar has a relatively low acoustical output, and this calls for fairly close microphone placement. The instrument may be amplified, and this extends the range of pick-up options. Figure 23-9 shows some of the common techniques.

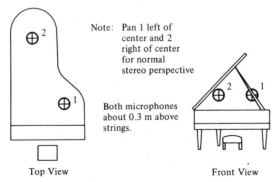

**Figure 23-8.** Keyboard pickup (stereo).

### 23.4.7 Electronic Instruments

This section deals with all instruments whose sound is generated or amplified for presentation over a loudspeaker. As shown in Figure 23-10, pickup can be from line outputs on the amplifier, from the loudspeaker output via a direct box, or by way of a microphone placed close to the loudspeaker. All options should be tried in an effort to get the most natural sound. Many synthesizers have stereo outputs, and these should both be used and preserved as stereo ingredients in the mix. Equalization may be necessary to get the correct spectral balance.

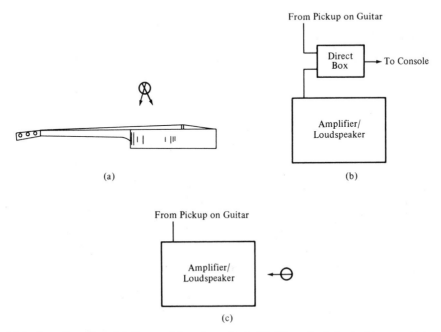

**Figure 23-9.** Acoustic guitar. (a) Stereo pickup (top view). (b) Direct feed from pickup on instrument. (c) Microphone placed close to loudspeaker (about 0.3 meter).

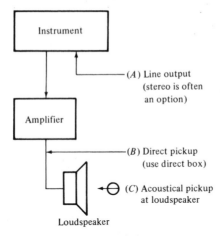

**Figure 23-10.** Pickup from electronic instruments. Three options are given.

A direct electrical pickup will nearly always result in more low bass than will a microphone placed in front of the loudspeaker, due to inherent low-frequency limitations of the loudspeaker. Signals are at line level, and input padding in the console must be adjusted accordingly.

### 23.4.8 Vocal Pickup

The greatest problem in vocal pickup is controlling level. If the vocalist moves back and forward, as part of the kinesthetics of performance, inverse square level variations may be considerable. Wherever possible, the vocalist should sit on a stool, and the microphone should be placed slightly above, as shown in Figure 23-11.

It is customary to use directional microphones with vocalists, inasmuch as some degree of low-frequency emphasis, due to proximity effect, is normally expected. The choice of

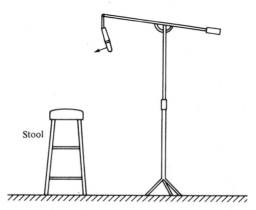

**Figure 23-11.** Vocal pickup. Microphone should be about 0.5 meter (20 inches) from the mouth.

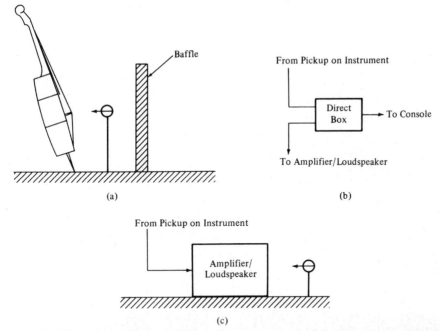

**Figure 23-12.** Bass viol. (a) Microphone pickup. (b) Direct pickup. (c) Microphone at loudspeaker.

microphone is important. Some older, large diaphragm capacitor microphones have a pronounced rise on axis, and this may or may not complement a given singer's voice. Highly sibilant singers are often best served by older dynamic and ribbon microphones whose high-frequency response may be slightly rolled off. The use of a wind screen to avoid "popping" p's and b's, and so on, is recommended.

When a singer has too wide a dynamic range, a compressor will be useful in controlling level.

### 23.4.9 The Acoustic Bass (Bass Viol)

There is usually one bass in a popular group, whether it be mainstream pop or rock, and for many applications, the electric bass, which has no acoustical output of its own, is preferred. Balance and tone quality are critical, and no effort should be spared to get the right sound.

The bass viol can be picked up three ways:

1.   With a microphone, as shown in Figure 23-12(a). The microphone should be about 0.5 meter (20 inches) off the floor, and the use of an acoustical baffle is recommended. This pickup method is useful in jazz, where bass solos are important and where the sounds emanating from the fingerboard are an essential musical ingredient. A variation here is to place a small capacitor microphone between the tailpiece and lower body of the instrument, wedging it in place with a piece of foam rubber. This will ensure consistent

levels from the player, but at the expense of cutting down on finger sounds from the strings.

2.  Direct electrical pickup, as shown in Figure 23-12(b). Most bassists today have pickup transducers connected directly to the bridge of the instrument. The connection to the console is normally made from transducer using a direct box. When possible, use an active direct box so that a line level signal from the transducer reaches the console.

3.  Microphone pickup at the loudspeaker, as shown in Figure 23-12(c).

Methods 2 and 3 may be used with the electric bass.

## 23.5 NOTES ON THE USE OF REVERBERATION

The ambience heard in most popular recording usually has little relation to actual performance environments. It may be thought of as an "enhancement" of the program, and it is generally added only to certain components of the program. Typically, reverberation times on the order of 2 to 2.5 seconds are common, but, since the return level from the reverberation generator is usually low, the effect is not usually one of long reverberation time.

Most of current practice in this area is simply a perpetuation of what has been done over the years, and the producer's desire to provide what the listener traditionally expects. Popular recording came of age with the rather primitive acoustical "echo chambers" of the 1950s, and these have set directions for most current practice. Experimentation is always welcome, but the old art is really quite good.

In most popular recording, a single reverberation send signal is sufficient, if the reverberation unit has stereo return capability (see Section 17.2.2). The stereo returns are fed left and right in the stereo mix. In this arrangement, the diffuse nature of the reverberant signal will be the same for all individual feeds, regardless of their positioning on the stereo stage. This is shown in Figure 23-13(a).

In earlier days, mono reverberation was handled as shown in Figure 23-13(b). Cross-patching of the return signals was common, in an effort to increase a sense of space perspective. The attendant patching for this method can be rather complex, and it is not often done today. Modern digital reverberation units accept stereo input and provide stereo returns. It is easy enough to experiment with stereo reverberation send signals, as shown in (c). In some instances, this may produce a richer reverberation texture than can be produced with only a mono send signal. Experimentation is always in order.

Figure 23-14 shows some variations on reverberation decay times and return levels. The usual approach in popular recording is shown in (a). Here, a relatively long (2.5 to 3-second) reverberation time signal is returned at a moderately low level, just enough to fill in the empty spaces, as it were. The same return signal returned at a higher level, as shown in (b), is much too intrusive.

By comparison, a short reverberation time (1 second or less) returned at a too low level, as in (c), will hardly be heard. Given enough return level, as in (d), the short reverberation return can enhance certain brass and percussion instruments. This situation often exists naturally in some live studios, and engineers may use spaced omnidirectional microphones high in the studio to pick up this natural, but fairly short, reverberation.

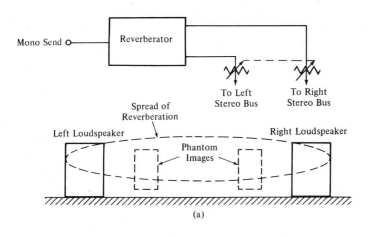

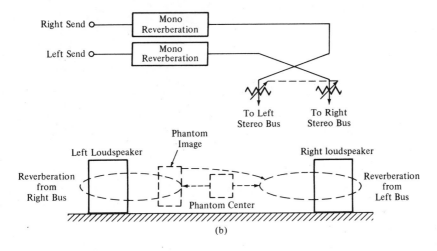

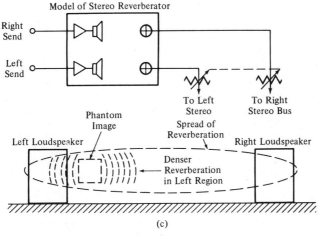

**Figure 23-13.** Reverberation patching. (a) Effect of stereo return from mono reverberation send. (b) Using two mono reverberators cross-patched. (c) Using a reverberator with both stereo send and return.

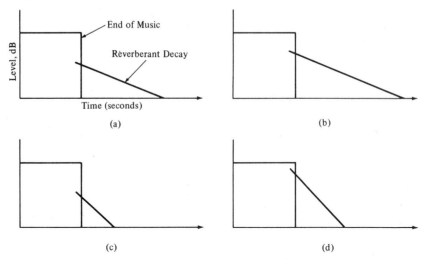

**Figure 23-14.** Adjusting reverberation time and return level. (a) Fairly long reverberation time; low return level. Effect: not necessarily natural, but quite pleasant. Traditional in jazz and pop recording. (b) Fairly long reverberation time; high return level. Effect: usually unpleasant; reverberation tends to get in the way of the music. (c) Short reverberation time; low return level. Effect: adds signal density, but otherwise not readily perceived by the listener; rarely used in jazz and pop recording. (d) Short reverberation time; high return level. Effect: good feeling of liveness; useful with full brass sections and some percussion instruments.

Other variations on the use of reverberation include using more than one reverberation unit, with each set to different reverberation times for enhancing different instruments.

## 23.6 EXAMPLES OF JAZZ RECORDING

Typical studio situations will be outlined, discussing in detail the musical values that must be maintained and the technical decisions that support them. Jazz is essentially an "acoustical" event, and every effort should be made to create as natural a sound as possible, avoiding the excesses of signal processing. It is also an intimate musical form, whether big band or solo piano, and all details must be heard. One may say that the goal should be to bring the players into the listening environment, rather than transplanting the listeners into another performance environment.

### 23.6.1 Small Jazz Forms

A typical jazz trio might be made up of piano, bass, and drums. In laying out the stereo stage, we should place the most prominent instrument in the center, with remaining instruments in flanking positions. Figure 23-15(a) shows how this might be done. The piano is picked up in stereo and panned inward as need be, so that is occupies perhaps the center one-third or one-half of the stage. Drums would be picked up via an overhead pair, as well as a microphone on the kick drum. The overhead pair could then be panned so that the left signal appeared in the center of the stage, with the right signal at far right. The kick drum would best be panned center, for purposes of mono compatibility

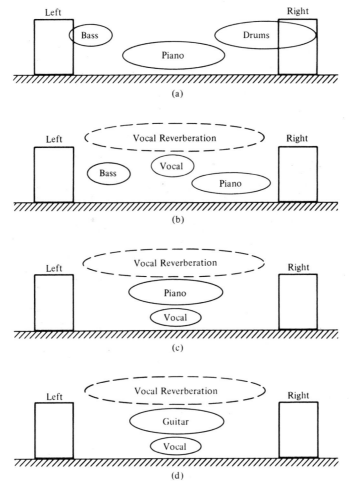

**Figure 23-15.** Stereo representations for some small jazz groups. (a) Piano, bass, and drums. (b) Piano, vocal, and bass. (c) Vocal with piano. (d) Vocal with guitar.

and FM broadcasting. The bass, picked up by a single microphone, or by direct pickup, should be panned slightly in from the left in order to maintain overall musical and stereo stage balance. The overall intent is to feature the piano, as it were, with both drums and bass as musical support functions.

It is important that the players be physically located in the same array in which they appear on the stereo stage. This will ensure that normal acoustical leakage in the studio will reinforce their positions on the stereo stage. Little, if any, artificial reverberation would be needed here, and the only gain manipulation required by the engineer would be to raise extended solo passages slightly.

A vocal solo with piano and bass might be arrayed as shown in (b). Here, the vocalist is clearly in the center, with piano and bass moved out to flanking positions. The piano remains in stereo. Reverberation is essential for the vocalist, but it should be subtle and in good perspective.

For a vocalist accompanied only by the piano, the piano should be restored back to the center for the sake of stereo balance, as shown in (c).

Vocalist and guitar would get similar treatment, as shown in (d).

### 23.6.2 Small Jazz Groups

A basic rhythm section for a small jazz ensemble consists of piano, bass, drums, and possibly guitar. Against this background, up to three wind instruments are often used in instrumental arrangements, or as backup for a vocalist. Figure 23-16 shows some of the possibilities here.

It makes good stereo interest if instruments that are in dialogue with each other can be placed on opposite sides of the stereo stage. The group shown in (a) places the Hammond organ and the guitar on opposite sides, with no inward panning. Much the same can be said for the tenor and alto saxophones and their placement at far left and far right. In (b), the drums are featured and are thus given center stereo stage. The piano is featured in (c), and an expanded group featuring the vocal is shown in (d). The major emphasis in these examples is on interesting stereo placement, both through panning as well as natural stereo pickup.

In setting up the basic mix, the engineer proceeds as follows. First, a good balance is made between the drum set and the bass. When that has been made, the piano and guitar may be brought in, one at a time. Then, the saxophones are brought in to the mix and their proper levels established. Finally, the vocal is brought in to the mix.

During this experimental phase, the musicians can be asked simply to improvise, with all players involved. Levels should be watched carefully from the outset.

Bear in mind that the ear has its limits as to how many musical elements can be sorted out. Make sure that the important elements are out front, while those of lesser interest are pulled back.

Referring to the setup described in Figure 23-16(a), note that the only conventional stereo pickup is the drum overhead pair. However, normal leakage in the studio environment itself will contribute to a natural feeling of good stereo. Further, if the players are physically arranged in the studio as they are on the stereo stage, this effect will be all the more natural.

Outside of added reverberation on the two saxophones and the vocal, little signal processing should be required in a setup such as this.

### 23.6.3 Big Band Jazz Ensembles

The usual makeup of this ensemble is:

| | |
|---|---|
| Trumpets | 4 |
| Trombones | 4 |
| Saxophones | 5 |
| (1 baritone, 2 tenors, 2 altos) | |

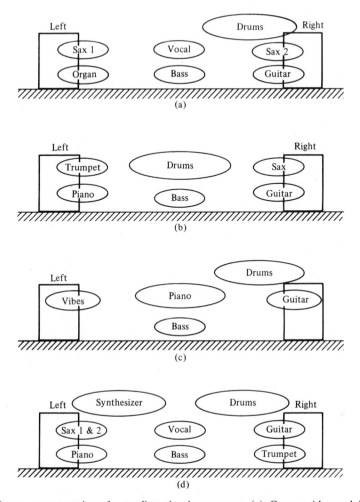

**Figure 23-16.** Stereo representations for medium-size jazz groups. (a) Group with vocal lead. (b) Group featuring drums. (c) Small group with piano lead; no winds. (d) Vocal with 8 players; drums and synthesizer in stereo pickup.

| Bass | 1 |
|---|---|
| Drum Set | 1 |
| Guitar | 1 |
| Piano | 1 |

This basic ensemble may be augmented by added percussion players, French horn, electric organ or synthesizer, and possibly one additional player each in the wind instrument sections. The saxophone players may double on woodwind (clarinet, flute, or oboe), as required. Attention here will focus only on the basic ensemble.

A typical studio layout is shown in Figure 23-17. Good stereo spread, with images

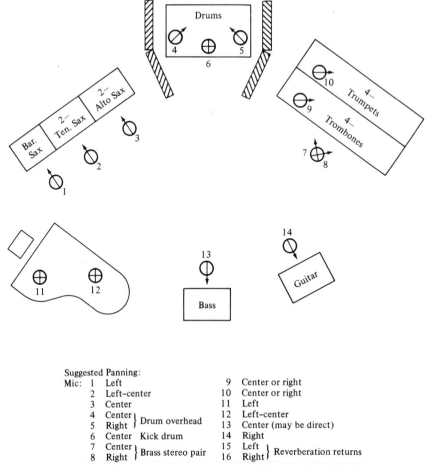

Suggested Panning:

Mic: 1  Left
2  Left–center
3  Center
4  Center  } Drum overhead
5  Right
6  Center  Kick drum
7  Center  } Brass stereo pair
8  Right

9  Center or right
10  Center or right
11  Left
12  Left–center
13  Center (may be direct)
14  Right
15  Left  } Reverberation returns
16  Right

**Figure 23-17.** Suggested studio layout for big band jazz ensemble.

across the entire stereo stage, can easily be achieved here through panning assignments as shown. Instrumental solos usually require that a player move in more closely to a microphone, and the engineer must be cued by the producer so that he can quickly make necessary level adjustments in time. The trumpets and trombones are picked up as a section via an overhead stereo pair. Microphones are spotted in each section to accommodate solos. The nature of trumpet and trombone writing is such that they can be treated as one large brass section; however, some engineers prefer to treat them individually, as in the case of the saxophone section.

**23.6.3.1 Getting the Right Balance.** It is essential that the recording engineer arrive at an acceptable balance as quickly as possible, because of the high cost of large sessions. As before, he begins with the rhythm section, bringing in each component at a time. Then, the saxophones and brass are brought in separately.

At the same time, the cue busses must be adjusted for those players who wish to monitor over headphones. It is customary for the softer rhythm and vocal inputs to be made more prominent in the headphone mix, deemphasizing those instruments that are louder in the studio. The recording engineer should monitor the cue busses over headphones so that he knows exactly what the players are hearing, both in terms of balance and level. Consideration should be given to operating the cue system in stereo, inasmuch as that will lessen listening fatigue over long periods. More than one set of stereo cue busses may be used for those players who wish to monitor a different mix. For this purpose, many modern consoles have four or more cue busses.

**23.6.3.2 Acoustical Isolation Requirements.** No more acoustical isolation in the studio should be used than is really necessary. The players are happiest when they can hear each other without benefit of headphones. On the other hand, too close microphone placement tends to be destructive of good blend, and it can produce harsh textures. Softer instruments, such as the guitar, bass, and piano, require special attention. The bass is easiest to work with if it is picked up directly. In this case, the bass amplifier-loudspeaker can be placed close to the player so that he can hear himself comfortably. The other players may rely on headphones to hear the amount of bass they want.

The same comments apply to the guitar, and the guitar amplifier-loudspeaker should face the player so that he can hear himself without having to operate the amplifier at a high level. An alternative to direct pickup of the guitar is to place a microphone directly in front of its loudspeaker. This signal may require some equalization in order to get the desired sound in the control room.

If required, the guitar microphone can be reoriented toward the instrument for acoustical pickup in quieter pieces, assuming, of course, that an acoustic guitar is being used.

The piano should be oriented so that its cover directs sound away from the rest of the players. For this reason, it is quite common to place the piano in the left channel of the stereo stage, since that position matches its most effective position in the studio.

**23.6.3.3 Visual Cues.** It is essential that the recording engineer maintain eye contact with the principal players in the studio. In this way, he can easily tell when a player is about to play a solo, which of course may require a gain change.

It is common in a big band setup for a soloist to stand up, although not all players choose to do this. The microphone placement must be such that it can accommodate players when sitting or standing.

**23.6.3.4 Notes on Signal Processing.** If the recording is made direct to stereo, then all balance, equalization, and reverberation decisions must be made at the time of the session, since there can be no "fixing it in the mix." There must be no question about the integrity of the monitor system, since this is the key to what is really getting on tape. As handy as a compressor is for keeping maximum levels in check, an experienced, quick hand at the fader is usually better.

Reverberation is not normally used with the rhythm instruments, but there are always exceptions. Reverberation cannot be successfully added to a stereo big band jazz recording after the session, so it is important to get the right balance from the start.

Of course, if the recording is being made multitrack with a modern console, the best of both worlds can be had. A "dry" (without reverberation or equalization) multitrack safety can be recorded simultaneously with a direct to stereo finished master. Should the two-track tape, for whatever reason, be deemed unsatisfactory, the multitrack tape can be remixed as needed. The cost of this insurance is quite high but, once in place, the security of multitrack backup nearly always tends to justify itself.

As formidable as the task may seem, there are many recording engineers who can easily handle a direct to stereo big band recording. The skill is not learned overnight, and one must progress through the intermediate forms, while at the same time apprenticing with seasoned engineers. A genuine love for the music is essential in learning the art.

Automated consoles capable of sub-grouping facilitate the job of mixing large numbers of inputs directly to stereo. It is desirable that the automation system be of the "moving fader" type.

## 23.7 THE LARGE STUDIO ORCHESTRA

The studio orchestra considered here is the typical ensemble that would be used for recording the score for a TV or motion picture sound track. While it appears symphonic in dimension, the musical demands may vary from all-out jazz performance to large, massed string writing in a near classical context. Invariably, it does not enjoy a large string complement, and the ensemble is usually recorded in studios that require added reverberation.

### 23.7.1 Composition of the Studio Orchestra

A typical studio orchestra will have the instrumentation of the big band jazz ensemble discussed earlier plus a string section that includes the following:

| | |
|---|---|
| 1st Violins | 8 |
| 2nd Violins | 8 |
| Violas | 6 |
| Cellos | 5 |
| Bass viol | 1 |

There may already be an electric bass, which complements the jazz portion of the group. In addition, there is usually a harp, tuba, additional woodwinds, as many as three French horns, additional percussion instruments, and vocalists, as needed. There may be additional synthesizers and other electronic resources, depending upon musical requirements.

### 23.7.2 Track Assignments

Multitrack recording is the norm here, because of the demands for post-production flexibility. Sound tracks are usually mixed with effects and dialogue, and individual instruments may need to be emphasized. Typical track assignments might be as indicated in Table 23-1.

### Table 23-1. Typical track assignments for the studio orchestra

| Basic track assignments for a 24-track recorder | Useful VCA or automated fader subgrouping for mixdown |
|---|---|
| 1. Strings (left) | 1. Strings |
| 2. Strings (right) | 2. Brass |
| 3. Chorus (left) | 3. Saxophones and reeds |
| 4. Chorus (right) | 4. Chorus |
| 5. Vocal solo | 5. Rhythm |
| 6. Saxophones and reeds | 6. Vocal |
| 7. Saxophones and reeds | 7. Piano and guitar |
| 8. Saxophones and reeds | 8. Master |
| 9. Brass overhead (left) | |
| 10. Brass overhead (right) | |
| 11. Brass solo | |
| 12. Brass solo | |
| 13. Percussion | |
| 14. Drums (left) | |
| 15. Drums (right) | |
| 16. Kick drum | |
| 17. Bass | |
| 18. Guitar | |
| 19. Piano | |
| 20–24. Spares for effects, reverberation etc. | |

An important consideration here is how the tracks are to be used in post-production. The engineer should know which elements will require the most flexibility in rebalancing, and he should ensure that those elements are on tracks of their own. Conceivably, the entire string section could be recorded on a single stereo pair of tracks, if the post-production flexibility required only raising them and lowering them as a group. On the other hand, a lead vocal must remain isolated from background vocals, and certain critical rhythmic elements must remain separate. When mixed under dialogue or sound effects, the engineer often has to reach for musical details or thin out textures if they are to be easily heard. In some live recording events, a pair of tracks may have be assigned to pick up audience reactions.

All things considered, there are rarely enough tracks to satisfy everyone, so a good bit of planning is necessary.

VCA subgrouping, or automated fader subgrouping, will simplify the monitor mixing of a complex session with a studio orchestra. For example, the entire string ensemble, with all stereo and panning assignments, can be grouped under the control of a single fader. The rhythm tracks may be similarly grouped. Within such grouping, an individual microphone input may be adjusted as required.

### 23.7.3 Balance Considerations

The single greatest difficulty in making a recording of the type discussed here is keeping the sounds of the louder brass instruments from swamping out the softer string instruments. For this reason, many recording engineers place microphones very close to the string instruments in an effort to hold down leakage from the louder instruments. Unfortunately, this often results in a strident string sound. The use of contact microphones placed directly on the bodies of string instruments will certainly take care of leakage problems, but at the expense of natural string sound.

Some large studios have isolation rooms adjacent to the main studio, and these are ideal for recording both loud and soft instruments at the same time. A typical layout is shown in Figure 23-18. Details of direct visual, as well as video, contact are important, and of course headphone cue monitoring is essential.

Where the luxury of string section isolation does not exist, the recording engineer must rely basically on quick manual response to cues from the producer. It is always hoped that the arranger will avoid pitting strings against full brass tutti.

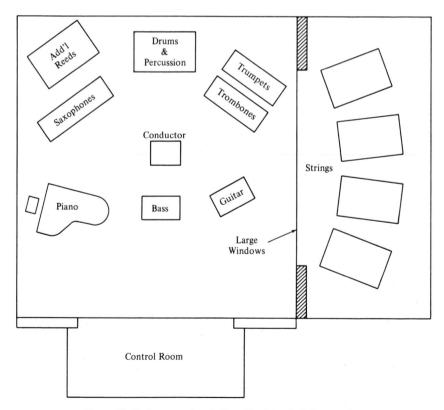

**Figure 23-18.** Layout of a studio with string isolation section.

## 23.8 ROCK RECORDING

Of all the forms of popular recording, rock recording relies almost totally on the tools of the modern studio for its very creation. It is in fact "born" over the control room monitors, and the expectation of a rock group on tour is that their live performances sound like their records!

The term rock comes from "rock and roll," the name given to a broad category of new music introduced in the mid 1950s. The Beatles and Rolling Stones typified developments during the 1960s, and today the term applies to a wide variety of styles, which evolve continuously and make heavy use of electric guitars and synthesizers, as well as traditional instruments. Such terms as jazz-rock, classical-rock, and country-rock describe the fusion that has taken place with certain mainstreams in popular music.

Most rock groups tend to be fairly small, usually numbering less than eight players. However, the way the creative art proceeds, there are usually many overdubs and many refinements in the musical plan as the sessions get underway.

The demands of rock recording have been responsible for considerable technological progress, especially in the signal processing area. The demand for 16- and 24-track recording came in the beginning solely from rock musicians and producers. The recording techniques themselves are extensions of what we have been discussing in this chapter, but there is a greater reliance on signal processing as a creative tool.

### 23.8.1 A Small Rock Group

A small rock band may consist of no more than three guitars, a keyboard instrument, a drum set, an electric bass, and a vocalist or other instrumental soloist. Often, the various instrumentalists double as vocalists.

The drum set alone may be picked up by as many as eight microphones, with an overhead pair augmented by many small microphones located adjacent to the drum heads and cymbals.

Most of the guitars will be picked up directly, preferably at the output of the amplifier, since the signal at that point will include all processing that may be a part of the instrument's own electronic system.

Instrumentation will likely vary from song to song, and synthesizers and additional percussion instruments may be added as needed.

It is easy to see how such a small ensemble can fill up most of the tracks on a 24-track recorder, if each input is recorded independently. The reason for this is that tracks are often played over again, and the older ones discarded. A high degree of acoustical separation is essential if this is to be done successfully. Insert recording is also common, even if it is only to change a small section of a take.

The roles of the recording engineer and players overlap that of the producer, and while there may seem to be a good bit if indecision in this kind of music making, we must remember that the whole creative process is usually one that can happen only in a recording studio.

Reverberation and the other tools of signal processing are experimented with, as the producer strives to obtain a specific sound. The creative process here is akin to composition itself, and may ideas are discarded before the right ones are found.

**Table 23-2. Track allocation
(typical) for a small rock group**

| | Section | Track allocation |
|---|---|---|
| 1. | Lead guitar | 1 |
| 2. | Rhythm guitar | 1 |
| 3. | Bass guitar | 1 |
| 4. | Keyboard | 2 |
| 5. | Synthesizer | 2 |
| 6. | Drums: | |
| | Overhead | 2 |
| | Kick | 1 |
| | Others | 5 |
| 7. | Vocal 1 | 1 |
| 8. | Vocal 2 | 1 |
| 9. | Vocal 3 | 1 |
| 10. | Effects | 2 |

### 23.8.2 Typical Track Assignments

With a group of the size considered here, the track assignments shown in Table 23-2 would be appropriate. Thus, six players have easily accounted for 21 out of 24 tracks, and it is easy to see how even 24 could be considered a marginal number.

Some of the tracks may be discarded outright and replaced with new ones. Alternatively, a successful mixdown of, say, the drum and bass tracks could be reduced from six occupied tracks down to two, thus freeing up another four tracks for further recording. Additional recording may take the form of laying in a new track, or in "sweetening" existing tracks (adding signal processing).

It is at this stage where successive overdubbing may come into play, using the technique discussed in Section 19.12. If at any point the 24-track capability is deemed insufficient for creative needs, a second machine can be locked into synchronization with the first (via time code on one track of each machine), and a total of 46 tracks then become available. The cost of this complexity may be very little, compared to the overall talent and production costs for a popular or rock album by major artist.

### 23.8.3 The Mixdown Process

When the producer and players feel they have the necessary musical ingredients in hand, the final step is to make a 2-track stereo mix. It is in this process where automated mixing is a valuable tool. With it, a given group of instruments, say, the rhythm section, can be submixed into stereo. When a satisfactory submix has been made, the automated system merely stores all the fader positions. Then, singly or in groups, the additional tracks can be mixed in. Any individual track can be altered without upsetting the rest of the mix.

After all tracks have been accounted for, the final physical transfer to 2-track can take place, with each fader operating solely from the memory of the automation system. Without the benefit of automation, the mixdown process can be lengthy, often involving many rehearsals or "dry runs" before a final mix is attempted. The resulting 2-track stereo mixdown will then be assembled with others into a composite master tape, digital or analog, for subsequent manufacturing of disc or tape product for the consumer.

## 23.9 SESSION PROTOCOL

A smooth-running studio session requires much preparation and clear assignment of authority. The producer is of course in charge of musical matters, and the engineer is in charge of all technical matters, including interfacing of electronic instruments with the console.

One or more assistant engineers are usually on hand, and their major functions are operating the recorders and keeping the tape log sheets. Communication between the engineer and assistants should be clear and to the point.

In one form or another, the communication between technical personnel needs to be almost a matter of verbal shorthand; it must be clear and direct. Verbal commands regarding operation of the recorders are normally given in the following manner: The engineer will say "Roll tape." On that command, the assistant will start the machines in the record mode, and when the machines are up to speed, he will will reply "Tape rolling." At that point, the engineer or producer will slate the take over the talkback system. At the end of the take, the engineer will say "Stop tape." The assistant will stop the machines, and no reply will be needed. For playback, the engineer or producer will inform the assistant of the desired take number.

Whatever terminology is used needs to be virtually standardized so that mistakes can be kept to a minimum. Just as the engineer hears everything the producer says, the assistant must hear everything the engineer says!

### 23.9.1 Keeping the Tape Log Sheet

The assistant fills in each take on the log sheet just after he starts the recorder. The following data is usually required:

1. Title
2. Take number
3. Time code reading at start
4. Time code reading at end
5. Identification of take as a full take, false start (FS), breakdown (BD), or any other codes the producer and engineer wish to use.
6. Track content

The recorders are not usually stopped after a false start, and the assistant should enter the new time code on the log sheet when the music commences, whether or not a new take number has been assigned.

Data which should be entered at the top of each log sheet should include: location, date, identification of artists, producer, and engineers, and any project numbers which are pertinent. The log sheet usually is affixed to the tape box and becomes the official record of the session proceedings.

The recording engineer may occasionally ask the assistant how much time is remaining on a roll of tape. With a knowledge of time code or tape counter reading and the reel capacity, the assistant should be able to estimate the time remaining to within a minute or two.

Multitrack sessions require extra work in that the content of each track must be indicated on the tape log. All details of overdubbing and track combining must be scrupulously documented.

The producer may or may not keep detailed notes, and may rely completely on the accuracy of the assistant engineer in this regard.

## BIBLIOGRAPHY

1. J. Borwick, *Sound Recording Practice*, Oxford, New York (1987)
2. M. Dickreiter, *Tonmeister Technology*, Temmer Enterprises, New York (1989).
3. J. Eargle, *The Microphone Handbook*, Elar, Commack, N.Y. (1982).
4. J. Eargle, "An Overview of Stereo Recording Techniques for Popular Recording," *J. Audio Engineering Society*, vol. 34, no. 6 (1986).
5. A. Nisbett, *The Technique of the Sound Studio*, Focal Press, London (1962).
6. R. Rundstein and D. Huber, *Modern Recording Techniques*, H. Sams, Indianapolis (1986).
7. M. Thorne, "Studio Microphone Techniques," *Studio Sound*, vol. 15, no. 7 (1973).
8. J. Woram, *Sound Recording Handbook*, H. Sams, Indianapolis (1989).
9. J. Woram and A. Kefauver, *The New Recording Studio Handbook*, Elar, Commack, N.Y. (1989).
10. W. Woszczyk, "A Microphone Technique Applying the Principle of Second-Order Gradient Unidirectionality," *J. Audio Engineering Society*, vol. 32, no. 7/8 (1984).

# 24

## RECORDING THE SPOKEN VOICE

### 24.1 INTRODUCTION

This chapter will discuss the problems of recording the voice, both for narration and for drama, with emphasis on microphone choice and placement, local acoustical considerations, signal processing, and monitoring.

### 24.2 RECORDING A SINGLE VOICE

#### 24.2.1 Microphone Considerations

The microphone chosen for this application normally should have very flat on-axis response. The position that works best is generally about 20 to 25 cm (8 to 10 inches) above the head of the talker, and some 50 to 60 cm (20 to 24 inches) in front, with the principal axis aimed at the mouth of the talker. In this position the microphone will not interfere with sightlines, and it will be free of air disturbances caused by the talker. If the speaker is using a music stand to hold notes, the microphone will be just slightly above the top of the stand.

The directional pattern usually selected is cardioid, and accordingly there will be some LF boost due to proximity effect. It is important to monitor the sound over accurate loudspeakers, and it is important in new studio environments to have on hand some known recordings so that the overall effect of equalization on the voice can be assessed, and any adjustments quickly made. The microphone will normally be placed in front of the speaker, but is possible to place it off to one side, if the principal axis is pointed at the speaker's mouth.

There will be times when a flat microphone will sound too bright. Some talkers produce more sibilant sounds than others, and often the best solution is to use a microphone with rolled-off high frequencies. Many older dynamic microphones work well in this regard. Often, the talker will know which models have worked well with his or her voice.

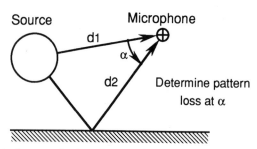

**Figure 24-1.** Source reflections from a table top; effect at the microphone.

### 24.2.2 Acoustical Considerations

Many voice recordings are made in small announcer's booths. Such rooms should be treated so that their boundaries are fairly absorptive at the lowest voice frequencies. Often, these rooms are too small for the purpose, or have insufficient damping at mid and low frequencies. If a fairly dead studio is available, it should be used. (On rare occasions, living rooms or other non-studio spaces are pressed into duty for narration recording, very often in the speaker's home. Every attempt should be made to ensure that things are as quiet as possible (all motors turned off), and that the room is will damped with blankets, carpeting, and the like.)

A good rule to remember is that if a reflected voice image (from a wall or a glass partition) is 10 dB or less, relative to the direct path, the effect of the reflection will be minimal in causing comb filtering effects. Figure 24-1 shows details of this. Normally, the directional pattern of the microphone is helpful in establishing the useful level ratio by means of its off-axis attenuation. With an omnidirectional pattern, the 10-dB requirement translates directly into a 3-to-1 distance ratio between the reflected and the direct sound paths.

In order to determine the loss of the reflected signal, calculate the inverse square distance losses, and add to that the off-axis microphone pattern loss:

$$\text{Overall loss in level} = 20 \log (d_1/d_2) + \text{Off-axis pattern loss} \qquad (24\text{-}1)$$

Acoustically transparent tables have been built (2, 3), which allow a microphone to be placed virtually anywhere over or on them, with no reflections. Details of this construction are shown in Figure 24-2. Even the standard desk stand, notorious for its susceptibility to reflections, fares very well with this table construction.

Script pages are a possible source of extraneous noise. They should not be bound, and they should lie flat on a table with ends turned up so that they can be removed quietly.

### 24.2.3 Signal Processing

If the right microphone choice has been made, then there should be no need for additional equalization. However, some degree of compression may be required, depending on the application of the recording. The engineer must determine, through good judgment and experience, whether normal manual gain riding can take care of any problems. If a

**Figure 24-2.** Details of an acoustically transparent table.

compressor is used, it should be set for no more gain reduction than necessary, and the recovery time constant in particular should be set so that gain is not restored too quickly, which might make breathing sounds overly prominent.

On the subject of breath sounds, they are perfectly natural if kept in proportion; ordinarily, no extreme attempts should be made to minimize them.

The normal ratio of average to peak speech signals is 12 to 14 dB. While this range may be suitable for a wide-range narration against music, it may be too great for other applications.

Whatever the signal processing judgements are, they should be made and carried out prior to the final mix with music.

Reverberation can be a useful tool in adding signal density to a voice recording. This can be done by adding a slight amount of relatively short reverberation, perhaps with a decay setting of no more than 0.5 seconds. This is hardly discernible as such, but its effect on the voice is to increase signal density and overall loudness. For special effects, more reverberation may be necessary, with a longer reverberation time setting.

The order of signal processing is critical. Normally, the recording is made without reverberation, since editing a recording with reverberation is apt to produce undesirable gaps in the reverberant signal itself. The dialogue should be edited, then equalized and compressed, if needed. Reverberation should be added last. The signal may be monitored with reverberation in order to let the narrator hear what the final program will sound like.)

### 24.2.4 Mono or Stereo?

It can be argued that a single voice needs no more than a single track, whatever the medium of presentation. However, recording engineers have long used a stereo pair for vocal or instrumental pickup in music recording, centering the soloist prominently in the middle of the stereo stage. The effect of the stereo pair, as opposed to a single mono channel panned to the center, is to add a feeling of space; even slight movements of the soloist are apparent as such, and the added subtle depth cues are important.

In some applications, the same can be said of the spoken voice. A case in point would be a prominent vocal narration in classical music. However, in most motion picture and television work, the added burden of the extra tracks would not normally be worth the effect.

If the engineer and producer choose to record in stereo, a coincident pair of cardioids is recommended. The outputs may be panned hard left and right. However, if too much movement is detected, then the signals may be panned half left and half right.

## 24.3 THE ONE-ON-ONE INTERVIEW

In the days of monophonic radio transmission, the standard method for picking up dialogue between two persons was with a ribbon figure-8 microphone, with the two sources located opposite one another along both major axes of the microphone. Today, most recording applications demand stereo pickup, and a pair of cardioid pattern microphones are normally used. Each microphone principally covers one of the participants, and any additional stereo cues are normally provided by slight artificial reverberation rather than through any sound reflections in the studio. The speakers would ordinarily be on opposite sides of a table facing each other.

There is an important departure to be made here. When musicians, for example a string quartet, are being interviewed in the dual contexts of performance and conversation, their conversation should be picked up by the microphone array used for music. There may be supplemental microphones as well, perhaps small lapel microphones, just to ensure that speech articulation does not suffer.

## 24.4 DRAMA

There is relatively little audio recording of drama today, since television has become the prime medium for presentation. In video production, audio is often relegated to hidden (wireless) microphones worn by the actors. This has become a matter of necessity for freedom of movement, and also because the video studio is apt to be a fairly noisy place.

The theater itself may not be the right place to record drama. When visual cues are present, details of time and place are inherent. When heard and not seen, the drama must rely on other cues; specifically, sound and spatial effects and details of ambience must often be slightly overstated in order to have the required impact. The theater is apt to be a bit noisy, and many nonverbal sounds, such as entrances, footfalls, rustling of clothing, and the like, are apt to sound tentative and too far away if picked up in the theater.

In a studio setting each problem can be separately addressed; for example:

1. A dead portion of the studio can be used for the recording of outdoor scenes, and appropriate sound effects can be added to convey naturalness. In the theater, the visual cues alone will suffice.
2. A live portion of the studio can be used for recording indoor action, and appropriate sound effects can be added.
3. Such movements as walking, entering or leaving a room, or pouring a cup of tea take care of themselves in the theater; in the studio, each of these, if important, will have to be conveyed by realistic effects recorded at the right level.
4. Certain stage movements will need to be carefully blocked on a grid and directed in the studio in order to take full advantage of the reproduced stereo stage. Dialogue

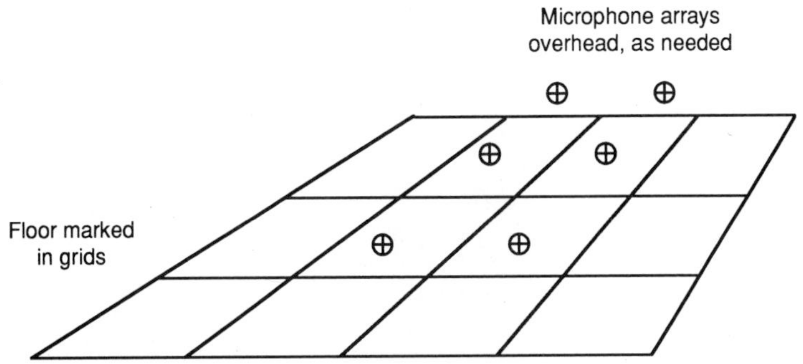

Microphone arrays
overhead, as needed

Floor marked
in grids

**Figure 24-3.** Grid and microphone arrangement for pickup of actors' movements.

between actors should appear naturally spaced, but should not necessarily seem to span the distance between the stereo loudspeakers.

5. In the theater, one is observing the action at a distance, and everything seems natural. In the recording, the action should appear much closer, perhaps no farther away than the playback loudspeakers themselves. This is an important matter for both engineer and producer to agree on at the outset.

### 24.4.1 Microphone Considerations

Actors experienced in radio production know how to "work" a microphone and are generally content to stay in the same place. Stage actors are used to movement and feel most comfortable when they are allowed that freedom. Frontal and overhead stereo microphone arrays will likely cover most movements, but there may occasionally be times when an actor is off-microphone. Details are shown in Figure 24-3.

While nobody expects a recording of a play to be done in one pass, it is a downright inconvenience for an actor to have to do something over again because the engineer missed it. Careful planning is called for, and a good case can be made for multichannel recording using numerous wireless microphone placed on the actors.

## BIBLIOGRAPHY

1. S. Alten, *Audio in Media*, Wadsworth, Belmont, Calif. (1986).
2. A. Nisbett, *The Technique of the Sound Studio*, Focal Press, London (1979).
3. D. Taylor, "The Spoken Word," chapter 15 in J. Borwick, *Sound Recording Practice*, Oxford, New York (1987).

# 25

# PRINCIPLES OF MUSIC AND SPEECH EDITING

## 25.1 INTRODUCTION

The advent of 0.6-cm (0.25-inch) magnetic tape recording after World War II brought with it the ready capability of editing, and a new creative world was opened to the record industry. Wrong notes could be corrected, noises removed, and the best sections of musical works joined together. Not everyone hailed this as a musical advantage, but there is no disputing that recording standards, not to mention consumers' expectations, have been raised through the skillful editing and assembly of the best takes. The vast majority of musical artists embrace the notion thoroughly.

There is remarkably little literature on music and speech editing. Of all the disciplines in recording, editing has traditionally been learned solely through apprenticeship, and that remains the best way of honing skills. Editing analog tape is mechanical, requiring the cutting of tape and subsequent splicing of the desired pieces together. With the advent of digital recording, tape cutting has largely gone, and the new process is entirely electronic. With digital editing have come new freedoms for the editor, including many techniques impossible in the analog domain.

This chapter will discuss the process of editing both analog and digital recordings, with special emphasis on studio techniques that facilitate the editing and assembly processes.

## 25.2 BASIC ANALOG TAPE EDITING TOOLS

The editing block, razor blade, splicing tape, and marker are the basic tools of tape editing. Figure 25-1(a) shows a 0.6-cm editing block of the type designed by Tall (4). The depression in the center holds the tape in a slightly concave position, and the slanted (45°) groove allows the razor blade to be drawn across the tape, cutting it smoothly. (The vertical groove is used for making rare "butt" splices.) Splicing tape is made of a thin plastic backing with a bleed-free adhesive that inhibits sticky splices.

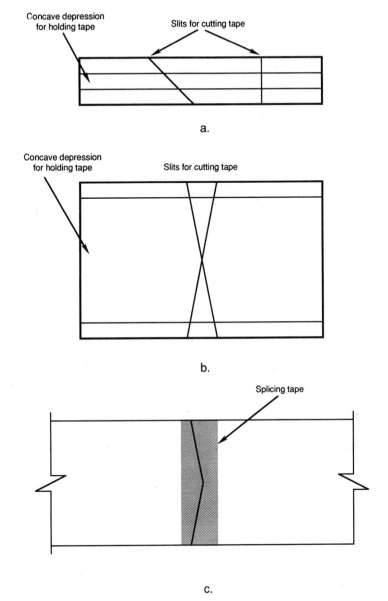

**Figure 25-1.** Editing blocks for 0.6-cm (quarter inch) tape (a) and 5-cm (2-inch) tape (b). (c) Example of arrow cut splice on wide tape.

A fresh supply of single-edge razor blades should be kept on hand, and old ones discarded at the first sign of becoming dull. Care should also be taken that the blades are free of any remnant magnetization.

Multichannel tape formats can be edited as well, and there are editing blocks for all tape widths. A 45° cut is not applicable here, because of the audibility of the time gap between

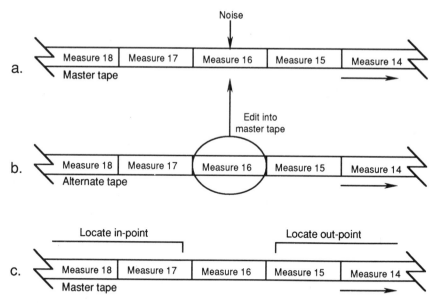

**Figure 25-2.** Principle of editing. (a) Master tape with noise in meaure 16. (b) Alternate tape without noise in measure 16. (c) Locating an edit-in point before the noise and an edit-out point after the noise.

outside tracks as the splice moves over the playback head. For editing 5-cm (2-inch) tape, the splicing block shown in Figure 25-1(b) is normally used. Note that there are two slants at steep angles. This facilitates making an "arrow" cut in the tape, as shown in (c).

## 25.3 MUSIC EDITING

Assume that a piece of music has a noise in the master recording at a point indicated in Figure 25-2(a). Assume that in an alternate take, the same point in the music was noise-free, as shown in (b). The editor can insert a portion of the alternate into the master by identifying two workable editing points in the music, as shown in (c).

It is easiest to edit on musical attacks or chords in which all notes change at the same time, and the editor will slowly "rock" the tape back and forth over the reproduce head until the beginning of the incoming attack is identified. Then the editor will "back off" from the actual attack by a very small amount and then carefully mark that point on the tape. Then, going to the alternate take, the procedure is repeated.

The editor then places the master tape in the editing block so that the marked point is just over the diagonal slot, and then cuts the tape with the razor blade. This step is repeated with the alternate take.

Then the outgoing point of the master take is placed in the editing block, and the incoming point of the alternate take is placed in the block and butted up against it. A short piece of splicing tape is placed over that point and firmly pressed to make a sure contact, as shown in Figure 25-3.

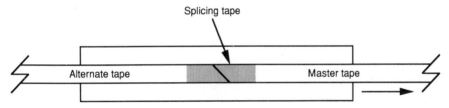

**Figure 25-3.** Making the splice.

At this time, the editor plays the splice to make sure that it works well and that it is not audible as such. If all has gone well, the editor then searches for another editing point to get back into the master take, and the whole process is repeated.

Note that a diagonal cut is shown for this operation. This seems to work best by providing a slight "time smear" which helps to make the transitions less audible. At a tape speed of 38 cm/sec (15 inches/sec), the 45° cut results in a time smear of a little less than 16 msec with 0.6-cm ($\frac{1}{4}$-inch) tape. At a tape speed of 19 cm/sec ($7\frac{1}{2}$ inches/sec), the time interval is just over 30 msec, which is reaching the range in which the ear might detect small timing differences in transitions between the left and right channels. For this reason, fine editing at a tape speed of 19 cm/sec ($7\frac{1}{2}$ inches/sec) is difficult and not recommended.

In ensemble playing, an attack may be marred by one player who enters a split second before the rest of the group. Often, the leading edge of the offending note can be cut out entirely (and not replaced). The amount of tape removed may be no more than 10 or 20 milliseconds, and the gap in the music will be virtually inaudible. The resulting attack can then sound quite precise and musical. Here, a butt splice might work best. On a larger scale, pauses in playing can often be tightened up slightly to great musical advantage.

This, in essence, is the editing process. As simple as it appears, it is very tricky. Even experienced editors will copy a recording and experiment with a difficult edit before attempting to execute it with the master tape. If an improper edit has been make, the tapes can be reassembled and the process begun over again. There is a limit to this, however, in that the tape will bear the bruises of all mistrials.

*Leader tape* is plastic base material without oxide and is used at the head and end of tape programs. Normally, at the end of a program, the tape or room noise is faded down to the lowest value before the leader tape is spliced in. If this were not done, there would be an abrupt cessation of room or tape noise as the leader tape passed over the reproduce head. At the beginning of a program, it is customary to use leader tape up to the start of music if the noise floor is fairly low. If it is high, many editors will "fade in" during the noise, editing the leader tape up to the start of the fade-in. Details of this are shown in Figure 25-4.

### 25.3.1 Planning the Recording for Editing

The experienced producer is responsible for running the session in a way that will provide the editor the needed flexibility for assembling an acceptable recording. Producers

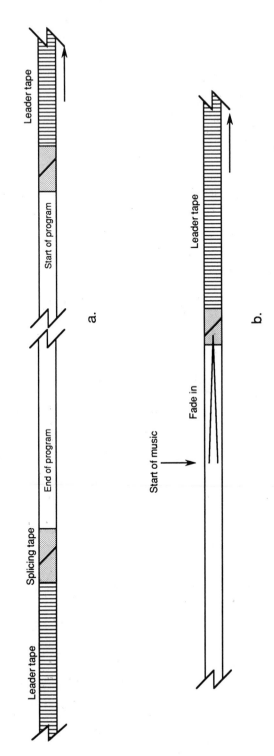

**Figure 25-4.** Use of leader tape. (a) At beginning and end of program. (b) Fade-in of room sound or background noise.

**Figure 25-5.** Example of a blocked score. Vertical lines indicate edit points, and large numbers indicate the incoming take number. Small numbers indicate the incoming SMPTE time codes to the nearest one-thousandth of a frame. The producer further notes the quality of a given take using personal shorthand; for example: N for noise; + for a good take; - or ≈ for a questionable take; → for rushing tempo.

generally use their own shorthand indications of things which have gone wrong or right in the score. On subsequent takes, or insert takes, the producer works with the artist to "cover" all problems with small sections that can be readily edited into the master take.

The producer then "blocks" the score (see Figure 25-5) and then gives it to the editor to work from. Often, there will be several choices for the editor, so that the one that works best (is least audible as an edit) can be used. Many producers are able to block as they go in the studio, while others prefer to do the blocking at another time. On some occasions, the artist may wish to be present for the blocking process.

The skilled producer has a number of tricks up his sleeve that will make editing easier and more efficient. Some of them are:

1. Overlapping takes to eliminate gaps for breathing. On occasion, a singer or wind instrument player will want to perform a long passage without taking a breath.

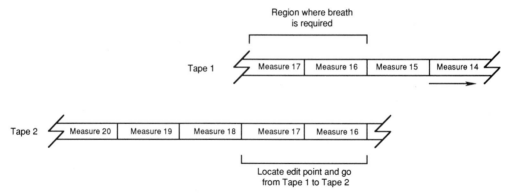

**Figure 25-6.** Editing a breath sound out of the program.

While this is often impossible in performance, it may be appropriate musically and can be done quite easily in recording. Instead of identifying one take as a master and another as alternate, there are in effect two master takes starting at different times, as shown in Figure 25-6.

2. Eliminating page turn and mute noises. Page turns can be noisy, as can be putting on and removing mutes. Page turn noises can be eliminated by having the players memorize the first one or two measures on the following page and playing through to that point without turning pages. Then the pages are turned and the previous one or two measures memorized. The second segment of music is played with the overlap, and the two takes can be edited without the noise of page turns. A similar technique allows string players to put on and remove mutes without noise.

Similar methods can be used to remove some of the noises inherent in registration changes on organs, many of which can be quite distracting.

The budding producer soon learns that a cold attack cannot be edited into a continuous performance, because there will be no continuation of reverberant sound into the incoming program. Unfortunately, this is often required, and the addition of artificial reverberation during the transition can often make these edits workable.

## 25.4 SPEECH EDITING

Speech editing is helped immeasurably by proper production techniques in the studio. Often, a speaker can be taught to correct mistakes by simply pausing, and repeating a sentence or portion thereof. The resulting segments can then be easily assembled by the editor. Many talkers will inadvertently emphasize a passage of speech as they are correcting it, and both mood and inflection may be different from what was originally intended. The producer must be quick to identify and correct this. Experienced narrators generally do not fall into this trap.

The editor must learn to recognize the sounds of consonants with the tape playing at half or quarter speed, since this will be of great help in identifying an edit point as the tape is rocked back and forth over the reproduce head. Normally, speech editing is done at the beginnings of consonants, so it is essential that they be identified correctly. Vowels and diphthongs are far more difficult to identify at slower speeds and will require more practice.

## 25.5 DIGITAL EDITING

The DASH and PD reel-to-reel digital recording formats provide for normal razor-blade editing, and the points presented thus far in this chapter are appropriate. These systems, along with the video-based systems, can be edited electronically through a process known as assembly editing. The principle is shown in Figure 25-7.

In this method of editing, source tapes (1 through $n$) are placed on machine 1, played into the editor, and recorded on machine 2. Figure 25-7(a) shows the system in *rehearsal* mode; a tape previously composed of segments 1 and 2 from master tapes 1 and 2 is to be edited to a new segment 3. In this mode, the editor can audition the crossfade from segment 2 (played back on machine 2) to the new segment 3 (played back on machine 1). By comparing address codes, the system allows the editor to select the desired edit point, $t_0$, between segments 2 and 3.

When the editor has located the desired edit point, the system is put into the *record* mode (Figure 25-7(b)). When this is done, both tapes run in synchronism, and precisely at moment $t_0$ machine 2 will be in record mode and will add segment 3 to the end of segment 2. Machine 2 has the capability of going into record mode at the beginning of a video frame, without loss of previous information; thus, the edit will be seamless and smooth. In this way, a final composite master tape may be assembled while the original master tapes remain intact.

The editor has many options in refining the edit point, among them:

1. Change of level and channel balance of incoming segment. Often, a better edit can be made if the level of the incoming signal can be adjusted up or down, as needed.
2. Variable cross fade times. Unlike razor blade editing, where there are limited options, the editor working in the digital domain can select crossfade times over a range up to several seconds.
3. Flexibility in identifying precise in and out points on both incoming and outgoing tapes. The region around the intended edit point can be stored in random access memory (RAM) as a convenience for the editor. The edit point can be auditioned repeatedly and quickly with no movement of tape. Precise in and out points can be altered by small degrees, and a high degree of refinement is possible. Only when the edit is exactly what was intended will it be executed.

There are many small editing systems available today that are based on the capabilities of standard microcomputers with expanded hard disk storage capabilities. While such systems enable the small studio to carry out many assembly jobs quite effectively, the demands of detailed professional music editing for commercial release require greater speed. Multichannel disk-based systems capable of rapid editing were pioneered by

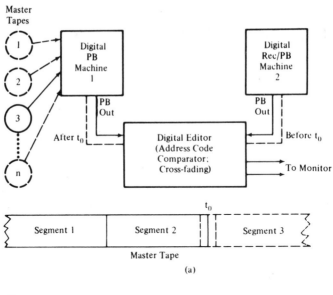

(a)

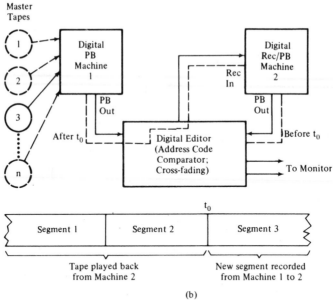

(b)

**Figure 25-7.** Digital editing. (a) Rehearsal mode. (b) Record–assembly mode.

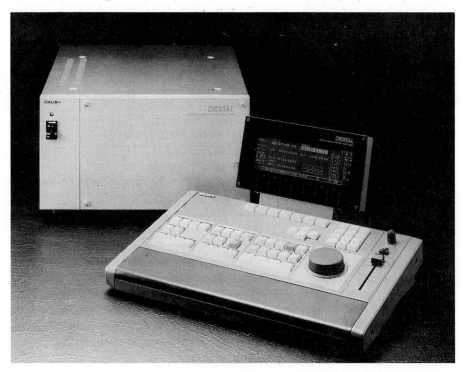

**Figure 25-8.** Photograph of Sony DAE-3000 editor. (*Courtesy Sony Corporation*)

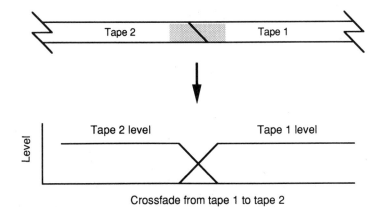

Crossfade from tape 1 to tape 2

**Figure 25-9.** Razor-blade editing of digital tape.

Soundstream during the 1970s (3), and the tradition has been carried forward by the work of Lexicon and Lucasfilm.

Somewhere between these extremes is the dedicated two-channel editor shown in Figure 25-8. The Sony DAE-3000 is widely used for rapid and flexible editing of two-channel and multichannel program material.

Those reel-to-reel digital tape formats that allow razor blade editing work on the following principle. The physical cut in the tape and subsequent joining up with another segment of tape are seen by the digital processing machinery as a massive dropout. Because of the redundancy of interleaved information along the tape path, there is enough information to determine both outgoing and incoming signals extending beyond the physical cut in both directions. When the discontinuity is detected, a program is initiated that produces a crossfade from the outgoing segment, which overlaps a crossfade to the incoming segment. Details of this are shown in Figure 25-9.

## BIBLIOGRAPHY

1. J. Bloom and G. McNally, "Digital Techniques," Chapter 4 in *Audio Engineering Handbook* (edited by B. Benson), McGraw-Hill, New York (1988).
2. D. Davis and R. Youngquist, "Electronic Editing of Digital Audio Programmes," *Proc. Int. Conf. Video Data Recording*, Southampton, England (1979).
3. R. Ingebretsen and T. Stockham, "Random Access Editing of Digital Audio," *J. Audio Engineering Society*, vol. 32, no. 3 (1984).
4. J. Tall, *Tape Editing*, Editall Corporation, Washington, D.C. (1978).
5. K. Tanaka, et al., "On Tape-Cut Editing with a Fixed Head Tape PCM Tape Recorder," *IEEE Transactions ASSP*, vol. 27, no. 6 (1979).

# 26

## MUSIC PREPARATION FOR COMMERCIAL RELEASE

### 26.1 INTRODUCTION

This chapter will deal with the problems of taking previously recorded program segments from various sources and compiling them for commercial release. Such matters as relative transfer level, signal processing, and even identification of the earliest sources will be discussed. The compact disc, with its performance characteristics that far outclass the stereo LP record, has brought new expectations to the record reissue market, and consumers routinely expect the best transfers possible.

### 26.2 SOURCE IDENTIFICATION

In compiling programs for reissue, the engineer often will have to work with material that is quite old, perhaps 25 years or more. When dealing with record companies who archive their material under vault conditions, the original tapes are usually easy to find and identify. However, where recorded material has been sublicensed or sold, such identification is not easy. More often than not, the original tapes were transferred, and the copies exchanged in the licensing procedure.

Older tape formulations were not stable, and many older recordings have been ruined by progressive delamination of oxide from the base material. In such cases, the only working copy of the recording may be one or two generations removed from the master.

On other occasions, the old tape will be playable, perhaps for only a few minutes at a time, due to the build-up of oxide on the reproduce head and consequent "squealing" of the tape as it passes, violin-bow fashion, over the head. There are some remedial steps that may be taken here (5).

The following points should be noted:

1. Examine the tape carefully, noting the quality of the wind. If it is smooth, then it is likely that the tape is wound tails out. It should not be rewound quickly, because

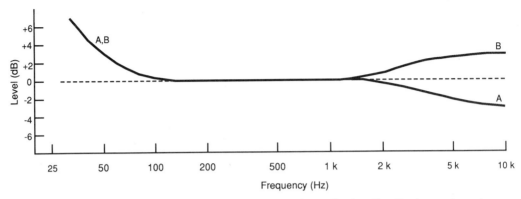

**Figure 26-1.** Correction curves for playing EIC tapes with NAB equalization. Equalization as shown in curve A should be added when transferring IEC 38-cm/sec tapes, and as shown in curve B when transferring IEC 19-cm/sec tapes.

this will almost certainly cause damage if the tape has any tendency to stick to itself, layer to layer. Place the tape reel on the feed side and rewind it by playing it at the slowest tape speed. (The tape lifters may be engaged so that there will be no unnecessary head wear.) Stand over the tape during this process and be prepared to stop the machine on a moment's notice if anything appears amiss.

This is also a good time to check the quality of splices. Anything questionable here should be redone using fresh splicing tape. Some engineers will use a slight amount of talcum powder to dry a sticky splice; this is not recommended since the powder and adhesive will eventually collect on the heads and cause other problems.

2. Check the tape equalization carefully. Most 19 and 38 cm/sec (7.5 and 15 inches/sec) tape recordings made in the United States will require NAB equalization. The occasional rare 76 cm/sec (30 inches/sec) tape will, if made before the middle 1970s, be of indeterminate equalization, requiring fine tuning by ear.

Every attempt should be made to correct for the various IEC (European) playback equalization curves by having switchable playback electronics for the purpose. If this cannot be done, the correction curves shown in Figure 26-1 can be used as a broad guideline for making transfers.

3. Check track configuration and azimuth carefully. Many older tapes made before modern standards were promulgated have odd track configurations that will result in channel noise and level differences of played back on modern machines. The exact track configuration can be observed by treating the oxide surface with a small amount of carbonyl iron solution. This liquid has very fine particles of iron in solution and can be painted over a small portion of the tape. The iron particles will align themselves with the part of the tape that has passed over the record head. Remove the solution when the determination has been made. If the tape appears to be far out of standard, a decision may have to be made regarding height adjustment of the playback head.

Azimuth determination must be done purely by ear if there is no azimuth setting tone on the tape. If the recording is stereo, it will be best to sum the tracks and listen carefully

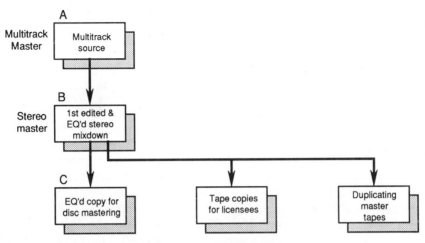

**Figure 26-2.** Normal hierarchy of master tapes.

for maximum HF output while the azimuth adjustment is varied. With full track recordings the single track will have to suffice.

## 26.3 DETERMINING THE EARLIEST USABLE SOURCE TAPE

Figure 26-2 shows a hierarchy of tape sources as normally used in the recording industry. The earliest is of course the multitrack master (A), and this is today generally recorded on 5-cm (2-inch) tape with 24 channels. Technically speaking, this is the "master" tape, since it represents the earliest generation of recording. In a practical sense, however, the two-track tape (B) which has been mixed from it is what most people in the industry would refer to simply as the "master." This tape represents the musical judgments made during the arduous mixdown process and is the approved recording that both artist and producer intended to be heard via the two-channel media of LPs, compact discs, cassettes, and FM radio.

In the pre-digital era, this tape was subjected to considerable activity. It was the source of the initial disc transfers for LP manufacture, the production of duplicating masters for cassette duplication, and the production of next-generation tape copies for the international licensees of the recording company. No wonder that it occasionally wore out and had to be remixed again. But many times the original producer, engineer, and artists were not available for this purpose, and the new mix was apt to be different.

As a hedge against this problem, an "EQ'd master" (C) was often made at the time of the original disc transfers. This tape reflected any last-minute changes in equalization or dynamic range control that the producer felt would make a better long-playing record. More to the point, this tape generally compensated for shortcomings in the LP record itself, and as such it was not a good candidate for later transfers. Unfortunately, the "C" masters are in great abundance, and the "B" masters are often relegated to the back shelf. It is worth every attempt to recover the "B" tapes and work from them.

Digital technology has changed this. The "B" master is now a digital tape (although some producers prefer a 76-cm/sec two-track tape for this purpose), and digital clones can be made for all applications.

## 26.4 MAKING THE ARCHIVAL TRANSFER

Today, great care is generally taken in making archival transfers of older tape sources. In the early days of the CD, "B" masters were routinely used for CD mastering, with critical damnation. It is commonplace now to engage the original producer to supervise latter-day transfers from original multitrack masters. CBS Records, RCA Records, and Mercury Records have done this with classical recordings, and EMI engaged George Martin to supervise the CD transfers of the early Beatles four-channel recordings.

If the engineer and reissue producer know exactly what they want in terms of equalization and signal processing, the final transfer may proceed, incorporating these changes. More often than not, it will be better to make a straight digital transfer using the local digital editing and assembly format. From this point, any signal processing and level adjustments can be made with little or no further degradation. This is also an appropriate time for decisions regarding any computer-based processing of the digital tape for the removal of noise. If it is decided not to do this, then the tape can be assembled into a finished program, making appropriate band-to-band level adjustments and any desired equalization changes.

### 26.4.1 Signal Processing

It is important that the engineer and producer in charge of program assembly work with an accurate monitor system and that they routinely "calibrate" themselves with a wide variety of recordings from many sources. In most cases, a living room ambience with consumer-type loudspeakers will be a better working environment than a control room with high power monitors.

The engineer and producer should not try to be "too creative" as they transfer older program material. That is, there should be no attempt to make the recordings sound as though they had been made yesterday. It will be more appreciated by the buyer if the sound is simply brought up to the best standards of its time. Identify the best sounding recording of the set, and attempt to make the others match it through careful broadband equalization. Levels should of course be matched so that the consumer will have no urge to turn the recording up or down as it plays.

The options of adding reverberation and processing mono program for pseudostereo should be made only after careful consideration, since both are quite obvious and may offend many listeners.

### 26.4.2 Transfers From 78-rpm Discs

While a few giant record companies still have their vaults intact and can even make new pressings from old metal stampers, most of the reissue market for old recordings depends on the largesse of individual record collectors and various non-profit recording archives around the country. Transferring from old discs is a special art and require a

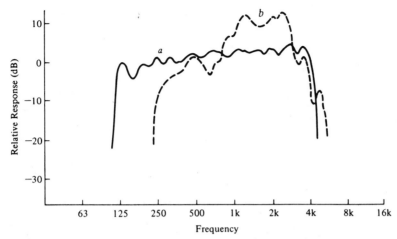

**Figure 26-3.** Typical acoustical phonograph response with electrical recordings (curve *a*) and acoustical recordings (curve *b*). (*Data after Maxfield and Harrison, as reprinted in (4)*)

collection of custom made styli and tone arms, a variable speed turntable, facilities for cleaning old discs, and various equalizers and filters.

The bandpass characteristics of early recordings varies considerably. Figure 26-3 shows what may be encountered. Curve *a* indicates the response that electrical recording provided when it was introduced in the late 1920s, while curve *b* shows typical response of an acoustical recording. Obviously, there is little recorded program above 4 kHz, and the decision could be made to use a lowpass filter set at 4 kHz on the assumption that it would not affect program material. This may be true, but the effect of the filter on random ticks and pops in the reproduced sound may be disturbing. Such filtering tends to color those sounds, making them sound unnatural. Often, it is better to set the lowpass filter at 7 or 8 kHz and be content with removing only some of the noise. Low frequencies can be boosted slightly, but there is obviously no point in trying to boost anything that is not present in the recording.

A good rule to remember is that the upper and lower frequencies of audio bandwidth should have a product of about 400,000. Most listeners do not feel comfortable with extended HF response unless it is accompanied with a corresponding extended LF response. Thus, if the lower frequency limit is 100 Hz, then the upper frequency limit should be no greater than 4 kHz. If the lower frequency limit is 200 Hz, then the upper limit should be no greater than about 2 kHz. Olson (3) made this determination many years ago based on psychoacoustical tests. Even in the early years of electrical recording, general practice was to limit the LF response of the system, even though it could have been extended relatively easily, simply because of the HF limitations of the day.

If continuous performances are to be assembled from 78 rpm records, there will be a need to match the sound from the end of each side as it is edited into the start of the next side. This is often very tricky, since it involves matching the sound quality of different cutter heads as well as the differences between the response of recordings at outer and inner diameters. Care should be taken to do this unobtrusively, even if it requires subtle

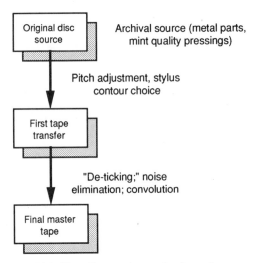

**Figure 26-4.** Flow diagram for tranfer from disc sources.

equalizing that must change during the course of playing each side. A more difficult problem here is the difference that might be evident in noise levels between consecutive sides, due to differences in record processing. Figure 26-4 indicates the normal steps used today in the processing of archival disc sources.

Overall, the art of making transfers from old discs rests in the hands of a few dedicated persons. Companies interested in having such work done should consult the Library of Congress, the Rodgers and Hammerstein archives at Lincoln Center, the Stanford University archives, and the University of Syracuse archives, since these organizations can identify skilled engineers in the art as well as provide sources for old recordings.

## BIBLIOGRAPHY

1. S. Feldman, "Preparation of Master Tapes," *J. Audio Engineering Society*, Vol. 34, no. 11 (1986).
2. F. Hoffman, *The Development of Library Collections of Sound Recordings*, Marcel Dekker, New York (1979).
3. H. Olson, *Acoustical Engineering* (Section 12.29), D. Van Nostrand, New York (1957).
4. O. Read and W. Welch, *From Tin-Foil to Stereo*, Howard W. Sams, Indianapolis (1958).
5. M. Stosich, "Archival Revival," *Audio Magazine* (November 1990).
6. *The Gramophone Jubilee Book*, The Gramophone, Middlesex, England (1973).

# 27

## OVERVIEW OF SOUND FOR FILM AND VIDEO

### 27.1 INTRODUCTION

Sound recording technology for the motion picture theater differs from that of the record industry in the following ways:

1. Presentation in the theater is normally via four channels: three behind the screen and a single surround channel.
2. Control of the playback acoustical environment. Unlike the wide variety of consumer playback environments (automobile, home, or headphones), motion pictures are primarily shown in environments that are not unlike those where the product was mixed.
3. Extensive postproduction activity. Music, dialogue, and effects are all separately recorded and premixed, and are brought together during a final mixdown operation after the film has been edited.

While microphone techniques for film recording are not fundamentally different from those that have been discussed in earlier chapters, there is more reliance on expedience. For example, the microphone at the end of a boom following the actors' movements and microphones hidden in actors' clothes or hair are some of the things that must be done to keep them out of the way of the camera.

### 27.2 MULTICHANNEL FORMATS FOR FILM

Films today are normally presented over three screen channels in LCR (left–center–right) format and a surround channel made up of 8 to 12 loudspeakers. The present formats for this include 70-mm film magnetically striped for six channels and 35-mm with dual

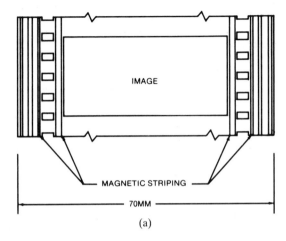

(a)

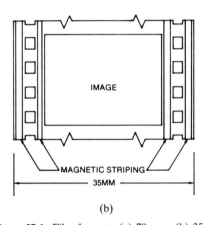

(b)

**Figure 27-1.** Film formats. (a) 70 mm. (b) 35 mm.

bilateral optical sound tracks, often referred to as Dolby Stereo Optical. An earlier 35-mm format provided four magnetic tracks. These formats are shown in Figure 27-1. The center channel is used primarily for dialogue, and the origination of dialogue from a real source (often referred to as "hard center") as opposed to the phantom center used in conventional stereo, ensures that all patrons in the theater will hear dialogue unambiguously from a single point.

The six magnetic tracks on 70-mm film are a holdover from an earlier day when five screen channels were used. Today, two of the tracks (left-extra and right-extra) are relegated to auxiliary subwoofer feed. Split surround operation is an option here as well, but it is rarely used. The Cinema Digital Sound format discussed in Section 10.2.2 brings new prominence to the notion of split surrounds, while retaining the LCR channels behind the screen.

## 27.3 CONTROL OF THE PRESENTATION ENVIRONMENT

Due to continuing efforts toward standardization, the typical film exhibition environment is very much like that of the dubbing theater where the final film sound balances were made. The dubbing theater is a moderate-size theater seating anywhere from 75 to 250 persons. In properly qualified venues, it is possible to ensure that the playback level in the field matches that at which balances were set in the dubbing theater.

### 27.3.1 Reverberation Time

Figure 27-2(a) shows the range of reverberation time at 500 Hz normally encountered in motion picture theaters. A theater has approximately 5.1 m$^3$ (190 ft$^3$) of volume per patron, so a house seating 1000 persons (a large house indeed) would have a volume of about 5400 m$^3$ (200,000 ft$^3$) and an average reverberation at 500 Hz of about 0.7 seconds. By concert hall standards this is quite short, but it is traditional in motion picture theater design, inasmuch as the sensation of ambience is generated not by local reflections but by the signals presented by the surround channel. As in other large spaces, the reverberation time at low frequencies tends to be longer than at 500 Hz and somewhat shorter at high frequencies, as shown in Figure 27-2(b).

### 27.3.2 Playback Levels in the Theater

The motion picture industry has established reference levels in both magnetic and optical media and locked them into reference sound pressure levels in the theater. For example, a surface fluxivity of 185 nWb/m on a magnetic track normally corresponds to a level of 85 dB, C-weighted, as measured in the house. The same acoustical level corresponds to the optical medium when it is modulated at 50% of maximum. It is thus possible for the film industry to maintain consistent playback levels in most locations.

### 27.3.3 Frequency Response

Another important standard is frequency response in the theater. Figure 27-3 shows guidelines here. At one time, the industry considered 10 kHz the highest usable frequency in the theater; today, systems are routinely equalized to 16 kHz.

### 27.3.4 Dynamic Range

It is ironic that current standards allow films to be mixed with a dynamic range that is greater than can be properly handled in many theaters. As a result of this, some low-level effects are often lost due to the high local noise levels generated by patrons in the theater. Some dubbing theaters are equipped with an acoustical noise generation system which simulates that of a typical noisy theater. When this system is turned on, the mixers use it as a guide for ensuring that all normally quiet details will be heard over the noise floor.

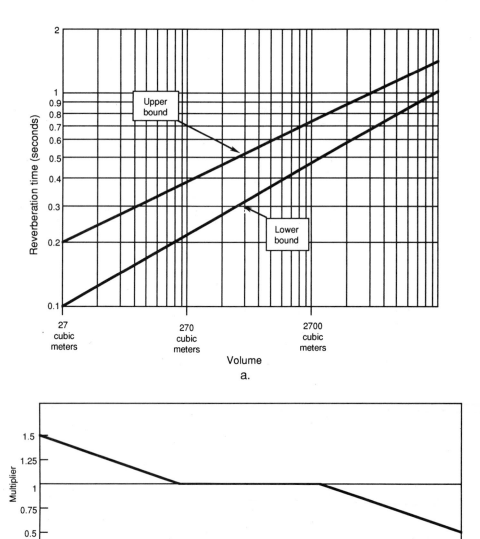

**Figure 27-2.** (a) Suggested reverberation times in motion picture theaters. (b) Suggested variation of HF and LF reverberation relative to midband reverberation.

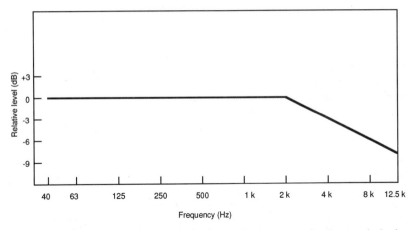

**Figure 27-3.** ISO 2969 standard playback equalization curves for theater playback.

### 27.3.5 Matching Subjective Response Between Large and Small Theaters

The industry is now concerning itself with methods of equalization that will result in better matches between large and small presentation spaces. The data shown in Figure 27-4 provides this subjective correction (1). The reader is referred to Section 14.5 for additional discussion of this problem.

### 27.3.6 New Technology in the Theater

In the 1970s, Dolby Laboratories introduced A-type noise reduction into the motion picture work, and with it came the first large-scale efforts toward loudspeaker system

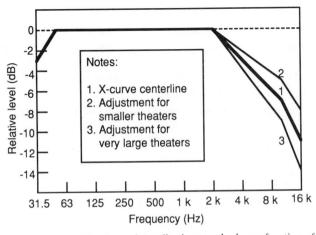

Notes:

1. X-curve centerline
2. Adjustment for smaller theaters
3. Adjustment for very large theaters

**Figure 27-4.** Suggested modifications of equalization standard as a function of room size.

equalization in the the theater. During the later 1980s, Dolby SR (Spectral Recording) has gained favor.

During the early 1980s, newer loudspeaker designs based on the concept of flat power response were introduced to the industry; these have vastly improved coverage in the theater and resulted in lower distortion (4, 6). Subwoofers have also been added and have extended LF response in the theater down to 25 Hz.

## 27.4 OVERVIEW OF POST-PRODUCTION TECHNIQUES

### 27.4.1 Music Recording

Outside of title music, which can be recorded at any time, the music cues that accompany action on the screen may not recorded until the picture has been edited. Actually, some of the music might not even be composed until the editing has taken place. The reason here is that often the conductor must pace the music so that it matches the action precisely.

The orchestral pickup is nearly always multitrack, and the engineer responsible for the original recording may not be involved with the final mixing. Multitrack recording is essential, inasmuch as the final use of the music may not be determined until later in post-production. At that point, the remix engineer may need considerable flexibility in creating the necessary balance.

### 27.4.2 Dialogue Recording

Although dialogue is always recorded on the set, the quality may vary considerably. The best quality results from a boom operator following the actors with a microphone on a stick—but always keeping it out of the picture! When this is impractical, small wireless microphones can be hidden on the actors. When this does not work well, a process called ADR (automatic dialogue replacement) is used. In this process, a segment of film is repeatedly shown to the actor (the old term was "looping"), who rehearses the segment of dialogue until timing and inflection are correct. In this way the dialogue is replaced under more favorable recording conditions. The process is expensive and is used only when necessary.

Dialogue editors have the job of making all of the dialogue sources sound consistent, and various equalizers and filters are part of their stock in trade. Reverberation is routinely added to dry tracks in order to maintain perspectives. The whole range of signal processing options, as discussed in Chapters 15 through 18 may be useful at one time or another.

### 27.4.3 Sound Effects Recording

The gathering of sound effects, whether for ambience or for specific action, is normally done in stereo. Today, the MS microphone method is preferred for this, even though the effects are stored in their resolved left and right (M + S and M − S ) forms (see

Section 9.2.3). The reason for this is the excellent mono compatibility of MS and the fact that effects are quite often used in mono.

It is difficult to record effects on the set because of high noise levels. For example, if two actors are walking down a corridor carrying on a conversation, the dialogue may be successfully picked up, but not the sound of footfalls on the pavement. Such effects as these are normally recorded on what is called a Foley stage, which has a number of pits filled with sand, gravel, concrete, and the like. The Foley "walker" then creates these effects while watching the picture.

## 27.5 THE FINAL MIX

Prior to the final mix, dialogue and effects will have gone through a number of premixes. For example, the various mono and stereo effects would have been premixed into useful LCR formats. The same is true for the dialogue tracks in order to give the operator level control flexibility over individual actors. There are usually three operators at the console, one each for balancing dialogue, effects, and music. Through the use of extensive premixing, each operator, at the time of the final mix, may be dealing with a limited number of input faders, and this gives each operator relative freedom to listen to the mix rather than search for its ingredients. Panning and level changes are the major options at this point, although added signal processing is available.

If a film is scheduled for 70-mm release, then one mix will be made monitoring in that format. The output of that session is a six-track print master that will be used for subsequent dubbing to magnetically striped positive prints.

For most other purposes a Dolby Stereo Optical release will be the standard, and when this mix is made it will be monitored through the Dolby playback matrix in order that the mixing engineers can detect any problems and correct them on the spot. The encoding matrix is similar to those discussed in Section 10.3 and has the following coefficients:

$$L_T = L + 0.7\,C + 0.7\,S\,(90°)$$

$$R_T = R + 0.7\,C + 0.7\,S\,(-90°)$$

$L_T$ and $R_T$ represent the two encoded stereo transmission channels. $L$ and $R$ signals are completely separate, while the C signal is in-phase in both transmission channels. By the use of $\pm90°$ phase shifting networks, a total of $180°$ phase shift exists between transmission channels for the surround signal. The playback matrix recovers each signal according to demand. If a given signal is detected as dominant, then the coefficients will be adjusted to favor its separation from the other three signals. The output of this mixing session will be a two-track print master for modulating the optical tracks on the final negative.

## 27.6 DOLBY STEREO OPTICAL

Dolby Stereo Optical results in release print costs that are normally about one-tenth those of 70-mm magnetic stripe prints. It is no wonder that the industry has adopted it, even though the matrix often requires a bit of "coaxing." With the advent of digital optical sound, the need for a matrix will go away, and 70-mm six-track film can be retired for good. What will remain for the Dolby matrix format is the vast market of video tapes and laser discs, which are limited to two-channel audio capability. For that application the Dolby matrix will be current for many years to come.

## 27.7 NEW POST-PRODUCTION METHODS

Traditionally, the motion picture industry has relied on sprocketed film as the means of maintaining synchronism during all aspects of premixing and editing. A consequence of this has often been a number of generations of audio transfer, with increase in noise and distortion. Today, there are available a number of digital disc-based random access editing systems that limit the effective number of generations of transfer. As these become more generally used in the film industry, better audio quality will be the result.

## 27.8 AUDIO FOR VIDEO

In general, video production proceeds at a rapid rate, so there is relatively less in the way of detailed audio premixing as compared with film making. Until recent years most audio for video was mono. The adoption of a stereo standard for commercial television broadcasting has changed this, and many network programs are done in stereo.

Motion pictures of course account for a great deal of television broadcasting, and the Dolby Stereo sound track can be transmitted. Those viewers with Dolby Stereo decoders (a growing consumer market) can enjoy the audio presentation over a loudspeaker array that approximates that found in the theater. Those viewers with mono television sets will hear left, center, and right channels in reasonable perspective, but the information in the surround channel will be attenuated.

## BIBLIOGRAPHY

1. I. Allen, *Technical Guidelines for Dolby Stereo Theatres: Updating for the Playback of Dolby SR Films*, Dolby Laboratories, San Francisco (1989).
2. S. Alten, *Audio in Media*, Wiley, New York (1986).
3. L. Blake, *Film Sound Today*, Reveille Press, Hollywood, Calif. (1984).
4. M. Engebretson and J. Eargle, "Cinema Sound Reproduction Systems," *J. Society of Motion Picture and Television Engineers*, vol. 91, no. 11 (1982).
5. T. Holman, "Postproduction Systems and Editing," Chapter 14 in K. Benson, *Audio Engineering Handbook*, McGraw-Hill, New York (1988).
6. T. Holman, *THX Sound system Instruction Manual; Architect's and Engineer's Edition*, Lucasfilm, Ltd, San Rafael, Calif. (1987).
7. D. Huber, *Audio Production Techniques for Video*, H. Sams, Indianapolis (1987).
8. *Cinema Sound System Manual*, JBL Incorporated, Northridge, Calif. (1990).
9. *Motion Picture Sound Engineering*, D. Van Nostrand, New York (1938).

# 28

## THE STEREO LONG-PLAYING (LP) RECORD

### 28.1 A BRIEF HISTORY

The stereo LP is rapidly declining in sales due to the immense success of the compact disc. Since 1947 to the present, however, the LP has represented a long period of compatibility between product and players in the history of consumer audio, exceeded only by the era of the 78-rpm disc in the early part of this century.

Technologically, the disc is an outgrowth of Edison's original cylinder apparatus, which dominated recording during the last quarter of the nineteenth century. Berliner's disc rapidly overtook it in the early years of the 20th century primarily because ease of replication.

Until the late 1920s, recording remained an acoustomechanical process, both in recording and playback. Maxfield and Harrison (9) developed electrical recording, and with it the problems of audio bandwidth and distortion were on their way to being solved. Problems of playing time were not to be dealt with until the introduction of the LP in 1947. Goldmark combined the advantages of a quiet vinyl plastic material with microgroove geometry and $33\frac{1}{3}$ rpm to produce playing times up to 30 minutes.

The stereo LP had been conceptually invented by Blumlein in the early 1930s, when he demonstrated that two independent modulation channels could be cut at $\pm 45°$ to the surface of the disc. It was not until 1957 that the stereo disc became a marketplace reality, and during the golden era of the stereo LP (1960 to 1985) many significant improvements were made in the electromechanics of both cutting master discs and playing the pressed discs. As a result, the medium attained audiophile status, compromised only by occasional pressing problems and attendant ticks and pops. Many consumers were inclined to overlook these, however, because of the high level of quality that was otherwise obtained.

While the CD is now in the ascendency, the LP is far from gone. While the great recordings of the past have been reissued in the new format, there are many other

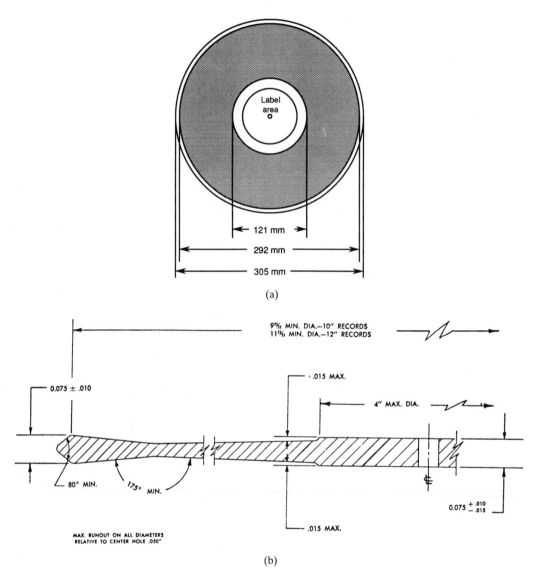

**Figure 28-1.** Physical view of the LP. (a) Surface view. (b) Section view.

relatively obscure recordings that are not likely to be reissued in CD form. For this reason alone, there will be LP enthusiasts for decades to come.

## 28.2 PHYSICAL PROFILE OF THE LP

Figure 28-1 presents physical details of the LP. The diameter is 301 mm (nominally 12 inches), and the maximum thickness in the center (label) portion is 3.8 mm (0.015 inch). The recorded portion of the disc is thinner than the center and outer diameter, a contour

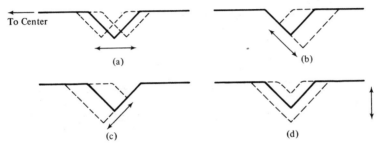

**Figure 28-2.** Basic stylus motions shown in section view. (a) Lateral (mono) motion. (b) Right channel only. (c) Left channel. (d) Vertical motion.

that saves vinyl and at the same time provides a degree of protection for the grooves when the discs are stacked on a record changer.

The various starting and stopping diameters of recording are standardized, as are the various pitches of lead-in and lead-out grooves. (*Pitch* here refers to the number of grooves per unit radius, not the frequency of a signal.)

## 28.3 STEREO MICROGROOVE GEOMETRY AND REFERENCE LEVELS

Figure 28-2 shows the basic movements of the cutting and playback styli in the plane of the master disc. Lateral motion (a) results from equal signals fed to the 45°/45° cutting coils. Motions in (b) and (c) represent right channel only and left channel only, respectively. The motion shown in (d) results from a 180° polarity relationship between the two input signals.

Figure 28-3 shows a scanning electronic microscope view of typical stereo modulation. Note that each groove wall is independently modulated. The outer groove of the stereo disc is modulated by the right channel and the inner groove by the left channel. The cutting stylus is chisel-shaped and is made of sapphire or diamond.

The nominal width of an unmodulated groove is about 0.064 mm ($2.5 \times 10^{-3}$ inch). During heavy modulation, the groove width and depth can increase by a factor of about three, while on upward swings of the cutting stylus the width can be as small as 0.025 mm ($1 \times 10^{-3}$ inch).

In the early days of disc recording, wax was used as the recording medium. Since the early 1940s, a lacquer formulation on an aluminum substrate has been used. It is customary to use a stylus heated by a small coil to facilitate cutting the lacquer material and to reduce noise that would otherwise be generated in the process.

The normal zero reference level in stereo disc cutting is defined as lateral peak stylus velocity of 7 cm/sec at 1 kHz. On a per-channel basis, this corresponds to peak velocity of 5 cm/sec.

## 28.4 RECORDING AND PLAYBACK EQUALIZATION

The input signal is pre-emphasized some 34 dB over the range from 30 Hz to 20 kHz. The need for this was determined early in the art, where it was determined that high

**Figure 28-3.** Scanning electron microscope photograph of stereo grooves, 100-times magnification. Note the independent modulation of each groove wall. (*Courtesy Victor Company of Japan*)

signal levels at low frequencies tended to cause excessive groove excursion, thus consuming valuable recording space. High-frequencies, on the other hand, tended to get lost in the noise of the medium. With a reduction of low-frequency signals and a corresponding boost of high frequencies, the stereo disc exhibits a desirable trade-off between adequate playing time and reproduced noise.

During the early years of the LP, there was no clear agreement between manufacturers regarding signal pre-equalization, and the proliferation of recording curves of the day was as shown in Figure 28-4. Today, the universal playback curve for both stereo and mono LPs is as shown in Figure 28-5. This is literally a worldwide standard and is known in the United States as the RIAA (Record Industry Association of America) standard.

## 28.5 OVERLOAD IN DISC SYSTEMS

Since the disc cutting and playback processes are mechanical, there are fundamental geometrical limits imposed on the system. These fall into three areas.

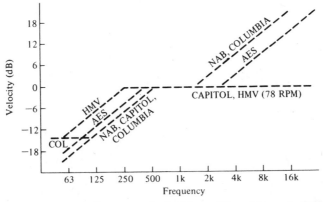

**Figure 28-4.** Recording pre-emphasis characteristics of the early 1950s.

### 28.5.1 Displacement Overload

At low frequencies, excessive signal input can result in one groove intersecting the preceding one, resulting in *overcut*. The simple remedy here is to increase the recording pitch so that the extra space needed by the excessive modulation is provided. The trade-off here is playing time; if a long side is required, the excursion will have to be limited to accommodate it. In severe cases, the cutting stylus may lift out of the cutting medium entirely (so-called "cutter lift"), if there is an excess of opposite polarity program content at low frequencies.

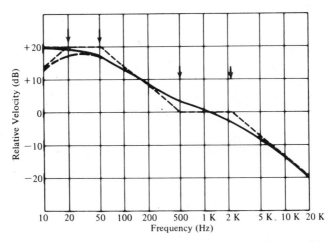

**Figure 28-5.** The RIAA playback de-emphasis characteristic. The three principal transition frequencies are: 50 Hz (3180 µsec), 500 Hz (318 µsec), and 2120 Hz (75 µsec). An optional roll-off below 20 Hz reduces effects of turntable rumble.

### 28.5.2 Slope Overload

In the midrange, high-signal levels may cause such rapid side-to-side motion that the back facets of the cutting stylus hit the freshly cut groove and scuff it.

### 28.5.3 Curvature Overload

At high frequencies it is possible for an overdriven cutting stylus to cut a groove that has curvature exceeding that of the playback stylus. When this is encountered in the playback process the result is distortion and accelerated record wear. The effect is more problematic at inner recording diameters, since wavelengths diminish as the tangential groove velocity diminishes.

In modern disc-cutting systems these forms of overload are monitored and compensated for through careful signal limiting.

## 28.6 PREDISTORTION OF THE STEREO SIGNAL

The master recording is made on a complex cutting lathe, and the cutting is done directly in flowed lacquer on an aluminum substrate, as shown in Figure 28-6. The simplest predistortion of the stereo signal comes from mechanically tilting the cutting stylus to that it moves in a non-perpendicular direction to the disc that matches that of the playback stylus. The action is shown in Figure 28-7, and the degree of mechanical tilt is in the range of 20 to 25°. If this precaution were not taken, the mismatch between cutting and playback vertical angles would produce undesirable self-modulation of the signal.

Another significant improvement can be made by further predistorting each groove wall so that the discrepancy between the chisel-edged cutting stylus and the spherical-tipped playback stylus is justified. Referring to Figure 28-8, note that the signal input to the cutting stylus is a sine wave. The playback of that signal with a spherical tip produces a locus of points that do not describe a sine wave; the signal is broad on top and pointed at the bottom. This can be simulated electrically and inverted during the cutting process. The result during playback of the predistorted signal is the recovery of an accurate sine wave.

## 28.7 CUTTING HEAD DESIGN

All modern stereo cutting heads are of the moving coil type and make use of inverse feedback to reduce distortion. The basic process is shown in Figure 28-9. Without feedback the motion of the stylus reflects its primary resonance, $f_0$, as shown in (b). When inverse feedback from the sensing coil is returned at negative polarity, the signal can be corrected so that its amplitude is flat (d). The process produces phase response in the signal current as shown in (c) and drive signal current as shown in (e).

A section view of the Neumann SX-74 cutting head is shown in Figure 28-10(a). Note that the cutting stylus cantilever is actuated at angles of $\pm 45°$ relative to the disc surface. The Ortofon design shown in (b) uses an isosceles T-bar to translate vertical motions of each coil into 45° groove motion.

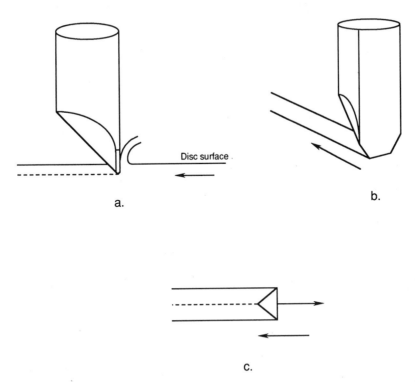

Disc surface

a.

b.

c.

**Figure 28-6.** Cutting styli. (a) View of stylus showing major surfaces. (b) Section view showing cutting action. (c) Normal view of disc during cutting action.

## 28.8 PLAYBACK STYLUS-GROOVE RELATIONSHIPS

Figure 28-11(a) shows a normal view of a recorded disc. The section view of the cutting stylus is shown at A. Further section views show three kinds of playback styli: line contact at B, elliptical contact at C, and conical contact at D. The details in (b) show contact areas and section views in the vertical plane for the three kinds of playback styli.

The best reproduction generally results when the area of contact is large and when the contact dimension is small in the direction of groove motion. These considerations favor the Shibata and elliptical stylus designs, as opposed to the simple conical tip designs. The large contact area results in minimal record wear, and the small contact dimension in the direction of grooved motion results in improved resolution of short recorded wavelengths.

## 28.9 DISC TRANSFER SYSTEMS

A disc transfer system is a specialized audio control system whose main function is to transfer a master tape to disc with the required signal processing. Ideally, a master tape that reaches this stage in production has been carefully prepared and should not require extensive last-minute treatment. Such is not always the case, and a flexible transfer system must be able to provide the following functions:

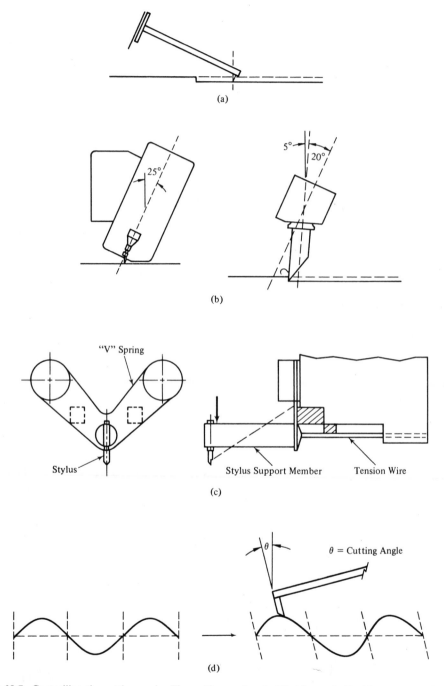

**Figure 28-7.** Controlling the cutting angle. The cutting motion is tilted by angle 0 with respect to the record surface in order to match the direction of motion of the playback stylus. Both actions are standardized to 20 to 25°.

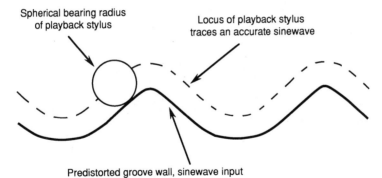

Spherical bearing radius
of playback stylus

Locus of playback stylus
traces an accurate sinewave

Predistorted groove wall, sinewave input

**Figure 28-8.** Tracing simulation. The cutting stylus must be fed a predistorted signal. For a sine wave input, as shown, the cutting stylus must execute the solid curve. The spherical bearing radius of the playback stylus will then execute a replica of the sine wave (dashed curve).

## Signal processing

    a. Comprehensive equalization and filtering; all functions easily resettable
    b. Compression and limiting; all functions easily resettable

## Signal routing

    a. Stereo input to stereo disc transfer mode
    b. Stereo input to mono disc transfer mode
    c. Left or right input to mono disc transfer mode
    d. Patching facilities in and out of major blocks in the system

## Monitoring and metering points

    a. Tape output
    b. Preview (advance head) output
    c. Signal processing output (cutter drive input)
    d. Cutter feedback signal
    e. Disc playback

## Signal conditioning

    a. Tracing simulation
    b. Slope and curvature limiting
    c. LF vertical limiting

## Calibration facilities

    a. Provision for constant velocity cutting and playback above 500 Hz
    b. Noise weighting filter and gain adjustment for reading low-level noise signals.

*Mechanical functions*

a. Flexibility for accommodating various tape speeds, disc diameters, and disc speeds
b. Comprehensive control of groove pitch and depth of cut (including duplication of signal processing elements in the preview system)

A block diagram for a complete disc transfer system is shown in Figure 28-12.

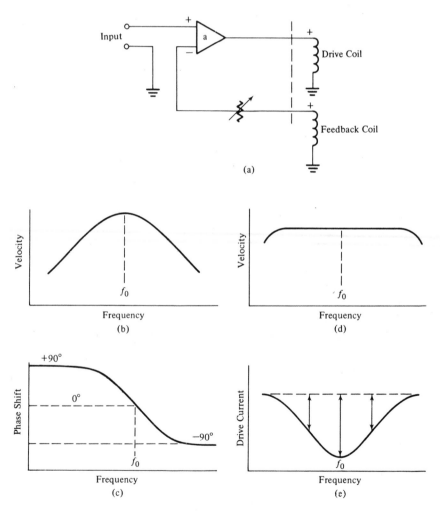

**Figure 28-9.** Principle of motional feedback. (a) Cutting stylus motion is monitored via a feedback coil, and any errors are corrected electrically. (b) Without feedback, the moving system has a pronounced resonant peak. (c) With feedback, the resonance is damped. (d) Phase response of system with feedback. (e) Drive current requirement with feedback.

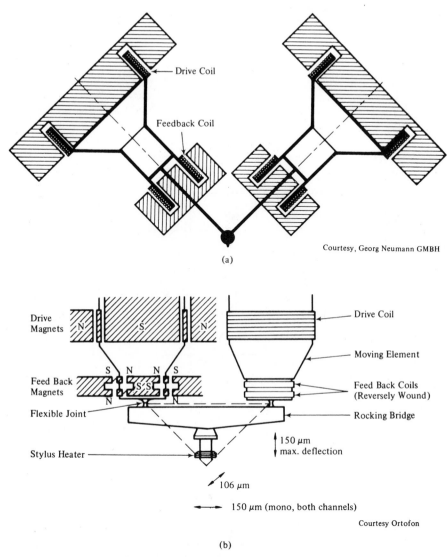

Courtesy, Georg Neumann GMBH

(a)

(b)

**Figure 28-10.** Section views of two cutting heads showing drive and feedback coil locations. (a) Neumann SX-74. (*Courtesy Georg Neumann GmbH*) (b) Ortofon. (*Courtesy Ortofon*).

## 28.10 VARIABLE PITCH AND DEPTH CONTROL

Variable pitch and depth control optimize both playing time and level capability on longer discs through the efficient use of space on the disc. Essentially, grooves are made narrower and spaced closer together when the level is low, and they are deepened and spaced farther apart as the signal level increases. It is no easy task to do this efficiently, and early methods of pitch and depth control were fairly coarse in their operation.

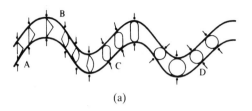

(a)

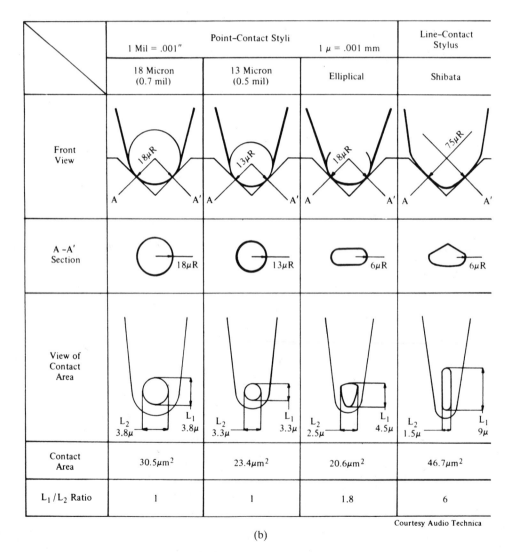

Courtesy Audio Technica

(b)

**Figure 28-11.** Playback stylus and groove relationships. (a) Trajectory of cutting stylus (A). Trajectory of Shibata playback stylus (B). Trajectory of elliptical playback stylus (C). Trajectory of conical stylus (D). (b) Some details of stylus–groove contact. (*Courtesy Audio Technica*)

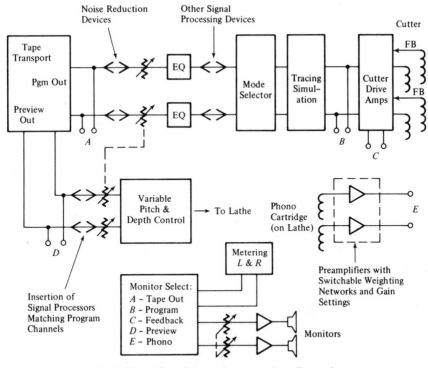

**Figure 28-12.** Signal flow diagram for a complete disc-cutting system.

In the most advanced cutting systems, the groove depth requirements are determined by the vertical components of the program at hand. The information for this is picked up by the preview head on the tape playback transport and stored until needed half a revolution later.

Pitch requirements are determined by three factors:

1. Left groove wall requirements. The left channel program input determines this need, and the information is stored for one revolution so that the right wall of the following groove will not interfere.
2. Right groove wall requirements. The right preview signal determines this need.
3. Pitch change as a result of depth increase. The preview vertical component determines this need; the information is stored for one-half revolution until it is needed.

The above actions are indicated in Figure 28-13(a), and typical performance is shown at (b).

## 28.11 DIAMETER LOSSES

An additional consequence of the mechanical aspect of disc recording is the attenuation of HF signals at inner cutting diameters. The reduced tangential velocity of the groove

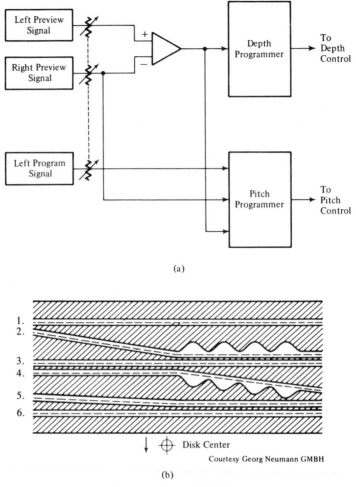

(a)

Courtesy Georg Neumann GMBH

(b)

**Figure 28-13.** Variable pitch and depth. In the Neumann VMS-70 cutting system, three signals, as shown in (a) are used to determine pitch and depth requirements. Typical action of the system is shown in (b). The right channnel modulation in groove 2 requires a decrease in pitch substantialy ahead of modulation so that there will be no overcut into groove 1. The decrease in pitch must be maintained one revolution so that groove 3 can be accommodated without overcut. Modulation on the left wall of groove 4 does not require a preview signal for proper pitch decrease; the signal that controls this is the left program input. Again, the decrease in pitch must be maintained one revolution in order to make room for groove 5. (*Courtesy Georg Neumann GmbH*)

at inner diameters increases wavelength-dependent losses, as shown in Figure 28-14. The losses are plotted versus recorded diameter for several frequencies for three disc sources.

The losses are due to several phenomena. Scanning losses result from the finite width of both burnishing facets on the cutting stylus and the width of the playback stylus contact in the direction of groove motion. Deformation losses result from the plasticity of the lacquer or vinyl medium. The master lacquer recording and the pressing are very much

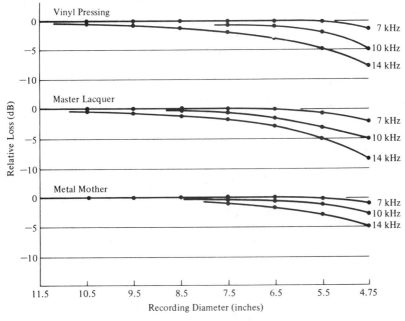

**Figure 28-14.** Diameter losses in disc recording.

the same as regards the losses. However, the metal mother (an interim step in the replication process) is virtually free of deformation effects.

## 28.12 RECORD PRESSING

The processing of a master lacquer disc through the various metal-to-metal replication operations and finally to the vinyl pressing is a very intricate one involving many disciplines. The basic operations in the three-step process are shown in Figure 28-15.

The master lacquer is carefully inspected, cleaned, sensitized, and "silvered" by reduction of silver nitrate on its surface. This renders it electrically conductive. It is then preplated at low electrical current density to build up a thin nickel surface that is a negative representation of the lacquer surface. Then the current density is increased to produce a substantial backing. The metal negative so produced is called the *metal master*. It is further treated so that a *metal mother* can be grown from it. The mother is a positive and can be played to check for problems in transfer. Minor defects can often be repaired.

Finally, the mother is plated and a stamper is produced. This is a metal negative which is used for final production. The stampers are ground on the back so that they will fit snugly into the press. The edges are crimped and the part is carefully centered in the press. The pressing cycle begins by placing a charge of hot vinyl plastic between the stampers in the press, along with the labels. Pressure and heat are applied, and the plastic is molded to conform with the stampers. When the molding is completed cold water is run through the channels of the mold, cooling the record so that it can be removed from

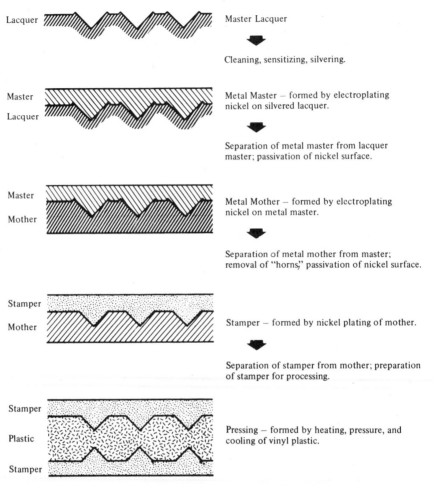

Lacquer — Master Lacquer

Cleaning, sensitizing, silvering.

Master Lacquer — Metal Master – formed by electroplating nickel on silvered lacquer.

Separation of metal master from lacquer master; passivation of nickel surface.

Master Mother — Metal Mother – formed by electroplating nickel on metal master.

Separation of metal mother from master; removal of "horns," passivation of nickel surface.

Stamper Mother — Stamper – formed by nickel plating of mother.

Separation of stamper from mother; preparation of stamper for processing.

Stamper Plastic Stamper — Pressing – formed by heating, pressure, and cooling of vinyl plastic.

**Figure 28-15.** The three-step disc replication process.

the press without warping. The remaining plastic around the edge of the disc, referred to as "flash", is trimmed and the process is finished.

## 28.13 RECENT TECHNOLOGICAL DEVELOPMENTS IN DISC RECORDING

Under the trade name Direct Metal Mastering (DMM), the Teldec company of Germany has introduced a process of cutting master discs directly on freshly plated amorphous copper, eliminating two steps in the replication process. Their efforts have complemented by those of Georg Neumann GMBH in the areas of lathe and cutter head development. The technology differs from the standard approach in the following ways:

1. The cutting is done on the copper layer, which becomes the metal mother for subsequent production of stampers. Figure 28-16 shows a view of the cutting lathe with a freshly cut master on the turntable.

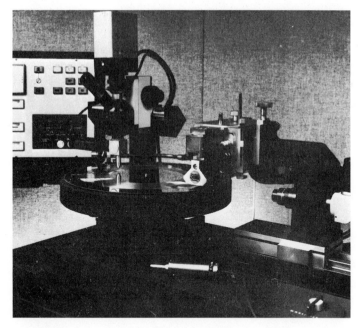

**Figure 28-16.** Lathe for cutting Direct Metal Masters (DMM). (*Courtesy Gotham Audio Corporation and Georg Neumann GmbH*)

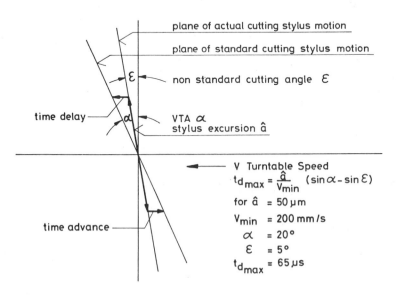

**Figure 28-17.** The effect of the vertical tracking angle converter for DMM. (*Courtesy Gotham Audio Corporation and Georg Neumann GmbH*)

2. There is no spring-back effect in the metal, as there is with lacquer, and deformation effects, such as "groove echo," are virtually eliminated.

3. The diamond cutting stylus does not require burnishing facets, and HF detail is much better than with conventional cutting.

4. A new, more powerful, cutting head is required to engrave the signal, and the physical cutting angle is about 5°. This necessitates electronic processing of the stereo signal by delay modulation to produce an effective cutting angle of 20°. Details of this process are shown in Figure 28-17.

Further advantages of the system include up to 10 dB improvement in noise performance and the ability to accommodate a general 15% increase in playing time, depending on the nature of the program.

## BIBLIOGRAPHY

1. G. Bogantz and J. Ruda, "Analog Disk Recording and Reproduction," Chapter 8 in K. Benson, *Audio Engineering Handbook*, McGrawıHill, New York (1988).
2. D. Braschoss, "Disc Cutting Machine—Computer Controlled," *Radio Mentor* (October 1966).
3. J. Eargle, "Record Defects," *Stereo Review* (June 1967).
4. J. Eargle, "Performance Characteristics of the Commercial Stereo Disc," *J. Audio Engineering Society*, vol. 17, no. 4 (1969).
5. E. Fox and J. Woodward, "Tracing Distortion—Its Cause and Correction in Stereo Disc Recording," *J. Audio Engineering Society*, vol. 11, no. 4 (1963).
6. F. Hirsch and S. Temmer, "A Real-Time Digital Processor for Disc Mastering Lathe Control," presented at the 60th Convention, Audio Engineering Society, May, 1978.
7. R. Narma and N. Anderson, "A New Stereo Feedback Cutterhead System," *J. Audio Engineering Society*, vol. 7, no. 4 (1959).
8. C. Nelson and J. Stafford, "The Westrex 3D Stereo Disk System," *J. Audio Engineering Society*, vol. 12, no. 3 (1964).
9. O. Read and W. Welch, *From Tin-Foil to Stereo*, H. Sams, Indianapolis (1958).
10. J. Stafford, "Maximum Peak Velocity Capabilities of the Disc Record, *J. Audio Engineering Society*, vol. 8, no. 3 (1960).
11. J. Woodward and E. Fox, "A Study of Program-Level Overloading in Phonograph Recording," *J. Audio Engineering Society*, vol. 11, no. 1 (1963).
12. *Disk Recording*, Volumes 1 (1980) and 2 (1981), Audio Engineering Society, New York.

# 29

## RECORDED TAPE PRODUCTS FOR THE CONSUMER

### 29.1 INTRODUCTION

The first recorded tape product for the consumer was in the form of 19-cm/sec (7.5-inch/sec) two-track stereo in reel-to-reel format and was introduced in 1953. The programs were less than one hour, and the costs for longer tapes were in the range of twenty to thirty dollars. Such were the prices that could be charged when tape was the only medium for stereo. When the stereo LP was introduced in 1957 the original tape format quickly died out.

It was later replaced by a 0.6-mm (0.25-inch) four-track reel to reel format, with stereo program recorded in each direction. The track layouts for the original format and the subsequent four-track format are as shown in Figure 19-23. The high costs of tape duplication could not keep pace with the improvements in stereo LP production, and eventually the four-track configuration gave way to the Philips Compact Cassette.

The cassette began as a lowly medium for dictating machines. Through many improvements during the years it has reached a degree of technical respectability that was quite unforeseen when it was introduced during the late 1960s. Today, the very mention of recorded tape brings to mind the cassette, and that format is, by any measure, the most popular medium for delivery of music into the homes and automobiles of consumers worldwide.

### 29.2 PHYSICAL PROFILE OF THE CASSETTE

Another problem of the reel-to-reel format was the nuisance of threading the tape through the often intricate guides of tape machines. The convenience of the cassette is that the tape is contained within a shell; the consumer simply inserts the tape into the player, and the machine does the rest, often including automatic reversing of the tape at the end of a side.

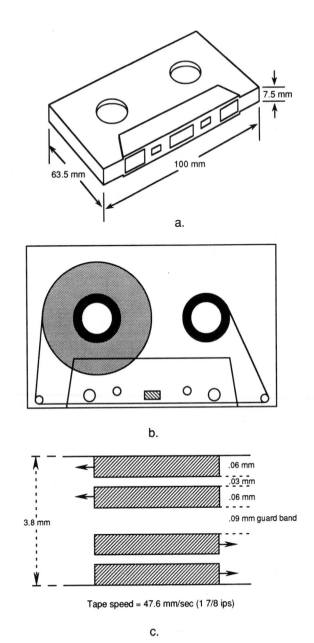

7.5 mm

100 mm

63.5 mm

a.

b.

.06 mm
.03 mm
.06 mm
.09 mm guard band

3.8 mm

Tape speed = 47.6 mm/sec (1 7/8 ips)

c.

**Figure 29-1.** (a) View of the cassette and dimensions. (b) Internal details. (c) Track configuration for the cassette.

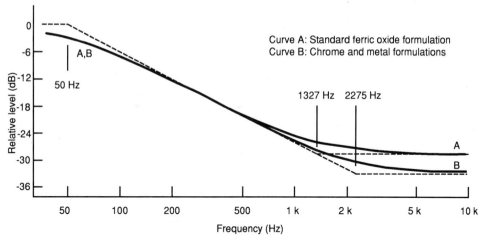

**Figure 29-2.** Standard playback curves for the cassette.

Figure 29-1(a) shows a view of the cassette. Functional views are shown in (b), and the track format is shown in (c). The tape speed is 4.75 cm/sec ($1\frac{7}{8}$ inches/sec). In some record/playback machines, the cassette must be removed from the machine and turned over to record or play on the alternate set of tracks. A few machines have dual drive capstans and require no removal from the machine.

## 29.3 ELECTRICAL ASPECTS

There are two primary playback characteristics (70 and 1120 μsec) for the cassette, and they are determined basically by the the magnetic characteristics of the tape stock. Representative curves are shown in Figure 29-2. Many machines are capable of recording on standard tape, chromium dioxide tape, and metal tape formulations. Since the recording equalization requirements are different for the three types of tape, recording equalization must also be switchable.

The best overall performance is obtained with metal tape. This formulation requires bias drive capability in excess of the normal oxide and chromium formulations and must be done on machines specifically designed for it. Metal tapes can be played back, however, on standard machines.

Dolby noise reduction is applicable to all tape formulations, and the B-type noise reduction is widely used today. For the quality-conscious consumer, C-type noise reduction offers the best response. In the immediate future is Dolby S-type noise reduction, which has certain advantages over C-type. Figure 29-3 shows the family of encoding curves for Dolby B-, C-, and S-type noise reduction. These curves show the maximum amount of HF boost that takes place at lower recording levels, but they do not necessarily indicate noise reduction action for specific program input conditions.

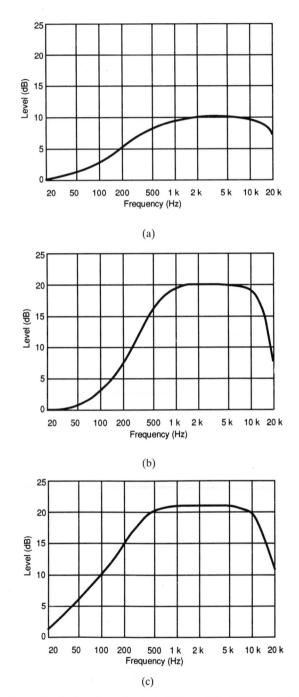

**Figure 29-3.** Dolby encoding action for low-level signals. (a) B-type NR. (b) C-type NR. (c) Dolby S. (*Courtesy Dolby Laboratories*)

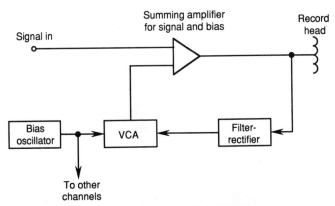

**Figure 29-4.** Circuit for Dolby HX-Pro.

### 29.3.1 Tape Characteristics

Recorded wavelengths on cassette tape are one-eighth those of the same frequency recorded at 38 cm/sec. At 20 kHz, the recorded wavelength is 20 μm at 38 cm/sec and 2.4 μm at 4.75 cm/sec. Tape for cassette use is optimized for short-wavelength recording, and this requires that the magnetic layer be quite thin in order to minimize recording losses at short wavelengths. Since thin magnetic coatings tend to increase noise, much of the research in cassette tape in the last two decades has addressed higher signal output capability. In particular, metal formulations are excellent in this respect.

### 29.3.2 HX Pro

In cassette recording, high frequencies at high program levels reaching the record head can act as additional bias, and the resultant overbiasing at short wavelengths can lead to diminished HF output. HX Pro (3) is based on developments by Dolby Laboratories and Bang & Olufsen and is a method of controlling the main bias signal during heavy modulation so that the effective bias operating on the signal at the record head is more or less constant. HX Pro is provided by the circuit shown in Figure 29-4. The incoming audio signal is summed with a bias signal that has been determined by a voltage-controlled amplifier (VCA) modulated by a signal from the record head itself. The filter-rectifier detects the amount of HF program and alters the bias oscillator output so that the net effective bias at the record head remains uniform. A tape recorded with HX-Pro will of course play back on any cassette machine.

Using the best available tape, Dolby C- or S-type noise reduction, and HX Pro, the quality of sound produced by a carefully made cassette is excellent. Great care must be taken, however, that the input program spectrum does not stress the system at high frequencies.

### 29.4 HIGH-SPEED DUPLICATION OF CASSETTES

A large part of the success of the cassette derives from the relatively low replication costs. A large part of this is due to the time saving aspects of high-speed duplication.

**Figure 29-5.** High-speed duplicating system for cassettes. (*Courtesy Gauss*)

Figure 29-5 shows a high-speed duplication system. The duplicating master is recorded at 19 cm/sec and runs in an endless-loop tape bin. The master normally runs at 610 cm/sec (240 inches/sec), resulting in a duplication ratio of 32-to-1. A 64-to-1 duplication ratio is possible if the duplicating master is recorded at 9.5 cm/sec ($3\frac{3}{4}$ inches/sec), with some reduction in quality. Higher duplicating speed ratios are desirable obviously because of cost savings.

Of all the consumer media, the cassette is the only one that is duplicated in a manner strictly analogous to making a cassette in the home. The basic differences are purely in scale and in the fact that the tape is duplicated in bulk on hubs, called "pancakes," which are loaded into empty cassette shells later after quality checks have been completed.

A recent improvement in duplicating technology involves the use of digital storage of the entire program in high-speed memory. This permits a duplicating ratio up to 80-to-1, while bypassing another generation of tape copying altogether.

### 29.4.1 MASTERING FOR CASSETTE DUPLICATION

Most cassette duplicating facilities prefer to make their own duplicating (running) master tapes, since this gives them complete control over such matters as overall tape level and HF level in particular. An incoming program is auditioned and potential trouble points are noted. When the program is transferred to the duplicating master, limiters that have been previously calibrated will reduce the level of HF passages in the program that could be troublesome. The alternative to such treatment is to reduce the overall duplicating level so that all signals can be accommodated.

For classical music, the spectral characteristic is generally as shown in Figure 2-15, and little if any HF treatment will be necessary. If the overall spectrum is flat, as is so often the case with rock program material, then limiting is required. HX Pro can be implemented at the duplicating stage just as it can in consumer recorders.

## BIBLIOGRAPHY

1. R. Dolby, "A 20 dB Audio Noise Reduction System for Consumer Applications," *J. Audio Engineering Society*, vol. 31, no. 3 (1983).
2. K. Gundry and J. Hull, "Introducing Dolby S-type Noise Reduction," *Audio Magazine* (June 1990).
3. K. Gundry, *Headroom Extension for Slow-Speed Magnetic Recording of Audio*, AES Convention preprint number 1534 (1979).
4. M. Martin, "Some Thoughts on Cassette Duplication, *J. Audio Engineering Society*, vol. 21, no. 9 (1973).
5. J. McKnight, Operating Level in the Duplication of Philips Cassette Records, *J. Audio Engineering Society*, vol. 15, no. 4 (1967).
6. D. Robinson, "Production of Dolby B-type Cassettes," *J. Audio Engineering Society*, vol. 20, no. 10 (1972).
7. J. Woram, *Sound Recording Handbook*, H. Sams, Indianapolis (1989).

# 30

## THE COMPACT DISC (CD)

### 30.1 INTRODUCTION

The introduction of the Compact Disc in the early 1980s heralded a new era of consumer enjoyment of recorded sound. While the LP had served so well for many decades, the lingering problems of ticks, pops, and inevitable record wear had long militated against it. The emergence of a digital playback medium came after many years of development in the allied fields of high-speed computation and digital signal processing. At first the replication costs were high, and the players were expensive. Now, as we enter the decade of the 1990s, the costs of both are fairly low. Only the continuing high market price of CDs seems to hold back wholesale adoption of the medium. Even so, unit sales of CDs exceeded those of LPs in 1987 and have been growing steadily since that time.

### 30.2 PHYSICAL PROFILE OF THE CD

Table 30-1 gives pertinent specifications for the compact disc, and Figure 30-1 shows an overall view of the CD. Program is recorded only on one side in spiral form of pits of varying length. The pit surface is metalized so that it will reflect light, and it is covered with a coating of clear plastic for protection. The pits are read sequentially with a fine laser beam. The disc rotates at a constant linear velocity, so the rpm is variable, as required. The disc plays from the inside to outside.

### 30.3 OPTICAL DETAILS

A scanning electronic microscope view of the pit structure is shown in Figure 30-2. Figure 30-3 shows a view of the laser reading assembly. The pit depth and laser wavelength are chosen so that light reflected from the metalized surface between pits will be constructively reinforced, while light reflected from the pit will be cancelled. Thus, it possible to distinguish between both pit and disc surface and recover binary data.

## Table 30-1. Specifications for the compact disc (2)

| | |
|---|---|
| Playing time | Upwards of 78 minutes |
| Rotation | Counterclockwise when viewed from readout surface |
| Rotational speed | 1.2–1.4 m/sec |
| Track pitch | 1.6 $\mu$m |
| Diameter | 120 mm |
| Thickness | 1.2 mm |
| Center hole diameter | 15 mm |
| Material | Polycarbonate (refractive index 1.55) |
| Minimum pit length | 0.833 $\mu$m (1.2 m/sec) to 0.972 $\mu$m (1.4 m/sec) |
| Maximum pit length | 3.05 $\mu$m (1.2 m/sec) to 3.56 $\mu$m (1.4 m/sec) |
| Pit depth | Approximately 0.11 $\mu$m |
| Pit width | Approximately 0.5 $\mu$m |
| Standard wavelength | $\lambda$ = 780 nanometers |
| Focal depth | $\pm2$ $\mu$m |
| Digital quantization | 16 bits |
| Sampling frequency | 44.1 kHz |
| Frequency response | Flat to 20 kHz |
| Signal-to-noise ratio | Greater than 90 dB |
| Channel capacity | 2 (4 with reformatting) |

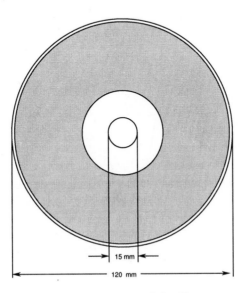

**Figure 30-1.** View of the CD.

**Figure 30-2.** Photomicrograph of CD pit structure. (*Courtesy University of Miami*)

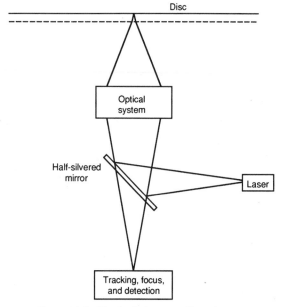

**Figure 30-3.** The basic laser reading system.

No details of the tracking system are given here, but suffice it to say that *all* sources of tracking error must be detected and compensated for during the playback process. These errors include departures from concentricity of the disc as well as up-down motions resulting from deviations from flatness of the disc.

The digital readout from the mechanism is subjected to signal conditioning and error correction as discussed in Chapter 21. Many players have a serial digital output (SPDIF format), enabling the player to be used with an external digital processor.

## 30.4 REPLICATION OF CDs

The replication process for CDs is remarkably like that used for LPs. The basic process is shown in Figure 30-4 (3). A photoresist coating is placed on a glass substrate, and a laser beam, fed by a properly formatted digital signal derived from the tape source, exposes the photoresist material. The surface is then developed, and exposed areas are etched away. Metal deposition then takes place, and this initiates the repetitive negative–positive replication cycles.

Direct metal mastering (DMM) can also be used to make the master disc. In this case the pattern of pits is imbossed on the copper blank by modulating a piezoelectric transducer.

## 30.5 P AND Q SUBCODES

Along with the digital audio signal, time code and other subcodes are included. These include information on lead-in, lead-out, track numbers, playing times, copy inhibit, and the like. Figure 30-5 shows a typical program code sheet that is sent to the disc manufacturer along with the Sony 1630 digital master tape. SMPTE time code is used to indicate the start and end of program, along with the exact frame timings for the start of each band. In this case, the program is indexed for continuous music presentation from beginning to end. That is to say, there is continuous "room sound" between the actual banded segments of the program. Note that subbanding is possible, enabling specific points within a musical movement to be accessed by the player.

## 30.6 PROGRAMMING FOR THE CD

The CD effectively can handle a flat power bandwidth signal. That is, the medium requires no pre- or de-emphasis, as do analog tape and disc mediums. This means that a signal does not have to be compressed, or otherwise limited in any part of its frequency range, in order to be accommodated on CD.

There is provided in the system specifications, however, an optional 10-dB pre-emphasis, which is a user option. When this is employed, a flag is entered into the digital word structure so that complementary de-emphasis will be automatically used during playback. It is the general consensus among mastering engineers that emphasis is not needed—and may be a source of confusion at some later stage in the mastering process.

Since the CD does not "know the difference" between 20 Hz or 20 kHz in a musical signal context, the mastering engineer does not need to worry about compression of high

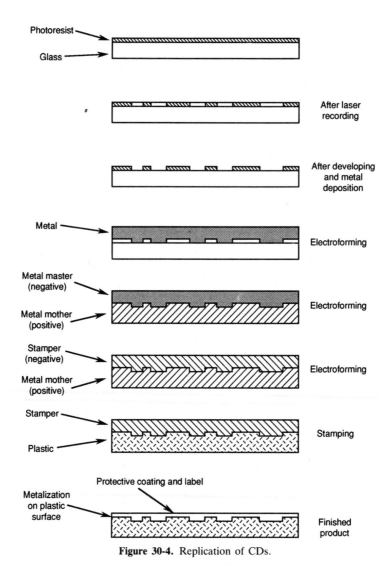

**Figure 30-4.** Replication of CDs.

frequencies, or any of the other problems that have plagued analog media since their inception. This is both blessing and pitfall. During the early rush to get product into the marketplace, many record companies routinely used equalized copies of master tapes to make CDs (1). The problem here was that those tapes had been "shaped" for the stereo LP, with its special characteristics and limitations. When used for making CDs, the resulting sound was more often than not quite bright, and even harsh. This was certainly the leading cause of critical objection to the earliest CD releases; and in many quarters this objection still remains long after most manufacturers have stopped using equalized masters.

Delos International, Inc.
Catalog #: D/CD 3073
Title: Howard Hanson:
Symphonies 1 & 2; Elegy

PQ Subcode Information
Date: 20 Dec 88
Mastered by: AS, LJW

Format:Sony 1630
Total playing time: 70:39
Last time present
on tape: 01:14:00:00

| Track# | Index# | Title | Time | SMPTE Codes Begin-end | Notes |
|---|---|---|---|---|---|
| | | Howard Hanson: | | | |
| | | Symphony #1, Nordic" | (29:19) | | |
| 1 | | Andante solenne | 12:41 | 00:02:00:00 | |
| 2 | | Andante teneramente | 6:05 | 00:14:45:00 | |
| 3 | | Allegro con fuoco | 10:24 | 00:20:55:00 | |
| 4 | | Elegy in Memory of Serge Koussevitsky | 12:37 | 00:31:30:00  (Note) | Use 31:30 as start of track although music begins slightly later |
| | | Symphony #2, Romantic | (28:20) | | |
| 5 | | Adagio | 13:34 | 00:44:19:00 | |
| 6 | | Andante | 7:21 | 00:57:59:00 | |
| 7 | | Allegro | 7:14 | 01:05:25:00--01:12:39:00 | |

**Figure 30-5.** Typical programming sheet for a CD. (*Courtesy Delos International*)

## BIBLIOGRAPHY

1. J. Eargle, "Do CDs Sound Different?" *Audio Magazine* (November 1987).
2. J. Hanus and C. Pannel, *Le Compact Disc*, Editions Techniques et Scientifiques Francaises, Paris (1984).
3. K. Pohlmann, The Compact Disc, A-R Editions, Madison, Wis. (1988).

# 31

## DIGITAL AUDIO TAPE (DAT)

### 31.1 INTRODUCTION

Since the introduction of the CD in 1983, consumers have wondered when a digital tape standard would complete the digital picture, so to speak, and provide an alternative to the analog cassette. The R-DAT (rotary head digital audio tape) standard was promulgated during the mid-1980s, and it has encountered hard going as a consumer medium. It is expensive; but what is more to the point, the RIAA (Record Industry Association of America) has vigorously opposed its importation from Japan into the United States on the grounds that it will further erode music copyright interests by providing a "virtually perfect" method for the consumer to copy CDs.

Whatever the merits of the consumer case may be, there is no doubt that DAT has become a new and highly portable standard for professional use. DAT machines can be quite small, facilitating field gathering of sound effects and audio data of all sorts. Many professional direct-to-stereo recordings are now done with DAT machines priced in the two to five thousand dollar range. The professional machines provide recording at 44.1 kHz so that transfer to digital editing formats can be made without sampling rate conversion.

It is unlikely that the record industry will promote the sale of prerecorded DAT tapes. Primarily, reasons are the high cost of duplication (one-to-one "real-time" methods are required at present), and the high cost of raw tape stock. The consumer satisfaction with the Philips Compact Cassette is too much of a good thing, and many in the record business consider promotion of the DAT as virtual suicide!

### 31.2 PHYSICAL PROFILE OF THE DAT

Figure 31-1(a) shows the profile of a DAT cassette. It resembles its analog cousin but is slightly smaller. When it is inserted into the player, a front cover is opened and the tape is pulled out of the cassette, as shown in (b), and is wrapped around a helical-scan record–playback drum, as shown in (c).

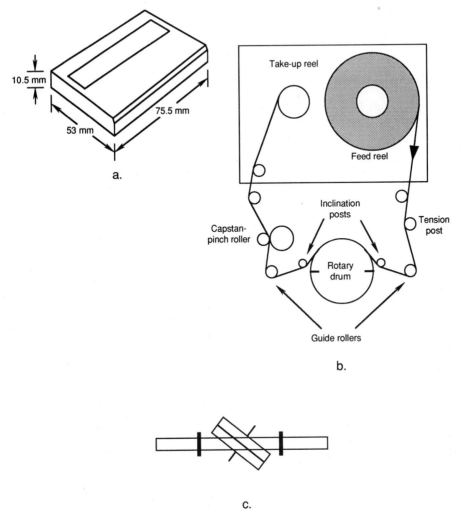

**Figure 31-1.** Details of the R-DAT. (a) View of the cassette. (b) In operation, the tape is pulled out of the cassette and wrapped around a helical scanning head. (c) Details of helical scanning head in contact with tape.

The resulting track pattern on the tape is as shown in Figure 31-2. On the edge are tracks produced by stationary heads, but the program modulation is represented by the slanted tracks occupying the bulk of the tape area.

## 31.3 OPERATIONAL CONSIDERATIONS

The actual tape-to-head speed is provided by the high tangential velocity of the helical scan drum. The linear tape velocity is only as fast as needed to keep the helical segments from overlapping each other. The angular "staggering" of adjacent record head azimuth relationships provides some immunity to crosstalk, enabling lower linear tape velocities.

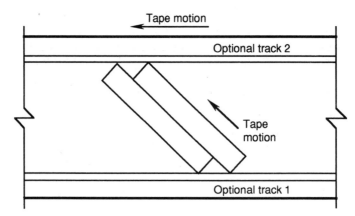

**Figure 31-2.** Track and helical scan layout on tape.

As a result, the linear tape velocity of the DAT is only 8.15 mm/sec, and the small cassette can accommodate 2 hours of recording time.

Like other digital systems, the DAT coexists with professional formats through standardized interface buses. Professional DAT recorders have AES-EBU and SDIF-2 outputs so that DAT tapes can be converted directly to the various professional editing formats. The machines include indexing facilities so that sequential take numbers can be encoded in the stationary tracks, further facilitating transfer and assembly of program segments during post-production.

DAT is directly adaptable to electronic editing systems, but the resolution of editing is only on the order of 1 msec. While this is excellent for many assembly jobs in video applications, it is not precise enough for detailed music editing for CD mastering. Figure 31-3 shows a photograph of a portable professional DAT recorder. Professional DAT recorders normally provide recording at sampling frequencies of 32, 44.056, 44.1 and 48 kHz. The quantizing is 16-bit linear.

## 31.4 PROSPECTS FOR S-DAT

S-DAT is an abbreviation for stationary head digital audio tape. Such a system uses relatively slow-moving tape, with a multiplicity of thin film recording and playback heads to provide the necessary recording density on the tape. In theory at least, an S-DAT recorder is simpler to manufacture from the mechanical point of view than a rotary head machine, but the electronic complexity is about the same.

While there are no officially promulgated standards, it is likely that the first S-DAT standard will address the consumer market. Philips of Holland has suggested that an S-DAT standard, called Digital Compact Cassette, would be a logical successor to their analog Compact Cassette, making use of the same size shell and linear tape speed. Time will tell; there is a powerful base for the analog cassette, but Philips feels, and rightly so, that it must be brought into the digital age.

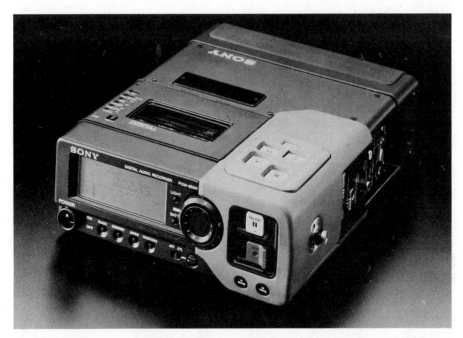

**Figure 31-3.** Photograph of a Sony PCM-2000 portable professional DAT recorder. (*Courtesy Sony Corporation*)

## BIBLIOGRAPHY

1. Anon, "DAT: Where it Stands and How it Will Work," *AudioVideo International* (January 1990).
2. *Operation Manual for PCM-2000 Audio Recorder*, Sony Corporation, Teaneck, N.J. (1988).

# 32

## RECORDING STUDIO DESIGN FUNDAMENTALS

### 32.1 INTRODUCTION

Regardless of scale, the requirements for successful studio operation are basically the same. A low-cost studio in the home environment deserves the same acoustical and technological considerations as a multichannel installation in a major metropolis if both are to successfully deliver useful services.

This chapter will cover some of the basic acoustic considerations in building a studio. More fundamentally, it will address the problems of site selection and the development of a business plan. The nature of professional equipment, its costs, and its rapid obsolescence will be discussed.

### 32.2 PLANNING FOR BUSINESS

It has long been the dream of many an engineer to build and operate a recording studio. Too often, the dream gets ahead of sensible financial planning, and the studio, whether built from the ground up or acquired through other channels, runs into trouble. The biggest pitfall is investing too much money and real estate in a large studio space, overlooking the income possibilities of more, and smaller, work spaces.

A conservative business plan is essential. Essentially, a business plan is an outline of income potential less the cost of getting into, and staying in, business. The first thing to do is determine what the income potential really is. Questions such as these need to be answered:

    a. Are there enough clients in the community to adequately "load" the facility at its break-even point? It is important to be conservative in these estimates. Take note of how other studios in the area have fared. In particular, analyze those that have failed, and determine why. Likewise, analyze those that have succeeded, and determine why.

b. What is the income growth potential for the studio? For example, if the intended specialty of the studio is advertising or video-related work, find out what the long-range growth potential is in your community. Any responsible lending institution will expect an analysis prepared by a financial analyst who understands the field.

c. What are your own qualifications for specifying, building, and operating a studio? A realistic appraisal is essential here. Identify those specialists in studio design and construction who can help you.

The next step is to outline the initial and ongoing costs of being in business:

a. Outline in detail the costs of leasehold or property development for the studio, and note the time required for this work.

b. Identify the equipment that must be purchased outright as opposed to that which may be leased against eventual purchase option.

c. Outline all personnel salary and benefit requirements for running the studio, as well as all items of overhead. (Incentives are a common thing in hiring competent recording engineers, and commissions are routinely paid for work that experienced engineers can bring to the studio. Deal with this openly and professionally.)

d. Take note of building codes, licenses, and other civic details.

e. Identify legal and financial counsel who have experience in this or in related fields.

Financial data should be presented in a balance-sheet format projected on a quarterly basis. Inflationary factors should be considered along with other factors affecting the community at large. Do not rely on a "rich uncle" who wants to finance an operation that the banks have turned down. The banks are probably right.

## 32.3 SITE SELECTION AND DEVELOPMENT

In most locations, studios are considered commercial enterprises and must be located in areas zoned for such purposes. Many small studios exist in residential locations only because they do not create a noise or traffic nuisance to such an extent that neighbors have complained.

In picking a site for a studio, take careful note of who your commercial neighbors will be and what their business hours are. It is expensive to acoustically isolate a studio, and the ideal situation is to have neighbors who do not make noise and who themselves are tolerant of moderate noise levels.

Avoid proximity to busy thoroughfares and approaches to airports. A little homework is advised in checking out future state and federal plans for a given site. For example, a freeway passing near the site could profoundly influence prospects, and not always for the better. Ensure that the neighborhood is stable by checking with those businesses already in place.

The ready availability of space in light industrial parks attracts many in the studio business. Landlords are quite willing to make changes, but the major problem is likely

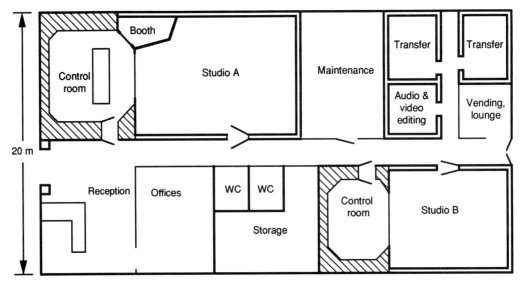

**Figure 32-1.** A typical floor plan for a studio complex in which studio work areas have been separated by acoustical buffer zones.

to be a problem with an insufficient total floor-to-roof distance. It is best to make such arrangements when such a facility is in the design stages. Another concern here is parking; make certain that there is enough space for your purposes.

### 32.3.1 Acoustical Considerations

The essential advice here is to engage a qualified acoustical consultant at the outset of the project. Pick one who has a good track record and good references. The acoustician can be of great help in laying out the basic floor plan for the facility, and with proper care at this stage many potential acoustical problems can be avoided entirely. Figure 32-1 shows an arrangement in which recording areas, which require good isolation, are separated from each other through buffer zones, such as storage areas, maintenance activities. This simple expedient means that the transmission loss (TL) between adjacent areas has to be sufficient only to reduce transmission of sound from the buffer zone to the recording area to the necessary degree. If the noise in the buffer zone can be controlled, then the TL between that zone and the studio can be minimal, and considerable cost savings can be realized. Many times, the buffer zone is simply an air space between two structural walls.

When a buffer zone has been defined, care must be taken that there are no flanking paths between recording areas that would defeat the buffer zone. Figure 32-2 shows some details: In (a) is shown the ideal case of a studio located on a concrete slab. There is virtually no transmission into or out of the studio through the floor, and the transmission loss $TL_S$ through the walls and ceiling may be, depending on construction, between 35 and 55 dB. Figure 32-2(b) shows what can happen when two studios are located on the

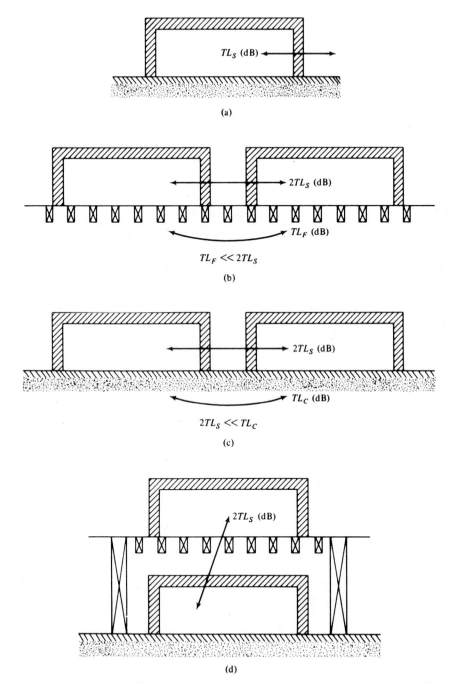

**Figure 32-2.** Isolation between studios and the environment. (a) Single studio on concrete slab. (b) Adjacent studios on wood floor. (c) Adjacent studios on concrete slab. (d) Studios on adjacent floors.

same floor where the substructure is made of wood. The airborne sound isolation between the studios will be about twice the *TL* noted at (a); however, the structure-borne *TL* through the common floor will be significantly less and will effectively obviate the excellent isolation provided through the walls. In (c) the excellent airborne sound isolation between studios will be preserved because of the great inertance (mass) of the concrete slab. It is generally massive enough that there will be very little structure-borne sound transmitted through it. However, any direct hammering on the slab is likely to be heard anywhere on the slab. Figure 32-2(d) shows two studios on adjacent floors. This works best when one studio is on a ground floor slab, where structure-borne sound transmission will be minimal. On adjacent floors of wood or steel structures, great care must be taken so that structure-borne sound transmission does not nullify an otherwise good job of airborne sound isolation.

It is in such matters as these that a consultant can be invaluable. Do not take the seriously the gratuitous advice, however honestly offered, of building contractors who have not had experience in studio building. They are likely to tell you that you are spending too much money on sound isolation. If anything, the opposite tends to be the case.

Allow for final space requirements in choosing a site. An undeveloped space may seem quite large at the outset, but it will be much smaller after all aspects of isolation and acoustical treatment have been dealt with. Space requirements for bass traps in the control room can easily be in the range of 1 m (40 inches). Dropped ceilings and air conditioning ductwork can also take up much space. As a general rule, no undeveloped space with a ceiling height less than 4.5 m (15 feet) should be considered for first-rate studio design.

Where existing sites are being considered for conversion to studio use, existing air-conditioning systems should be carefully assessed in the following regards:

a. Is the cooling effort equal to the maximum anticipated load?
b. Does the noise level of the system meet studio requirements ? (More about this later.)
c. Does the ductwork provide sufficient sound isolation between the studio and adjacent work areas? This question needs to be answered in terms of possible interference in *either* direction.

A facility that consists of a single studio is relatively simple to deal with; the cooling load must be carefully assessed and the ductwork gauged to avoid objectionable turbulence. Fans must be isolated so that their noise will not intrude. Where multiple studios are planned, there are specific problems to watch for. Figure 32-3(a) shows the worst case, two studios on a single air-conditioning feed. While the physical isolation of the two studios may be sufficient, sound leakage through the common air conditioning feed may well nullify it. In (b) there is a significant improvement; here, both studios have separate feeds from a common cooling plant, and the isolation will usually be sufficient. The best solution is shown in (c). While more expensive at the outset, the arrangement may also be most energy-efficient in the long run. Again, watch out for free advice from air-conditioning contractors who have not had studio construction experience.

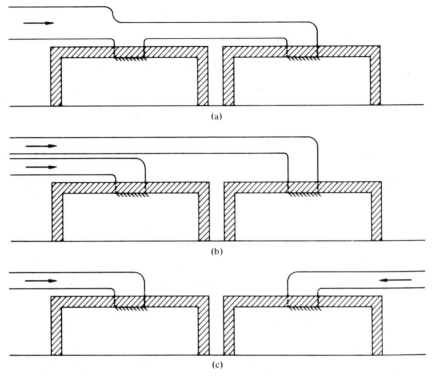

**Figure 32-3.** Common air-conditioning problems. (a) Two studios on a common feed. (b) Separate feeds from a common cooling plant. (c) Separate cooling plants.

### 32.3.2 Studio Noise Level Requirements

The foregoing remarks on studio noise levels are aimed at helping prospective studio builders avoid existing sites and structures that are basically unworkable, or appear to present extreme difficulties.

Once a site has been chosen, the remaining problems of studio isolation and quieting must be solved. Noise levels are customarily measured according to accepted Noise Criteria (NC) curves, which are shown in Figure 32-4. Note the resemblance to the Robinson–Dadson equal loudness contours discussed in Chapter 2. Like the Robinson–Dadson curves, the NC curves take into consideration the ear's relative insensitivity to LF noise at low levels.

With the help of a sound level meter and an octave band analyzer, the acoustical consultant can determine the existing NC rating in the studio space, as well as in the various spaces outside the studio area. A good studio should have an NC rating of 20 to 25. If the maximum noise levels outside the studio area can be measured or estimated with reasonable accuracy, the NC 20 values can be subtracted from the outside noise levels on an octave band basis to yield the actual isolation requirements for the studio.

If the studio is to be located in relatively quiet surroundings with office areas close by, then the main problem may not be from the outside into the studio, but rather leakage

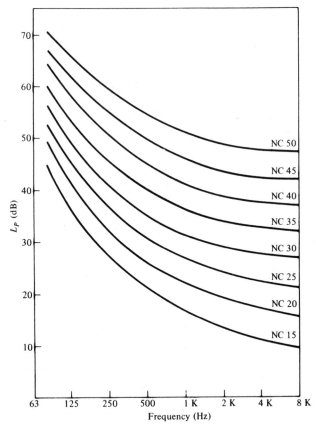

**Figure 32-4.** Standard Noise Criteria (NC) curves. In assigning an NC value, measurements are made on octave bands and compared with the family of curves given here. The NC value assigned is that lowest one for which the octave band noise levels do not exceed the values shown. NC curves are normally assigned in 1 dB increments.

from the studio activity into the relatively quiet surroundings. This is especially likely to be the case with pop-rock recording. The acoustical consultant must then make another set of measurements, this time assuming a reasonable NC rating for the office areas and estimating the highest levels to be encountered in the studio.

Both sets of isolation requirements, outside-to-studio and studio-to-outside, are then compared and the *maximum* values within each octave band are noted. These maximum values then define the isolation requirements for the studio, taking into account the possibility of sound transmission in both directions. The next step is to identify the wall and ceiling structures that will provide the required isolation. For general architectural purposes, various wall structures are rated according to their Sound Transmission Class (STC) value. These are a set of weighted curves that take into account the ear's relative insensitivity to low frequencies at low levels. The family of STC curves is shown in Figure 32-5. Note that these curves are roughly the inverse of the NC curves, a fortunate

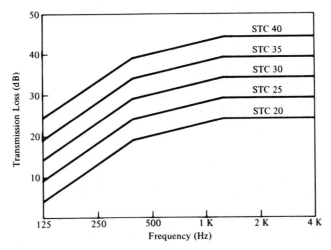

**Figure 32-5.** Family of Sound Transmission Class (STC) curves.

happenstance inasmuch as most wall structures are more effective in isolating the relatively short wavelengths of mid- and high-frequency sound than long-wavelength low frequencies.

The next step is to compare the maximum isolation requirements with the family of STC curves and choose structures that will meet the most stringent requirements. It is at this point that realistic construction costs for the studio complex can be estimated. It is possible that the target isolation requirements may put the project well beyond the intended budget. In that case, the acoustical consultant will have to make adjustments, possibly rearranging the studio floor plan to lessen some of the isolation requirements. This is the point in the design procedure where such decisions must be made.

Cooper (2) outlines these design steps in detail and give numerous examples of structures meeting various STC requirements. Due attention must be given to doors and fittings, using only those whose STC ratings are comparable with the wall, ceiling, and floor requirements of the space. A single small leakage path between adjacent areas is all that it may take to defeat an otherwise excellent job of sound isolation.

### 32.3.3 Impact Noise Isolation

The previous paragraphs have dealt only with airborne noise. Impact noise is that generated directly by vibration against structural members of a building. Some of the offenders are:

a. Footsteps on wood floors or thin concrete slabs in multistory buildings
b. Poorly isolated motors associated with air conditioners or elevators.
c. Noisy plumbing fixtures

It is surprising now far impact noise can travel in some structures; tapping and hammering on uncarpeted floors can be heard up to three of four floors away in some reinforced-concrete structures. While plumbing and motor noise may be expensive to isolate, the noise of footsteps on the floor above may be easily solved by offering the tenant the necessary carpeting and padding required to isolate them.

Impact noise is often one of the most elusive aspects of acoustical design. A proper assessment of it may require long-time monitoring of a proposed site. For example, a site survey made during the winter months may fail to pinpoint a problem due to air conditioning compressors located on a roof or the floor above. A survey limited to daytime hours may fail to identify noisy weekend or night-time activities on adjacent floors.

### 32.3.4 Acoustical Conditions within the Studio

So far, the discussion has dealt only with isolation of the studio from its surroundings. Now the treatment required to attain the necessary control over sound produced in the studio is considered. Most pop-rock studios are acoustically fairly dry, with reverberation time on the order of 0.5 second. There are good reasons for this. First, the relatively absorptive conditions provide for good separation between instrumental pickup; second, a live small studio has a tendency to be "boxy" through the predominance of widely spaced room modes well up into the midrange (see Section 1.11.6). Care should be taken that the room is not too dead, for this tends to make musicians uncomfortable.The best balance is a combination of moderately dry acoustics and isolation baffles. The baffles are used to provide more separation, and they can be moved out when not needed. Many engineers prefer a combination of live and dry acoustics in the same space. Variable wall panels that are absorptive on one side and reflective on the other can facilitate this.

Since so much monitoring in the studio is done over headphones, we can postulate a very dead studio in which all the musicians are immersed in an artificial and arbitrary acoustical environment. This is very often the case; but there will always be times when the headphones come off and the room must come into play. Again, use a good consultant in determining these options.

### 32.3.5 Vocal Booths and Drum Cages

The vocal booth is a room adjacent to the control room and the studio and is used for isolation of softer sounds. For example, a vocalist can easily be drowned out by a loud band in the studio, with consequent leakage into the vocal microphone. Placing the vocalist in a booth solves this problem. Monitoring in the booth is generally via headphones, but small loudspeakers are sometimes used. Acoustically, the room should be very dead so that there are no audible room modes in the voice range.

The drum set if often "semi-isolated" by placing it in a structure that surrounds the drum set to a height of about a meter. An absorptive canopy is placed overhead. This expedient allows the drummer to remain in the studio with the rest of the musicians, while diminishing the output of the drum set into the acoustical environment of the studio.

### 32.3.6 Matters of Decor and Atmosphere

Avoid making the studio look clinical and institutional. The feeling should be one of warmth so that the musicians will be at ease. Selection of colors and textures should be made early, preferably with the help of a studio designer, so that those choices can satisfy both esthetic and utilitarian needs. At the same, the control room must convey the presence of technology, not in the sense of wires, switches, and meters, but in the form of new equipment. The terms "state of the art" and "high-tech" are often invoked here.

Lighting is an important element in creating the right atmosphere. Provision should be made for high illumination when needed, but it should be remembered that recording activities will likely take place at moderate to low lighting levels.

## 32.4 EQUIPMENT SELECTION

Rapid changes in technology make it difficult for a studio owner to remain competitive for long without constant attention to upgrading facilities and acquiring new equipment. The disturbing thing here is that equipment must often be replaced—even while it is still capable of doing a superlative job!

Few studios can afford the luxury of outright purchase of expensive equipment, and leasing is the rule. Very often, the equipment is "obsolete" by the time the lease has expired, so the leasing terms should take this into account.

The extent of advice that can be presented here is to outline the major equipment areas in terms of their general directions and pace of development. From this discussion it will become clear which areas will require accelerated upgrading and which are relatively stable.

*Analog Multichannel Recorders.*    The bulk of multichannel recording is still done with analog machines, and the investment in a 24-track recorder is certainly justified. The associated noise reduction equipment here is clearly Dolby A-type and SR. Both standards are in for the long haul.

*Microphones.*    There is little in the way of new microphone technology, and development is basically in slow but steady refinement of the existing excellent performance. Studio owners are recommended to acquire vintage tube models when they can find them, since there is strong nostalgia in their favor.

*Signal Processing.*    This is a volatile area, especially where digital processing is involved. Fortunately, signal processing devices are not among the more expensive ones to buy. As with microphones, there is strong nostalgia for early classic models, especially tube-type limiter/compressors and equalizers.

*Consoles.*    Clearly the largest single budget item in the studio, a "name" console is looked upon as a drawing card for clients. The irony here is that many of the best recording engineers in the business use older consoles that have been kept in immaculate condition. In-line designs are in the ascendancy, but there is by no means agreement that they are more intuitively simple or ergonomically satisfactory to operate than split-configuration consoles.

There is almost nothing in the way of console upgrading that can be done, so signs of obsolescence should be taken seriously if a studio wishes to remain at the local leading edge of technology.

***Digital Multitrack Recorders.***   It is doubtful whether any of the handful of manufacturers of digital multitrack recorders has made a profit on the machines. Essentially, the industry is locked in a battle between two major Japanese companies, both of whom are seeking major studios, producers, and engineers who will endorse their products. For the present, most studios can afford to sit on the sidelines and watch.

***Digital Stereo Recorders.***   This is a different situation indeed. The ascendancy of the CD has made two-channel digital editing and assembly an important service activity at many levels in the recording industry. The preferred system is the Sony 1630 U-matic format, but the reel-to-reel formats, which can be edited by razor blade, are useful as well. Anyone interested in this facet of the industry is advised to contact the major CD pressing plants to see what their requirements are.

***Digital Work Stations.***   This is a general term describing computer-based systems for editing both audio and video. The scope runs the gamut from complex hard disk-based systems capable of film post-production and multichannel mixing to fairly simple PC-based systems for digital audio editing and assembly. Yearly Audio Engineering Society conventions keep the industry informed on what is happening here. The requirements for a studio will vary, depending on the clientele; the general situation is volatile and apt to change quickly.

***Digital Consoles.***   The vast majority of digital multichannel recordings are mixed to stereo through analog consoles. The costs of multichannel digital console are staggering, and it will be a long time before they are commonplace. Many in the industry doubt that this will ever happen. It is again recommended that most studio owners stand aside and observe.

## BIBLIOGRAPHY

1. J. Borwick, *Sound Recording Practice*, Oxford University Press, New York (1988).
2. J. Cooper, *Building a Recording Studio*, Recording Institute of America, New York (1978).
3. A. Everest, *Handbook of Multichannel Recording*, TAB, Blue Ridge Summit, Pa. (1975).
4. C. Harris, *Handbook of Noise Control*, McGraw-Hill, New York (1979).
5. V. Knudsen and C. Harris, *Acoustical Designing in Architecture*, Wiley, New York (1950).
6. M. Rettinger, *Acoustic Design and Noise Control*, Chemical Publishing, New York (1973).
7. J. Woram, *Handbook of Sound Recording*, H. Sams, Indianapolis (1989).

# 33

## STUDIO OPERATION AND MAINTENANCE

### 33.1 INTRODUCTION

Managing a studio complex requires as much business acumen as technical competence. It is essential to have on the studio staff many talents that complement one another, and one of the best assets a studio can have is a good recording engineer with a strong entrepreneurial bent.

This chapter will cover personnel requirements as well as the mechanics of day-to-day operation and client relationships. A final section will discuss the many aspects of general maintenance.

### 33.2 CLIENT RELATIONSHIPS

Clients demand first-class service on a timely basis at competitive rates, and a studio that fails to satisfy a client in any of these three areas is in trouble. A studio cannot operate effectively without clearly stated policies and internal procedures, and it is important that the client understand these. The following areas must be covered clearly.

*Booking Policy.* Scheduling of the studios should follow strict house rules, and exceptions should be a matter of executive decision. Rates are generally set on an hourly basis, and it should be clear to the client what will be included in the way of personnel and equipment. Normally, an engineer and assistant will be assigned to a recording session, but a remix session may involve only an engineer. Cancellation policy needs to be made clear; most studios have a 24-hour rule, and the client should agree to this.

Many clients wish to work with a particular engineer. If this is agreed to by the booking manager and engineer, then it should be honored. If it cannot be met then the client should be given the option of cancelling the session without penalty.

***Financial Arrangements.***   New clients may be asked to pay for services, or a portion thereof, in advance, and it is entirely at the studio's risk if this rule is suspended. The studio should bear all responsibility for determining the credit rating of a new client.

***Block Booking.***   Block booking of a studio allows the client, usually a rock group, to "move in," so to speak, and occupy the studio a week or more at a time at a negotiated rate. This can be a boon for both studio and client, and all services and personnel requirements must be spelled out. If there is previous hourly booking of the studio during the desired block period, that booking should not be cancelled unless the client has been informed and agrees. Every attempt should be made to offer the previously booked client alternate services so that the block booking can be made. The only acceptable alternative here is to inform a client beforehand of any anticipated block booking, and the reasons must be made clear to the client.

***Materials and Supplies.***   Most studios provide tape and other materials for clients, marking them up for a reasonable profit. Thus, clients are not allowed to bring their own materials unless by pre-arrangement.

***Client's Properties or Rental Materials.***   It is generally the client's responsibility to rent musical instruments and make all financial arrangements for them. The studio should bear responsibility for them while on the premises. Most studios will store client's tapes for a reasonable period of time; however, the client must understand that the studio cannot assume full liability for them.

***The Rate Card.***   The simplest way to make known studio policies is to publish a rate card and to keep it up to date. The rate card should clearly spell out the fees for services and materials and the other items that have been discussed in this section.

## 33.3 EMPLOYEE RELATIONSHIPS

Skilled studio managers are a rare breed, but they are just as essential to the operation of a facility as a skilled engineer. As is the case with many professionals, engineers and managers are often employed on an incentive basis. They are both essentially selling services, and their performance may rewarded accordingly. It is important that all details here be set by contract and that exceptions be spelled out for the benefit of all concerned.

A studio needs a continuing source of qualified technical personnel, and aggressive studios are regularly in touch with the many recording schools and training programs that now exist.

## 33.4 EMPLOYEE TRAINING

The orderly management of a studio requires that technical personnel follow the same rules. For example, such mundane things as coiling microphone cables, control room and studio clean-up, filling out equipment trouble reports, and "zeroing out" the console after sessions, need to be done the same way by all personnel. Most importantly, accurate documentation of tape logs is essential. Each studio must establish its procedures in these areas and enforce them. While this may seem like regimentation to some free-spirited persons, it is absolutely necessary for good business and will pay off in the long run.

All new technical employees should be specifically briefed on studio procedures and not relied upon to learn these things in a casual way. Further, all technical employees should be required to attend any training sessions on new equipment that may be scheduled by studio management.

## 33.5 VENDOR RELATIONSHIPS

The person in charge of materials and supplies for the studio complex must have a good sense for "making deals." Such things as yearly purchase orders with scheduled delivery are good for all concerned. Certain services, such as custodial care, may better be done by outside contractors rather than employees. Service contracts for air-conditioning, office equipment, and vending machines need to be considered. All landlord relationships must be considered here as well.

## 33.6 COMMUNICATIONS

There should never be anything casual about answering the telephone, and general calls to a recording studio should taken only by designated personnel who can route them as required. A fax machine is a requirement, and telephones in control rooms should generally be limited to local calls.

## 33.7 TRADE ORGANIZATIONS

Studios should consider membership of pertinent trade organizations, both local and national. Many credit problems can be averted, and business decisions can more sensibly be made if appropriate data is broadly available.

## 33.8 MAINTENANCE

### 33.8.1 The Chief Engineer

Not many people carry this lofty title nowadays, but it is essential that someone in the studio assume this function. Traditionally, the chief engineer is the person who makes sure that everything works, and is nominally in charge of the maintenance department. The chief engineer sets standards for all operations and takes charge of all technical training. The chief engineer's recommendations regarding technological improvements are generally binding.

### 33.8.2 Maintenance Procedures

With proper first-echelon maintenance on the part of studio engineers and technicians, the load on the maintenance department can be reduced significantly. First-echelon maintenance refers to the thoughtful care of equipment exercised by operating personnel as they do their work. Such matters as microphone handling, routine tightening of loose screws on any piece of equipment, gentle treatment of large items of equipment, and routine alignment of analog tape recorders are included here. It is surprising how many things *do not* go wrong with equipment if such care is taken.

Higher echelon maintenance involves such matters as:

a. Making of adaptors for interfacing nonstandard equipment and ensuring that operating levels are matched.
b. Making modifications and updates on equipment, as required.
c. Setting operating and calibration levels and equalization standards for all recorders.
d. Performing periodic maintenance on major pieces of equipment, including the following:
   – Many digital recorders require outside (manufacturer) maintenance after 1000 hours of operation. The maintenance department is responsible for seeing that this is done.
   – Analog recorders need to be checked out at regular intervals to ensure that standards are being met as regards bias settings, mechanical performance, and other "back panel" adjustments. The operating manuals for these machines outline the necessary procedures.
   – Checking of monitor loudspeaker response at regular intervals.

A proper area should be set up for performing maintenance, and there should be a complete set of test gear and hand tools. For more ambitious projects, some power tools will be necessary. Test jigs and fixtures for commonly aligned items may have to be made by the department.

Logs should be kept on each major piece of equipment, with indications of problems and how they were solved. There should also be a master file of all maintenance and users' manuals for equipment used in the studio complex.

It is recommended that all new equipment be unpacked and checked out in the maintenance department prior to being put into general service. This is as true of microphones as it is a recorders.

## 33.8.3 Maintenance During Recording Activities

The biggest nightmare for a studio is the prospect of massive equipment failure during a recording session with a studio full of musicians. Outside of motor failure in a tape recorder or console power supply failure, most problems can be "patched around" through various recorder and console options. However, a power amplifier or loudspeaker failure calls for immediate replacement.

The chief engineer must determine the degree of equipment redundancy necessary to keep all operations going; fortunately, the modular nature of modern equipment makes that job easier than it used to be. It is apparent that there should always be somebody on duty in the maintenance department.

The question of liability comes up often, and it should be a matter of policy. Manufacturers of equipment and supplies long ago indemnified themselves against failure, and their position is that the user (in this case the recording studio) must ensure that the equipment or material is suitable for the job at hand. This covers such matters as massive tape deterioration, as was adjudicated during the 1960s.

Thus, any failure of equipment or supplies remains the responsibility of the studio, including accidental erasure of clients' tapes.

## BIBLIOGRAPHY

1. M. Atkin, "Maintenance", Section 14 in J. Borwick, *Sound Recording Practice*, Oxford University Press, New York (1987).

# INDEX